Developing Mathematics through Applications: Elementary

Instructor Resources

Preliminary Edition

Developed by
COMAP, Inc.

Project Leadership
Solomon Garfunkel
COMAP, Inc., Lexington, MA
Susan Forman
Bronx Community College, CUNY, Bronx, NY

Authors
Nancy Crisler
COMAP, Inc., Lexington, MA
Gary Simundza
Wentworth Institute of Technology, Boston, MA

Key College Publishing
Innovators in Higher Education

The Consortium for Mathematics and Its Applications (COMAP)
Lexington, MA

This book was developed with the support of NSF Grant DUE 9950036. However, any opinions, findings, conclusions, and/or recommendations herein are those of the authors and do not necessarily reflect the views of NSF.

Key College Publishing was founded in 1999 as a division of Key Curriculum Press® in cooperation with Springer-Verlag New York, Inc. We publish innovative texts and courseware for the undergraduate curriculum in mathematics and statistics as well as mathematics and statistics education. For more information, visit us at www.keycollege.com.

Key College Publishing
1150 65th Street
Emeryville, CA 94608
(510) 595-7000
info@keycollege.com
www.keycollege.com

Key College Publishing and
Key Curriculum Press:
DEVELOPMENT EDITORS: Jacqueline Meijer-Irons,
Allyndreth Cassidy
PRODUCTION PROJECT MANAGER: Michele Julien
EDITORIAL PROOFREADER: Linda Ward
PRODUCTION DIRECTOR: Diana Jean Parks
COVER DESIGNER: Design Deluxe
COVER ILLUSTRATOR: Jeff Brice
PRINTER: Data Reproductions Corporation
EXECUTIVE EDITOR: Richard Bonacci
GENERAL MANAGER: Mike Simpson
PUBLISHER: Steven Rasmussen

COMAP:
PROJECT EDITOR: Pauline Wright
PRODUCTION EDITOR: Tim McLean
PRODUCTION DIRECTOR: George Ward
PRODUCTION: Daiva Kiliulis
PHOTO RESEARCH: Lynn Aro, Gail Wessell

Printed in the United States of America
10 9 8 7 6 5 4 3 2 1   06 05 04 03 02
ISBN 1-931914-05-2

Project Leadership
Solomon Garfunkel, COMAP, Inc., Lexington, MA
Susan Forman, Bronx Community College, CUNY, Bronx, NY

Advisory Board Members

Philip Cheifetz, Nassau Community College, Garden City, NY
William Haver, Virginia Commonwealth University, Richmond, VA
Robert L. Kimball, Jr., Wake Technical College, Raleigh, NC
Karen Larsen, National Alliance of Business, Washington, DC
David R. Mandel, MPR Center for Curriculum and Professional Development, Washington, DC
Pamela Matthews, National Council of Teachers of Mathematics, Reston, VA
Marilyn Mays, North Lake College, Irving, TX
Henry Pollak, Teachers College, Columbia University, New York, NY
William Thomas, University of Toledo, Toledo, OH

Field Testers

Susan Forman
Bronx Community College, CUNY, Bronx, NY

Pei Taverner
Frederick Community College

Jeffrey Morford, Larry Smyrski, Deborah Zopf
Henry Ford Community College, Dearborn, MI

Julane Crabtree
Johnson County Community College

Susan Wood
J.S. Reynolds Community College

Jan Roy
Montcalm Community College

Tim Chappell
Penn Valley Community College

Janet Ray
Seattle Central Community College

Reuben Farley, William Haver,
Gwen Turbeville, Kathryn Wallo
Virginia Commonwealth University, Richmond, VA

Focus Group Participants

Susan Enyart
Otterbien College

Nancy Johnson
Manatee Community College

Michelle Merriweather
Southern Connecticut State University

Charles Patterson
Louisiana Tech University

Don Ransford
Edison Community College

Rochelle Robert
Nassau Community College

Sharon Siegel
Sam Houston State University

About the Authors

Nancy Crisler, COMAP, Inc.

Ms. Crisler was a high school mathematics teacher and for ten years served as the K–12 Mathematics Supervisor for the Pattonville School District in St. Louis County, Missouri. She has taught at Washington University in St. Louis, Missouri. She is the co-author of the COMAP texts *Discrete Mathematics Through Applications* 1st and 2nd editions, a member of the writing team for *Mathematics: Modeling Our World Courses 1–4,* 1st and 2nd editions, and a co-author of *Precalculus: Modeling Our World* (2002) and *College Algebra: Modeling Our World* (2002), all published by W.H. Freeman.

Gary Simundza, Wentworth Institute of Technology

Mr. Simundza is Professor of Mathematics at Wentworth Institute of Technology in Boston, Massachusetts, where he has taught mathematics and physics for over 25 years. As director of the NSF-supported "Mathematics in Technology" project, he led an interdisciplinary team of faculty in creating a set of extensive laboratory activities for college mathematics. These were published by Prentice-Hall as *Precalculus Investigations: A Laboratory Manual* (1999).

Contents

Preface   *vii*

To the Instructor   *ix*

To the Student   *xxii*

Instructor Notes

    Chapter 1   I1

    Chapter 2   I16

    Chapter 3   I28

    Chapter 4   I36

Chapter 1   Measurement   1

    1.1 Measuring Length   2

    1.2 Linear Measurement and the Pythagorean Theorem   9

    1.3 Describing the Results of a Measurement   35

    1.4 Measuring a Surface: Area   67

    1.5 Volume, Surface Area, and Geometric Models   93

    1.6 Other Kinds of Measurement   119

    Chapter 1 Review   138

Chapter 2   Linear Models   148

    2.1 Measuring Indirectly   150

    2.2 Exploring Algebraic Expressions   156

    2.3 Solving Linear Equations   173

    2.4 Functions and Their Representations   205

    2.5 Linear Functions   223

    2.6 Creating Linear Models   271

    Chapter 2 Review   294

Chapter 3   Modeling Behavior from Data   305

3.1 Collecting Data and Determining a Model   307

3.2 Scatter Plots and Data-Driven Models   314

3.3 Lines of Best Fit   341

3.4 Using Models to Make Predictions   365

Chapter 3 Review   393

Chapter 4   Polynomials   405

4.1 Introduction to Polynomials   407

4.2 Exponents   412

4.3 Operations with Polynomials   435

4.4 Factoring Polynomials   455

4.5 Modeling with Polynomial Functions   471

Chapter 4 Review   496

Appendix   504

Index   508

Preface

Since the 1980s the "typical" college student profile has been changing as more non-traditional students have started their higher education later in life. Some students are entering their post-secondary education after a period of time in the work force, others after starting a family. Often students who have been away from school for extended lengths of time need to refresh and rebuild their mathematical skills and their confidence in their ability to solve challenging problems. Likewise, traditional students need to hone their mathematical skills to enter today's competitive job market. Developmental mathematics courses are offered as the first step in student success in mathematics-related programs.

Students in developmental mathematics courses are particularly in need of course materials that are written at an appropriate reading level and capture adults' interests. It is important to keep in mind that these students often bring with them life experiences, particularly from the workplace, that can be used to connect the mathematics taught in the classroom to their worlds. Yet many developmental mathematics programs simply present concepts and ask students to replicate the results while working through voluminous end-of-section exercises.

We now have an opportunity for real and positive change. Both *Crossroads in Mathematics: Standards for Introductory College Mathematics Before Calculus*, published by the American Mathematical Association of Two-Year Colleges (AMATYC) in 1995, and the National Council of Teachers of Mathematics (NCTM) *Principles and Standards for School Mathematics*, revised in 2000, advocate an integrated approach to mathematics content. They call for an increased emphasis on data analysis, the development of meaningful contemporary applications, and the use of appropriate technologies, as well as activity-based and collaborative learning.

Given students' needs in developmental mathematics, the vision of the AMATYC and NCTM Standards, and COMAP's experience, we have created a one-year sequence, *Developing Mathematics through Applications: Elementary* and *Intermediate,* which takes a different approach from traditional developmental mathematics textbooks.

- The rich applications are equally appropriate for students coming straight from high school with plans to enter technical fields, and those with work experience.

- The approach integrates topics from probability, data analysis, and geometry with the traditional developmental mathematics curriculum, making it a suitable foundation for students in diverse career paths, including engineering and the sciences as well as non-technical occupations.

- The context-rich, activity-based curriculum motivates critical thinking about fundamental concepts while building the analytical and graphical skills needed for further study of mathematics.

- Solving the problems posed in these books calls for integrating technology in a more natural manner then the traditional "drill-and-practice" use of technology commonly employed.

Many people and organizations have been helpful during the creation of this book. We would like to extend a special thank you to Professors James Sandefur of Georgetown University and Bobby Righi of Seattle Central Community College for their ideas and insights during the early development of this book. Thanks, too, to Larry Smyrski for his suggestions for refinement of the manuscript.

We would also like to acknowledge and thank the following:

Professors Peter Rourke, Larry Decker, Marty Kemen, and Philip Comeau, all of Wentworth Institute of Technology; David Joliat, Project Manager with Thoughtforms Corporation; and the people at Zymark Corporation and the USDA Forest Service.

Our sincere gratitude goes to Sue Martin of COMAP. She has always been there when we needed her. And, as always, we wish to thank the members of the COMAP staff. Without their help, this book would not have been possible.

<table>
<tr><td align="center">Sol Garfunkel
CO-PRINCIPAL INVESTIGATOR</td><td align="center">Susan Forman
CO-PRINCIPAL INVESTIGATOR</td></tr>
<tr><td align="center">Nancy Crisler
AUTHOR</td><td align="center">Gary Simundza
AUTHOR</td></tr>
</table>

To the Instructor

This book is a different kind of developmental mathematics text. We believe that any mathematics worth learning is best learned in the context of its use by real people in real jobs. Without neglecting necessary practice with fundamental skills, we emphasize connections between mathematics and the workplace, both in the body of the text and in the exercises. Interesting applications motivate students to learn, and guided discovery helps them succeed in their learning by developing habits of persistence necessary for achievement.

The AMATYC Standards have been thoroughly embraced by this book: Active investigation of mathematics is emphasized throughout with the expectation that students will conduct much of this investigation in small, collaborative groups. The content integrates data analysis, measurement, and geometry with traditional topics in elementary and intermediate algebra. A modeling theme runs throughout the text, as students learn to construct a variety of models, using equations, graphs, tables, arrow diagrams, narrative descriptions, geometry, and statistics. Access to computing technology is assumed, although the text can be used successfully without it.

In addition to competence with mathematical skills and concepts, this text intends to provide familiarity with the "new basic skills" demanded by the modern workplace, as reflected in such documents as the SCANS Report and various Industry Skills Standards. These include critical thinking, team-building, interdisciplinary connections, and communications skills.

Unfortunately reading is frequently not a strength of developmental mathematics students. Our philosophy is that students should be encouraged to improve their reading skills as they develop mathematical facility. Many of the contextual situations in the text require students to read for mathematical content. Indeed, an essential part of acquiring the ability to model the world with mathematics is learning to see how mathematics is embedded in various situations. We hope students will be encouraged to increase their reading ability as they see that careful reading helps them achieve mathematics competence. To this end, vocabulary is kept accessible and unfamiliar concepts are clearly explained in terms that students are able to understand.

Some topics that are not always considered part of developmental mathematics are introduced as they arise naturally in context. For example, vectors are mentioned in Chapter 1 as quantities whose measurement requires more than one number. Functions are introduced early as a way of describing dependency relationships between variables, and graphs of polynomials are touched on briefly in Chapter 4. These topics provide the underpinnings for in-depth work in precalculus and help lay the groundwork for more advanced mathematical study.

Organization

Each chapter is divided into four to six sections sharing similar pedagogical elements.

- **Goals of the chapter:** The first element of every chapter is a list of goals to be accomplished by learning the material presented.

- **Preparation Reading:** Each chapter begins with a brief introduction that sets the stage for the mathematics to come, and may include contextual connections or discussions of modeling aspects.

- **Chapter Review:** This section summarizes the key concepts of the chapter and contains a sampling of exercises from each section.

- **Glossary:** Each chapter concludes with a summary of the new terms introduced in the chapter.

The various sections of each chapter serve different purposes. The sections build on each other, incorporating the following tools.

- **What You Need to Know** and **What You Will Learn:** Each section starts with two lists. The first states the necessary prerequisite knowledge and the second defines the mathematical objectives to be learned.

- **Activities:** The first section of each chapter contains an *Activity* that requires students to work in groups and perform an experiment or otherwise collect data. They are then guided through the exploration of a core mathematical concept that will recur throughout the chapter.

- **Discoveries:** Later sections frequently contain explorations that are similar to *Activities* in that they are intended to be done in groups. A *Discovery* is usually a more focused examination of a single mathematical topic and does not necessarily involve active experimentation. If data are needed, they are often provided rather than collected.

- **Examples:** Numerous examples with detailed solutions are provided in the body of each section.

- **Exercises:** The exercise sets consist of three different types of problems. *Investigations* should be considered as adjuncts to the body of each section and may present new material. Some are in-depth examinations of particular subtopics or applications, and some are guided explorations similar to *Discoveries*. *Investigations* provide an opportunity for instructors to customize the text for their own purposes and students' needs. *Projects* and *Group Activities* are similar to the *Activities* that begin each chapter. They require students to work cooperatively and often involve research or experimentation of some sort. *Additional Practice* problems provide necessary skill practice, including some contextual problems. They are not necessarily in order from easy to difficult, partly so that students will not quit after trying a few easy problems.

Detailed solutions and answers to all questions asked in the *Activities, Discoveries,* and *Exercises* are provided embedded within the text in this Instructor Resources book.

Instructor Notes

Detailed instructional suggestions are provided for each chapter. These are intended to help instructors make choices regarding pacing of the course and exercises to assign. Many of the features in the Instructor Notes section are provided for ease of use and convenience. For example, each Instructor Notes section starts by restating the goals of the chapter. Next, the list of objectives to be learned and the list of prerequisites are provided. The bulk of the Instructor Notes is comprehensive material about the teaching of each section, such as amount of time required, and hints and suggestions for presenting the material.

In order to help instructors choose *Investigations* that are most appropriate for their students, the symbol $\Rightarrow$ is used to indicate any exercise that contains instruction on a topic not otherwise appearing in the body of a section.

Exercises that require, or explain the use of, computing technology for the solution of mathematical problems are indicated with a o symbol. No particular form of technology is required. Since many students own, or have access to, graphing calculators, calculator screen shots appear throughout the text. (TI-83 screens are shown only because this type of calculator is common, although the particular uses discussed are meant to be generic.) Computer graphing programs such as *Fathom Dynamic Statistics*™, which also provides data analysis capability, can be used, and spreadsheets and geometric drawing utilities such as *The Geometer's Sketchpad*® may also be helpful.

Nancy Crisler	Gary Simundza
AUTHOR	AUTHOR

To the Student

(This material appears in the Student Edition and is repeated for your convenience.)

This book is different from mathematics textbooks you have used before. We believe that mathematics should be learned by seeing how it is used day to day. The reason for learning the mathematics presented here is not simply to prepare you for the next math course but to prepare you for your next job and for using mathematics to solve problems that arise in other areas of your life. Yes, the mathematics that you learn will help prepare you for further schoolwork. But it is also important as a life skill, something you will use and value.

This book encourages active exploration of mathematics. You will learn to construct a variety of mathematical explanations of real problems. To do this, you will use equations, graphs, tables, verbal descriptions, geometry, and statistics. Here are a few tips that will help you use this book successfully:

- Much of the mathematical exploration should occur in small groups. Every chapter of the book includes *Activities* or *Discoveries*, which will most likely be done during class time. Discussions with other students will help you grasp new mathematical concepts.

- You will have to read carefully in order to understand the connections between mathematics and the workplace. This is especially important in some of the exercises.

- Many of the *Activities*, *Discoveries*, and *Exercises* require written responses. Try to write clearly and in complete sentences in order to show your understanding of the mathematics.

- When appropriate, use a graphing calculator or computer.

- Each section begins with *What You Need to Know*. This is a list of prerequisite skills that should be familiar from earlier mathematics courses.

- *What You Will Learn* lists the new mathematics you will study in the section.

- There are three types of exercises at the end of most sections:
  - *Investigations* are "thinking" exercises that will test your understanding and challenge you to apply the mathematics you have just learned. Some investigations will present new mathematics topics that build on the work of the section.
  - *Projects* and *Group Activities* involve experiments or research, many of which are intended to be done in small groups.
  - *Additional Practice* exercises allow you to master the computational skills introduced in the section.

In order to use mathematics to describe the world around you, you need to see how mathematics is part of that world. Our goal is that, by the end of the text, you will be able to recognize certain mathematical principles when you are outside the classroom. We hope that you enjoy using this text to develop your mathematical skills and understanding as much as we enjoyed writing it.

Nancy Crisler
AUTHOR

Gary Simundza
AUTHOR

Instructor Notes

Chapter 1: Measurement

Goals of the Chapter

- To accurately express and compute with measured quantities
- To determine geometrical properties of two- and three-dimensional figures
- To describe one-variable data numerically and graphically
- To begin to create and use mathematical models

What You Will Learn

Section 1.1 Measuring Length

- To estimate lengths of objects using various units
- To state the precision of a measuring instrument
- To express the accuracy of a measurement
- To compute perimeters of some two-dimensional figures

Section 1.2 Linear Measurement and the Pythagorean Theorem

- To change the units of a measured or computed quantity
- To use the Pythagorean theorem to compute certain distances
- To use the correct order of operations
- To use arrow diagrams to help identify correct order of operations
- To use formulas to find perimeters of two-dimensional figures

Section 1.3 Describing the Results of Measurement

- To compute the mean, median, mode, and range of a data sample
- To use inequality symbols to indicate relative sizes of quantities
- To construct a dot plot of a data set
- To construct a frequency histogram from a data set
- To use technology to create histograms

Section 1.4 Measuring a Surface: Area

- To compute areas of some plane figures

- To use formulas to compute areas

- To change units of area

- To distinguish between the quantities perimeter and area

Section 1.5 Volume, Surface Area, and Geometric Models

- To compute volumes of some three-dimensional figures

- To use formulas to compute volumes

- To use formulas to compute surface areas of some three-dimensional figures

- To change units of volume

- To construct geometric models

- To distinguish among the quantities perimeter, area, volume, and surface area

Section 1.6 Other Kinds of Measurement

- To identify rates as indicating relationships between variables

- To convert the units of any type of quantity into other units

- To write numbers using scientific notation

- To identify vector quantities

- To distinguish between exact and approximate values

What You Need to Know

Section 1.1 Measuring Length

- How to perform basic arithmetic operations

- How to round numbers

- How to identify basic polygon shapes

Section 1.2 Linear Measurement and the Pythagorean Theorem

- How to perform basic arithmetic operations, including powers and square roots
- How to multiply numerical fractions
- How to identify place value of a digit in a number
- How to round numbers

Section 1.3 Describing the Results of Measurement

- How to plot numbers on a number line

Section 1.4 Measuring a Surface: Area

- How to compute perimeters of plane figures

Section 1.5 Volume, Surface Area, and Geometric Models

- How to calculate areas of two-dimensional figures
- How to change units of length and area

Section 1.6 Other Kinds of Measurement

- How to use a protractor to measure angles

Instructor Notes for Chapter 1

Introduction to Chapter 1

The primary focus of Chapter 1 is on measurement techniques in the context of a review of geometry computations. It assumes that students have at least some familiarity with basic shapes and the concepts of perimeter, area, and volume.

Expressing appropriate accuracy is stressed continually throughout the chapter so that students develop the habit of being conscious of the information being conveyed anytime they communicate results of numerical measurement or computation. Estimation skills are stressed and practiced as well in an attempt to instill an appreciation of how such skills can complement and even facilitate computational accuracy.

In order to integrate nontraditional content, as promoted by the NCTM and AMATYC standards documents, Chapter 1 also provides a rudimentary introduction to elementary one-variable statistics and data analysis. This provides the base for bivariate data analysis in Chapter 3.

It should be noted that a large variety of topics is introduced throughout Chapter 1. Many of these are not intended to be mastered at this level. It is assumed that a few (e.g., ratio and percent) have been studied previously and that their use in a measurement context will refresh students' abilities with them. Several (e.g., notion of a function, definition of a vector quantity, rates of change, scientific notation) are intended as precursors to fuller treatment either later in this text or in more advanced courses.

The content is intentionally kept simple at first, being limited to measurement of length only in Sections 1.1 and 1.2, later expanded to other dimensions, and finally broadened beyond geometry, in order to allow students to focus more fully on each stage of familiarity with what are likely to be unfamiliar measurement issues.

Preparation Reading

This reading sets the stage for the modeling theme that is emphasized throughout the entire course. General models are discussed first, since most students can identify with these. The concept of mathematical models is then introduced.

As we begin our study of models and modeling, it is important for the instructor to continually reinforce this theme.

Section 1.1

This section requires one class period.

This section (as well as the first section of every chapter) focuses on an activity that actively involves students. The concepts derived from Activity 1.1 along with its real-world connections will weave in and out of the remaining sections of the chapter.

Because this activity is the first of a series of activities and discoveries, it sets the stage for the tone of the course by getting students involved in mathematical explorations. It is assumed that the students will work in groups of 2–4 people.

The room measurement exercise was chosen because it requires no special equipment other than something with which to measure. Metric rulers are suggested for ease of calculation, although students must convert results to U.S. Customary (formerly known, and still sometimes referred to, as British Engineering) units. Also, meter sticks are preferred to tape measures, not only from a cost standpoint but also so that data are more likely to show the variability essential to learning some of the key measurement ideas.

It is assumed here that classrooms are essentially rectangular. In cases where the classroom has a significantly different shape, it may be wise to take the class to a rectangular room in order to complete the activity.

When using a meter stick ruled in millimeters but numbered in centimeters, students typically write a length such as 32.7 cm correctly but may write 46 cm when the actual measurement is 46.0 cm, saying something such as "It was exactly 46." They should be encouraged to recognize that exact measurement is an essentially meaningless term and that writing 46.0 cm correctly expresses the precision of the measurement.

Sample measurements are included, but class results may show considerably more variability than seen here.

> **Important Note:** It is extremely important that groups keep their data, as they will be used throughout the remainder of the chapter. You may want to keep a copy of the data yourself, in case any students misplace theirs.

Items 11–14 have students verbalize methods of finding perimeter. These verbal rules will be translated into formulas in Section 1.2.

Some of the common prefixes are introduced here, but the list is restricted to those associated with length measurement. A more complete list is given in Section 1.6.

At the end of each activity throughout the book is an Extend the Activity section, which provides several different types of questions. In this section's extension, practice of skills developed in the activity is presented in items 15 and 16. Item 17 provides the instructor with an opportunity to introduce a concept that may or may not be appropriate for his or her individual course. In this item, students will need to be familiar with percents.

Extensions also provide opportunities for students to connect the activity to the real world (items 18 and 19).

Section 1.2

One day is required for this section.

Writing Geometry Formulas

This section introduces formulas as an example of an algebraic model. Stress that these particular formulas use variables to express relationships (such as the verbal rules from Activity 1.1) for perimeter in terms of the dimensions of the object.

Order of Operations and Arrow Diagrams

Arrow diagrams are introduced in this section and are used here to reinforce the order of operations. Even though these may be unfamiliar to both student and instructor, continue to examine them carefully. For some students, this visual model is invaluable.

Example 1

Item (c) provides an example of a fraction bar acting as a grouping symbol. This provides an opportunity to discuss how this or similar expressions are entered into a calculator. Emphasize that the parentheses must be included, e.g., $\dfrac{12}{2+4}$ is entered as $12/(2 + 4)$ or $12 \div (2 + 4)$, depending on the calculator.

Other Linear Measurements

Because students may not be familiar with basic algebraic operations at this point, alternate forms of the Pythagorean theorem are explicitly provided. Examples are provided for finding both the hypotenuse and a leg. These skills are practiced in the exercises.

Unit Conversions

Throughout this chapter, the method shown here for changing units is the method used in most technical and science courses.

Special Notes on Exercises

A reminder: Exercises labeled "Investigations" or "Projects and Group Activities" offer the instructor an opportunity to customize the text. Some of these exercises include a more in-depth treatment, or enrichment, of topics discussed in the body of the text; others examine extended applications. A few introduce new and related topics that not all instructors will wish to include in a developmental course.

You will occasionally see one of two icons that are used to identify exercises in the Teacher Notes.

- The symbol $\Rightarrow$ identifies exercises that contain instruction on topics not otherwise discussed in the body of the text. It is up to the teacher whether or not to include these topics in this course.
- The symbol ❏ identifies exercises that either require or explain the use of computing technology such as graphing calculators or electronic spreadsheets.

Important Note: Throughout this chapter when students are asked to change units, encourage them to use the Appendix to find convenient unit equivalents.

⇒Exercises 1, 2, and 3 treat measurement and computational accuracy in detail, introducing the concept of significant figures in recorded measurement and computation. These are optional and may include more elaboration than some instructors care to address. However, students intending to major in highly technical fields such as engineering may benefit greatly from this work.

It should be noted, however, that even among engineers, the terms *precision* and *accuracy* are not uniformly defined, and the typical definitions in mathematics texts are often at odds with engineering practice. An engineer is likely to use an operational analogy: If, when aiming for the bull's-eye in target practice, all of the shots hit the center, we have both accuracy and precision. If all of the shots cluster elsewhere, we have precision without accuracy. And if the shots are scattered, we may have neither, although the *averaged* result is accurate without being precise. Mathematics usage tends to focus on number of decimal places as an indication of precision, with the number of significant figures indicating accuracy. Although it is understood that not all instructors will assign these exercises (and the related Exercise 6 of Section 1.4), rounding of computed results in all subsequent exercises will generally follow the guidelines discussed here. There is occasional passing reference to the concept of significant figures later on as well.

In Exercise 1, the use of the term *significant variation* is meant to exclude the kind of variation that is due only to the idiosyncrasies of our decimal number system. For example, if one of the measurements in the piston diameter data were 9.196 cm, the 1 in the tenths place would not constitute a significant variation at that digit but would only be an artifact of the base 10 number system.

In Exercise 3 (b), notice that only the result is rounded. If each number were rounded to the nearest integer value before addition, the result would have been 871 pounds.

⇒Exercise 5 discusses scale factors and asks students to find actual measurements from plan dimensions.

⇒❏Exercise 6 is a calculator (spreadsheet) exercise that encourages students to use calculator lists to deal with data.

Exercises 8–15 provide practice with precision and accuracy.

Exercises 16–18 provide data and ask students to find the sample mean.

Exercises 19–22 are contextual and provide practice converting units, while Exercises 23–34 provide noncontextual practice.

Exercises 35–37 ask students to model given formulas with arrow diagrams.

Exercises 38–41 practice order of operations.

Exercises 7, 42–52, 62, and 63 are problems dealing with the perimeters of polygons or the circumferences of circles. In Exercise 62, assume 300 identical circular loops for simplicity. (The actual shape is a spiral, or helix).

Exercises 4, 53–61, 64, and 65 ask students to use and/or apply the Pythagorean theorem.

Section 1.3

This section requires two days to complete. The first day can be devoted to Discovery 1.1 and inequalities. A second day will be needed for Visual Models of Data Sets (dot plots and histograms). Exercises 1, 2, and 7–24 can be assigned after the first day. The remaining exercises involve dot plots and histograms.

This section provides a rudimentary introduction to data analysis and descriptive statistics, inclusion of which is recommended by the AMATYC Standards. An introduction to inequality notation follows naturally from a discussion of comparison of sample means.

Discovery 1.1

Measures of central tendency are introduced in the context of the analysis of the data the entire class collected during the activity in Section 1.1.

There should be a minimum of 10–12 data items. If you did not have that many measurements, you may want to supplement with additional items that are in the range of those collected by students.

The range of a data set is introduced as a measure of variability because of its ease of computation. Although the sample standard deviation is often used to measure variability, its use is beyond the scope of this text.

After students have computed descriptive statistics by hand, you may wish to discuss the use of calculator lists for data treatment.

Choosing among the Mean, Median, and Mode

Students should be alerted to the fact that the word *average* is often used (incorrectly) when a median for such things as home prices or salaries is given in news reports.

Using Inequalities to Compare Two Sample Means

Inequalities are introduced contextually. This lays the groundwork for a discussion of solving inequalities in Exercise 5 of Section 2.3.

Making Decisions Based on Sample Means

This brief section shows the value of making multiple measurements of a quantity of interest.

Visual Models of Data Sets

Dot plots and frequency histograms are introduced as ways of visualizing the distribution of single-variable data. This is the first use of graphical models in the text. The discussion of histograms is straightforward and omits details of the construction of grouped frequency tables and relative frequency histograms. These are included in the exercises.

❏ A sidebar on the use of a calculator to create histograms is included. Some instructors may wish to suggest that students use a calculator for Exercises 5, 6, and 27–29.

Special Notes on Exercises

⇒ Exercises 1 and 2 examine variations on computing sample means (trimmed and weighted means) that are used in some contexts. Exercise 2 presents one of the fundamental ideas behind the probabilistic approach to PERT/CPM project scheduling methodology, which is a key component of modern quantitative management.

⇒ Exercises 3 through 6 introduce extensions of the discussion of graphical displays of data as presented in the section. Bar graphs of categorical data (Exercise 3) see widespread use in newspapers and other media. A special type of bar graph called a Pareto diagram (Exercise 4) is used extensively in manufacturing.

Guidelines for constructing histograms (Exercise 6) and relative frequency histograms (Exercise 5) provide a more in-depth treatment of this topic.

⇒ Exercise 7 (statistical quality control) is an important application of mean and range in manufacturing and may be of interest to technical students.

Exercises 8–16 provide contextual drill on numerical measures of data.

Exercises 17–24 involve practice with writing and interpreting inequalities.

Exercises 25–31 involve construction and interpretation of dot plots and histograms.

Section 1.4

This section can be done in one day.

This section introduces the concept of area, explores converting units of area, and presents common area formulas.

Discovery 1.2

Important note: Students need their data from Activity 1.1 for the discovery in this section.

In this discovery, students are asked to share their group data with the entire class, and from the class data set, a mean floor length and width is calculated. Finally, a mean area is calculated and the maximum possible error in the area measurement is examined.

Area Formulas

It is important to recognize that although the formula for a rectangle's area is almost always written $A = lw$, the two dimensions of the rectangle may not be called length and width. For example, the terms *width* and *height* might be used to describe the dimensions of a computer monitor screen, so the formula might be written $A = wh$. Mechanical or civil engineers use the areas of rectangular beam cross sections in structural calculations but refer to the dimensions as *base* and *height*. Thus, formulas for rectangular area in such applications are written $A = bh$.

Example 27

Throughout this chapter, students will be asked to calculate cross-sectional areas. This example is designed to give students the idea that a cross section is a slice of the object, without trying to present a formal definition that goes into the idea of it having to be perpendicular to the axis, etc. Taking a few minutes of class time to point out to students cross-sectional areas of objects in the classroom may be worthwhile. (Suggestions: cross section of a pencil, table leg, or chalk tray.)

Special Notes on Exercises

⇒Exercise 1 asks students (for customary reporting purposes) to change a nonmetric measurement from its decimal form to a form such as feet and inches. It also suggests that when using these measurements in calculations, the decimal equivalent is preferred.

Exercise 2 asks students to find the area of a pentagon by breaking it into five congruent triangles. Area of a triangle and the Pythagorean theorem are practiced here.

⇒Exercise 4 is a brief introduction to surface area. This exercise is designed to get students thinking about the topic (an in-depth discussion of surface area appears in Section 1.5). This could be a challenge for students, as it asks them to think about a two-dimensional drawing in the third dimension.

⇒Exercise 6 continues the discussion of significant figures with accuracy by examining how results are handled when measured numbers are multiplied or divided.

❑ Exercise 7 asks students to explore maximizing area of a rectangle with constant perimeter. Once the table in (d) is completed, the problem is left very open ended. Encourage students to explore.

Exercises 8, 27–36, 38, and 39 provide contextual practice finding the area of specified figures, many of which come from technical fields. If students have difficulty seeing how to divide more complicated figures into simpler, familiar figures (e.g., Exercise 32), hints on breaking up the figure may be needed.

Exercises 9–15 provide noncontextual practice finding the area and/or perimeter (circumference) of polygons (circles).

Exercises 16–26 provide practice in changing units of area.

$\Rightarrow$Exercise 37 introduces the concept of packaging efficiency.

Section 1.5

This section will take two days to complete. The first day can be spent on calculation of volumes. Discovery 1.3 and surface areas will require a second day.

Exercises 1, 2, 6, (a) of 9–12, 13–23, and 25–31 can be done before Discovery 1.3 is completed.

Calculating Volume

A brief discussion of terminology may be worthwhile here. Students should be aware that other words like *capacity* or *size* can be used when *volume* is intended, but these words can also be used to describe length and area, or even nongeometrical quantities. And of course volume has other meanings, as in "turn up the volume" of a stereo. But for geometrical applications, volume always measures three-dimensional space. One of the objectives of this section is to help students develop the ability to substitute specific words such as *volume* or *area* for more generic words such as *size* or *amount*. Similarly, variable names such as h can occasionally refer to a length instead of a height. (See Example 31.)

Discovery 1.3

This discovery is based on the classic "box problem" optimization typically used in precalculus and calculus courses. In this discovery, it is intended to be more open ended and to introduce the notion of geometric models. Students are encouraged to do some systematic exploration of optimal dimensions, but their limited algebra skills at this point preclude much in-depth analysis. (Exercise 4 allows students to begin a more algebraic approach to this problem.) Item 3 of the discovery is an opportunity to encourage the use of calculator lists or spreadsheets to efficiently investigate the relationship between the lengths of folds or cuts on the flat sheet and the volume of the resulting box. Items 4 and 5 are intended to encourage students to relate the exercise to workplace issues.

Special Notes on Exercises

Exercises 1–3 continue to reinforce the ability to estimate and to formulate real problems in mathematical terms. With regard to the Pentagon problem (Exercise 2), official statistics list its volume as 77 million ft^3, which is significantly less than the answer provided. The lower figure is most likely based on internal space. In any case, there are large open depressions in the roof that would also reduce the actual volume of the building.

$\Rightarrow\square$ Exercise 4 may be difficult for some students. However, it provides a first look at the underpinnings of some important mathematical concepts such as domain and, in particular, the notion of recognizing that many situations have a "problem domain" that is a subset of the true domain of a function. In this sense, it lays the groundwork for later work in mathematical modeling.

⇒Exercise 6 completes the sequence of classroom geometry investigations begun in Section 1.1 and requires the data taken during the initial activity.

Exercises 7 and 8 are open-ended extensions of Discovery 1.3. Regarding the cylinder problem (Exercise 8), it can be shown (using calculus) that the volume of a cylinder for a fixed surface area is maximized when $r = h$. This relationship will not be strictly true here, where some of the material from the rectangular sheet may be discarded during construction of the cylinder.

Exercises 9–12 are fundamental drills on volume and surface area calculations, while 13–19 practice volume unit conversions. The remaining exercises 20–44 are contextual volume and surface area problems. Exercises 24(b) and 35(b) involve some critical thinking. Exercises 26(a) and 44 provide practice with terminology. Exercise 36 is open ended, in that many combinations of cylinder dimensions will provide the same volume.

Section 1.6

This section can be covered as a survey section in one day. Another option is to split it up as desired to deal separately and more in depth with a few topics:

Units and rates of change, exact and approximate numbers; Exercises 2–4, 7, 30–32.

Scientific notation; Exercises 6, 8–29.

Vectors; Exercises 1 and 5.

Time Measurement and Angle Measurement

These quantities are explicitly discussed because they are needed in exercises and for the introduction to the concept of a vector.

Rates

The discussion of rates of change presents the notion of compound units. It also helps lay the groundwork for the introduction of slope of a line in Chapter 2 and, ultimately, for derivatives in calculus.

Scientific Notation

This is intended as just a basic introduction using positive exponents. Negative exponents are introduced in Chapter 4, at which point the discussion of scientific notation is extended. Many students, however, may be expected to use scientific notation in other courses even while taking this course.

Vectors

Vectors are included here only to contrast them with scalar quantities as another kind of measured quantity. A detailed treatment awaits an introduction to trigonometry, although this is an excellent place to become familiar with vectors in a nontrigonometric context, especially if Exercises 1 and 5 are assigned.

Example 40

A detailed look at the inherent error in the volume calculation is included in Exercise 2.

Special Notes on Exercises

⇒Exercise 1 continues the discussion of vectors and asks students to identify some vector quantities.

Exercise 2 extends the previous discussions of maximum likely error to volume computation.

Exercise 3 asks students to express changes in quantities as rates.

Exercise 4 contrasts *unit* and *dimension*. There are also two uses of the word *length* here: a generic use of length as a dimension and a specific use of length as the longest measurement of a box-shaped object.

Exercise 5 provides practice in sketching vectors and compares distance with displacement.

Exercise 6, estimating orders of magnitude of (mostly) everyday things, could be a good group activity. A competition could even be arranged, with the group coming closest to the correct order of magnitude in each item getting a point, etc.

Exercise 7 brings closure to the chapter and provides a capstone to the work with measurement. Students should be encouraged to devote some time to this project, preferably working in groups, and to treat the report as an actual presentation to a supervisor or design group.

Exercises 8–15 provide practice with scientific notation.

❏ Exercises 16–21 help students distinguish between calculator displays and correct scientific notation form.

Exercises 22–29 are contextual practice with unit conversions and scientific notation.

Exercises 30–32 ask students to distinguish between exact and approximate numbers in calculations.

Chapter Review

The first question of each Chapter Review in this course asks students to summarize the important mathematical ideas found in the chapter. This has been designed to get students to think about what they learned in the chapter.

The breakdown of the exercises in the Chapter Review by section is:

Chapter Summary	Exercise 1
Section 1.1	Exercises 2 and 3
Section 1.2	Exercises 4–8
Section 1.3	Exercises 9–13
Section 1.4	Exercises 14–19
Section 1.5	Exercises 20–24
Section 1.6	Exercises 25–29

Instructor Notes

Chapter 2: Linear Models

Goals of the Chapter

- To model linear relationships using expressions, equations, graphs, and tables
- To recognize linear behavior and represent it mathematically
- To evaluate mathematical expressions
- To solve linear equations

What You Will Learn

Section 2.1

- To evaluate simple expressions

Section 2.2

- To use the distributive property
- To use the order of operations rules when evaluating expressions
- To use a calculator and/or spreadsheet to evaluate expressions
- To model real-world situations with algebraic expressions

Section 2.3

- To translate statements into mathematical equations
- To identify terms, factors, and coefficients in an expression
- To use algebraic operations to solve an equation for the value of one unknown quantity
- To solve literal equations and formulas

Section 2.4

- To identify the independent and dependent variables in a given situation
- To identify the range and domain of a function
- To recognize a function when given the equation or graph
- To recognize and use different representations of functions such as verbal descriptions, equations, arrow diagrams, tables, and graphs
- To determine if a point lies on the graph of a function when given its graph or equation

Section 2.5

- To recognize a function as a linear function given an equation, a table, or a graph
- To construct a graph of a linear function from a table of values
- To find the intercepts of the graph of a linear function
- To find the slope of a line given two points on the line
- To use slope-intercept form to sketch the graph of a linear function
- To find an equation of a linear function given the slope and y-intercept of its graph

Section 2.6

- To find an equation of a line given its slope and one of its points
- To find an equation of a line given two of its points
- To find an equation of a line given its graph
- To identify parallel and perpendicular lines by examining their slopes

What You Need To Know

Section 2.1

- How to use a pan balance

Section 2.2

- How to find the area of a rectangle
- How to evaluate simple expressions

Section 2.3

- How to use the order of operations guidelines
- How to use the distributive property
- How to construct expressions

Section 2.4

- How to solve an equation
- How to read simple graphs and charts

Section 2.5

- How to identify the independent and dependent variables for a given situation

- How to identify the range and domain of a function

- How to recognize a function when given a table or graph

- How to recognize and use different representations of functions such as verbal descriptions, equations, arrow diagrams, tables, and graphs

Section 2.6

- How to find the slope of a line

- How to find an equation for a line given its slope and y-intercept

- How to graph the equation of a line

Instructor Notes for Chapter 2

Introduction to Chapter 2

This chapter introduces the general concept of modeling relationships involving two or more variables and, specifically, the properties of linear relationships between two variables.

The chapter begins with an examination of how algebraic expressions can be used to model real situations. Evaluation of expressions leads naturally into the solution of linear equations. Methods of solution begin with arrow diagrams and include algebraic operations, tables, and graphs.

Functions and their properties are introduced for the general case before concentrating on linear functions for the remainder of the chapter. Multiple representations are discussed: verbal statements, algebraic expressions and equations, arrow diagrams, tables, and graphs. Students are encouraged to view all of the various representations of a function as interchangeable.

After completing this chapter, students will be prepared to examine and analyze bivariate data in Chapter 3.

Preparation Reading

The discussion is intended to provide a transition from the emphasis in Chapter 1 on a single variable and statistical variation, along with basic geometric models, to algebraic and graphical modeling involving more than one variable.

Section 2.1

The activity in this section may require one class period.

The notion of a function providing a means of determining the value of one quantity from the value of another is examined here. The robotic system referred to at the beginning of the section demonstrates the need for such a relationship.

Activity 2.1

This activity gives students direct experience with the concepts of input and output variables and the construction of algebraic expressions. The weights of various quantities of nails are found in order to provide an easily measured set of data that, in contrast with the volume/weight example preceding it, produces a uniformly linear relationship.

A balance that measures in grams can probably be borrowed from a science department storeroom. The reason for the reliance on units of grams is that most balances having the required precision use metric units. (A balance measuring in ounces would have to be accurate to the nearest 0.01 ounce.) It is technically incorrect to speak of the weight of an object as being measured in grams, since the gram is a unit of mass. However, it is common in many professional fields to use this terminology, and it would be awkward to continually refer to mass measurement with an audience that is unlikely to be familiar with the concept of mass as distinct from weight. It is perhaps unfortunate that it has been traditional for metric measurements of "heaviness" to rely on mass, whereas the older English (now U.S. Customary) system continues to use weight. The unit of mass in the U.S. Customary system is the slug, while the unit of force (and weight) in the SI (metric) system is the newton.

If balances or nails are not available, give students the completed table as presented in item 4 of Activity 2.1.

Any size nails can be used for the activity, but 10d nails are common. (A nail's "penny rating" originally referred to its price per hundred, but is now used primarily as a measure of length. For example, a 10d nail is 3 inches long, an 8d nail is $2\frac{1}{2}$ inches, and a 16d nail is $3\frac{1}{2}$ inches. The abbreviation "d" is derived from the denarius, an early Roman coin.) There should be virtually no variation in the weight of a 10d nail if measured to the nearest 0.1 gram, so it is suggested that students measure only to that precision. It is essential that the weight increments as nails are added to the balance be as constant as possible.

If time permits, any or all of the four exercises in Extend the Activity can be performed to provide further insight into creating expressions to model real quantities. Alternatively, they may be assigned as homework, provided that the required data is collected in class.

Section 2.2

This section requires one class period, although some instructors may wish to assign only Exercises 1–6 for the first night's homework and reserve the Additional Practice exercises for a second night.

This section lays the groundwork for the study of algebra, focusing on the origins and structure of algebraic expressions along with the distributive property and order of operations. Area models are introduced in order to provide a visual representation for expressions. Such models are used throughout the text in various mathematical contexts. Arrow diagrams are used to construct expressions, in preparation for their use as an aid in solving equations and representing functions later in the chapter.

Discovery 2.1

Encourage students to work in pairs. This invites them to verbalize their thoughts and questions as they build an understanding of the use of algebraic expressions to represent relationships among real quantities. The distributive property is "discovered" as providing an alternative way to write certain types of expressions.

As the students are becoming familiar with the distributive property, you may need to point out that the distributive property applies to any number of addends. For example, $a(b + c + d) = ab + ac + ad$. Furthermore, since division is equivalent to multiplication by the reciprocal of the divisor, the distributive property can be applied to division, as in $\dfrac{b+c+d}{a} = \dfrac{1}{a}(b+c+d) = \dfrac{b}{a} + \dfrac{c}{a} + \dfrac{d}{a}$.

You may also wish to point out that since multiplication is commutative, the distributive property also applies to $(b + c)a$. Example 1(e) shows this.

Using Technology to Evaluate Algebraic Expressions

In this section, students can see how the rules of algebra are adapted to calculators and computer spreadsheets. Since many students will use (and may already have used) spreadsheets in connection with their work, the identification of "cell A2" with the variable in the algebraic form of the expression can be particularly effective in reinforcing the notion of "variable." Students should check their calculator manuals if their calculators use different commands than those illustrated in Figures 2.4–2.10.

Special Notes on Exercises

Exercises 1–6 provide important practice in modeling real-world situations with expressions, according to appropriate algebraic rules.

Exercise 7 is an Internet research project and might be appropriate as an extra credit assignment.

❏ Exercise 8 is optional. Virtually all contemporary calculators employ algebraic logic, but there are some, especially older models and some financial calculators, that do not. They merely perform operations in sequence without regard to order of operations priorities.

Exercises 9–41 are primarily drill exercises on algebraic expressions and operations: 9-21 involve evaluation of expressions (17 with a calculator, 18–21 contextual), 22–28 and 39–41 involve modeling with expressions, and 31–38 involve the distributive property.

Section 2.3

Unless students are already skilled at solving equations, two class periods may be needed for this section. Discovery 2.2 and the fundamentals of equation solving (through Example 6) can be done in one period. A second day should be devoted to the remainder of the section.

Exercises 1–5, 7–14, and 16–26 can be assigned after the first day. The remaining exercises can be assigned after the second day.

Discovery 2.2

Working in pairs, students learn to use arrow diagrams to model equations and are introduced to the use of inverse operations to "undo" the results of algebraic operations.

The Hints for Solving Equations box is meant to provide general guidelines. Students should understand the need for flexibility in their application. Sometimes more than one sequence of operations will work in solving equations. (Exercise 6 deals explicitly with the latter.) Students should be especially encouraged to identify which inverse operations are needed to undo connections in an equation (see Exercise 1). In Example 5, an alternative solution to that presented in the text could be examined: first subtract 16, then divide by –3, since the parentheses override the normal order of operations.

The distinction between exact and approximate solutions, as in Example 5, is worth emphasizing here, especially for technical students and as a follow-up to the development in Chapter 1. Examples 12 and 13 are also important for technical students, as they contain the kinds of numbers often found in technical work.

The Formulas and Literal Equations section is especially important for technical students, as solving for different variables in formulas is often an important part of technical work. For further examples, refer to any physics textbook.

Special Notes on Exercises
Exercise 1 involves critical thinking regarding the concept of inverse operations.

Exercise 2 is an application of equation writing and solving in the interesting contemporary application of cryptography, which can be extended (as suggested in Exercise 8) to allow students to challenge each other to "crack" codes by solving equations made up by the students. Exercise 8 also uses matrices in the context of making codes more difficult to crack.

❏ Exercise 3 discusses the use of the TABLE feature of a graphing calculator to solve equations numerically.

Exercise 4 provides practice in writing equations to model real-world problems.

⇒Exercise 5 explains the principles for solving inequalities. Some instructors may wish to supplement this exercise with additional practice in solving inequalities.

Exercise 6 illustrates that more than one sequence of operations may be used to solve some equations.

Exercise 7 provides another opportunity for students to test each other by making up equations to solve.

Exercises 9–45 provide necessary practice in solving equations (9–17 being contextual).

Section 2.4

The material in this section is designed for a single class meeting. However, it may be beneficial to split the exercises into two homework assignments. Exercises 1–6, involving critical thinking regarding functions, could be assigned the first night. The second class period could be devoted to Group Activities in Exercises 7 and 8, with the Additional Practice Exercises 9–34 assigned the second night.

Properties of functions are discussed: dependent and independent variables, domain (and restrictions), and range. The concept of problem domain is introduced. The various ways of representing a function—verbal description, arrow diagram, equation, table, and graph—are explored. Students gain experience in reading and interpreting graphs and in identifying functions given in the various representations.

When defining a function, if the "exactly one output" concept causes trouble, use an analogy with calculator keys. We expect calculators to give the same result if the same input and key are used, but it is okay for two different input/key combinations to give identical results.

Special Notes on Exercises

Exercises 1–5 involve critical thinking regarding the definition of a function, domain, and problem domain.

⇒Exercise 6 introduces the vertical line test and asks students to justify why the test is valid.

The main purpose of Exercises 7 and 8 is to encourage students to examine graphs qualitatively; that is, to look at the key features of a graph and interpret those features in a given context. Exercise 7 asks students to choose which graph is most appropriate for a given situation, while Exercise 8 asks students to sketch a qualitative graph when given a situation.

Additional Practice Exercises 9–34 provide practice in applying and interpreting the multiple representations of functions: verbal descriptions, arrow diagrams, tables, equations, and graphs.

Section 2.5

This section could be done in one class period, although most instructors will probably prefer to devote two days to it (and possibly three—see Exercise 8 note). The first day can be spent on Discovery 2.3, with a discussion on average rate of change and on tables and graphs of linear functions. The second day would then start with Slope of a Line.

Exercises 1, 3–5, 10, and 12–21 can be assigned after the first day. The remaining exercises require knowledge of slope.

Discovery 2.3

We return to the situation that introduced the chapter. Although the robotic system modeled here uses a direct weight measurement to determine volume, this activity examines weight as a function of volume primarily because it results in straightforward interpretation of the vertical intercept. (The V-intercept, on the other hand, is not in the problem domain.) Students search for patterns in a table and observe a constant rate of change. They are then introduced to constructing the graph of a function and will notice the linear behavior of this particular function. The sidebar just before item 8 points out that the horizontal and vertical axes of a graph are often referred to as the x-axis and y-axis even when the variables on the graph have other names. Item 14 can be used as a springboard for a discussion of rates of change, beginning with an examination of why the shape of the graph changes for different liquids. (Notice that the slope of the graph in this context is numerically equal to the density of the liquid.)

The discussion under Identifying Linear Functions initially emphasizes *average rate of change*, since in general only an average rate (as distinct from an instantaneous rate) is defined over a finite interval, although for a linear function the distinction becomes irrelevant.

The short section Using Tables to Graph Linear Functions asks students to begin with an equation and construct a table and graph of the function, whereas in Discovery 2.3 students began with a table and then found the equation and graph. Notice that the graph (Figure 2.58) in Example 19 has different scales on the x- and y-axes. It may be worth pointing this out to students, as at this stage they may tend to assume that the slope of a line always corresponds to the actual geometrical steepness of the line as it appears on a graph. For purposes of clarity, graphs are often constructed with different scales on the two axes. (This topic is explicitly discussed under the heading Interpreting Graphs in Section 2.6.)

The remainder of Section 2.5 introduces the slope-intercept form of the equation of a line and its connection to the graph of a linear function. Students may need to be reminded that the equation $y = 2.5x - 7$ can be written as $y = 2.5x + (-7)$ in order to conform more closely to slope-intercept form.

Special Notes on Exercises

⇒Exercise 1 contrasts graphs involving discrete and continuous independent variables and asks students to consider whether a continuous line is appropriate as the graph of any function. Although (as is noted in the text) graphs of discrete variables are often drawn as if they were continuous, students should be aware of situations where such graphs mask the underlying discrete nature of the variables. Not examined are cases in which the independent variable is continuous and the dependent variable is discrete (e.g., postage versus weight of a letter), which would require step functions.

Exercise 2 involves practice in creating and interpreting a linear model of a real-world situation.

⇒Exercise 3 explores direct variation and is particularly important for technical students. In (g), the stated weight of 0.45 pounds for 100 requisitions is an estimate.

⇒Exercise 4 illustrates graphing a line using intercepts.

❑ Exercise 5 explores graphing calculator issues related to linear functions.

⇒Exercises 6 and 7 introduce equations of vertical and horizontal lines.

⇒Exercise 8 is an introduction to systems of linear equations. Instructors for whom an early and thorough introduction to this subject is necessary may need to supplement this exercise with extra drill problems.

Exercises 9–12 are contextual in nature, examining linear functions.

In Exercises 13–15, students examine tables and graphs for linearity.

Exercises 16–20 involve using tables to create graphs.

Exercise 21 asks students to determine whether points lie on the graph of a given function.

Exercises 22–35 involve slope, slope-intercept form, and sketching graphs.

Exercises 36–42 ask students to sketch graphs of lines when given a point and a slope.

Exercises 43–52 ask for the equation of a line given various kinds of information.

Exercises 53–56 involve critical thinking regarding graphs of linear functions.

Section 2.6

The material in this section is designed for a single class meeting.

This lesson provides students with the necessary tools to find equations of lines given specific information such as a point on the line and the slope of the line.

The rule of thumb shown in the graph in Figure 2.78 can be stated as follows: A person 5 feet tall should weigh 100 pounds; for each inch over 5 feet, add 5 pounds.

Discovery 2.4

Students are asked to create a mathematical model (find an equation) for a given graph. The items in the activity point out the need for additional ways of finding an equation of a line other than using the slope-intercept form.

Item 4 asks students to find the y-intercept for the graph. You may need to point out to students that the zigzag on the x-axis indicates a break in scale. The x-coordinate of the y-intercept is 0, and students cannot simply extend the graph to see where it crosses the y-axis. How they go about finding the y-intercept will vary. Some students may notice the pattern that for every 10 inches of decline in height, the weight decreases by 50 pounds. Others may redraw the graph to include the missing part of the x-axis. Either method works well.

After students have completed the activity, discuss with the class why the rule of thumb model is not a good model and that if we need a model to predict ideal weight from height, we would have to refine this one.

Talk about how the linear model might be refined. This context can be used at a later time to introduce nonlinear models.

Point-Slope Form

In the exposition following Discovery 2.4, the point-slope form for the equation of a line is introduced using the slope m and a point (h, k). The reason for using (h, k) rather than the traditional (x_1, y_1) is that subscripts, which often cause problems for students, are avoided. Using the variables h and k will also prepare students for translations of graphs such as circles.

Parallel and Perpendicular Lines

When discussing parallel and perpendicular lines, you may want to ask students why we specify that the lines must be distinct and nonvertical.

Special Notes on Exercises

Exercises 1 and 2 provide contextual practice with many of the chapter objectives.

Exercises 3 and 4 lay the contextual groundwork for some of the modeling explorations in Chapter 3.

⇒Exercise 5 discusses piecewise linear functions and how they can be used to model certain situations.

❑Exercise 6 continues the theme of deceptive graphs, but this time calculator graphs are explored.

Exercise 7 leads students through the proof (for one particular case) that two lines are perpendicular if their slopes are negative reciprocals of each other.

Exercises 9–28, 33, and 34 ask students to find an equation given various kinds of information.

Exercises 29–32 ask students to examine equations of lines and tell if the lines are parallel, perpendicular, or neither.

Chapter Review

The breakdown of exercises by section is:

Chapter Summary	Exercise 1
Sections 2.1 and 2.2	Exercises 2–5
Section 2.3	Exercises 6–12
Section 2.4	Exercises 13–18
Section 2.5	Exercises 19–25
Section 2.6	Exercises 26–33

Instructor Notes

Chapter 3: Modeling Behavior from Data

Goals of the Chapter

- To explore two-variable data analysis

- To further understanding of linear relationships

What You Will Learn

Section 3.1

- To create a scatter plot from collected data

- To examine a scatter plot for linear patterns

- To estimate a line of best fit to model data in a scatter plot

Section 3.2

- To examine scatter plots for linear patterns

- To use trial and error to create linear models describing data in scatter plots

- To use linear models to make predictions

Section 3.3

- To describe the direction, form, and strength of scatter plots

- To calculate residuals

- To use a calculator or spreadsheet to determine an equation of the least-squares line

- To use the least-squares equation to make predictions

Section 3.4

- To apply the modeling process in order to refine mathematical models

- To develop criteria for assessing the quality of fit of a model

- To use residual plots to assess whether a model is adequate to describe given data

- To use the correlation coefficient as a measure of strength and direction of a linear relationship

- To recognize the influence of outliers

What You Need to Know

Section 3.1

- How to plot points in the coordinate plane
- How to find the slope of a line
- How to find the equation of a line given two points on the line

Section 3.2

- How to create a scatter plot from given data
- How to find the equation of a line when given various properties

Section 3.3

- How to recognize linear patterns in scatter plots
- How to create linear models that describe data in scatter plots
- How to use linear models to make predictions

Section 3.4

- How to use a calculator or spreadsheet to determine an equation of the least-squares line
- How to identify patterns in a scatter plot

Instructor Notes for Chapter 3

Introduction to Chapter 3

The main goal of this unit is to reinforce the concept of linearity begun in Chapter 2 and to examine how it is used to create mathematical models.

Taking into account the time and curriculum constraints for this course, instructors may choose to do all or only parts of this chapter. Suggestions for several paths through the chapter are as follows:

- It is suggested that all courses cover Sections 3.1 and 3.2, as these sections provide additional insight into the concept of linearity and using linear models.

- If the curriculum suggests the topics of residuals and/or using technology to find the least-squares line, all or parts of Section 3.3 should be used.

- Section 3.4 formally introduces the modeling process and explains how residuals are used to help assess the quality of linear regression models.

Preparation Reading

This reading provides the student with insight on how a mathematical model might originate. It also discusses two uses of data. The Reflect and Discuss questions are designed to encourage students to think about using data and models in the real world.

Section 3.1

The material in this section is designed for a single class meeting.

The activity in this section requires students to collect data. Remind students that because the data will be pooled with the entire class, some decisions on measurement techniques and accuracy need to be addressed prior to data collection. It is probably easier to use metric units, but this decision can be left to the class. Whatever the decision, group data should all be in the same units.

As students are taking their measurements, make note of sloppy procedures. These can be talked about after all data are collected, recorded, and displayed in a scatter plot. This provides a good basis of discussion for data that do not seem to fit the pattern.

Caution! Before making a scatter plot of the data, make sure that the data are pooled. You want at least 20–30 ordered pairs of data before proceeding with item 3. If the number of students in class is smaller than this, suggest that students collect data from people outside the classroom.

If students were assigned Exercise 3 in Section 2.6, have them compare their equation from item 9 to the relationship given between the forearm length and the height of a typical female. Ask why the models are not the same. Answers may include the following: The students in class may be very different from the "typical" female, data in class includes males and females, and errors may have been made in measurement.

Extend the Activity

This extension begins by asking students for a contextual interpretation of the y-intercept of their algebraic model. It also provides height versus forearm data for practice. Students are then asked to compare the results from their own data and the one given here.

❑ Item 13 asks students to use technology to make a scatter plot and to graph their equation on the plot.

Section 3.2

This section is designed for a single class meeting or can even be assigned as homework after Section 3.1.

It may be worth noting in class the use of the word *versus*. This term helps distinguish the independent and dependent variables in a relationship.

Example 2

You may wish to point out that it is possible to choose a model that passes through none of the data points. In that case, students should choose two points on their line to find an equation.

This example illustrates using both a graphical model of the data (c) and an algebraic model of the data (e) to make predictions. Following this example is a discussion of using models to predict within the range of the data and outside the range (extrapolation). Caution is urged when extrapolation is used.

Special Notes on Exercises

In Exercise 1, as well as in other places throughout the chapter, students may wonder how the independent and dependent variables were chosen. Sometimes it is clear and sometimes it is not. It is also worth pointing out that there are times that it really does not matter. This always leads to a good discussion.

Be sure to assign Exercise 2 because it requires students to use data to evaluate a model that was created in a previous exercise. Remind students that this is all part of the modeling process.

In Exercise 3(a), the year 1970 can be thought of as year 0, with the independent variable being time t. In this case, the equation would be $P = 16.8t + 310$. For the data on the percent of women physicians in (d), the equation using time since 1970 as the independent variable would be $W = 0.53t + 7$.

Exercise 4 asks students to use their line of best fit to predict within and outside the range of the data. Students are asked to comment on how accurate they think their predictions are.

❏ Exercise 5 utilizes the Texas Instruments CBL or CBR. This provides a perfect opportunity for students to collect their own data. This activity gives students a real sense of rate of change.

Exercise 6 asks students to repeat the activity in Section 3.1 but to use different measurements. They are asked to compare the original model and the new one created in the activity and decide which model would be more reliable in predicting height.

Exercises 7–10 ask students to create scatter plots from tables of data.

Exercises 11–15 ask students to estimate a line of best fit and find the equation of the line drawn.

In Exercises 16 and 17, students are given a scatter plot with a line of best fit drawn in. They are asked to find the equation of the line and use the equation to make predictions.

Exercise 18 is a comprehensive question that gives a table of data and asks for predictions.

Exercises 19–22 ask students to look for patterns in scatter plots.

In Exercise 23, students draw a line of fit by using the criteria of "half the points above the line and half below the line." They are then asked to explain why this is not a good model for the data.

Section 3.3

The material in this section may take more than one day to cover. If that is the case, this section can be broken into Parts I and II. Part I (up to and including Example 4) covers assessing a scatter plot and the geometric introduction to residuals. Part II then covers the concept of the least-squares criterion and the use of technology to find the least-squares line. Exercises 1 and 7–14 can be assigned after Part I is covered. Any or all of the remaining exercises can be assigned after Part II.

Discovery 3.1

Discovery 3.1 requires students to create a data-driven model and to compare their model with others in the class. Because the model is found by "eyeballing" the data, models will differ. This activity provides the perfect opportunity to talk about optimization and which model is best. Also discuss item 5, listing different student-suggested criteria.

Example 4

In Example 4, make sure students understand that the geometric interpretation of residual is the vertical segment from the point (actual y-value) to the line (predicted y-value). It is not the segment defined as "distance from the point to the line," which is the segment from the point perpendicular to the line.

Special Notes on Exercises

Exercise 1 describes and gives data for an experiment that measures the force needed to move a brick(s) at a constant velocity. You may want to mention that a brick moving with constant velocity is in equilibrium and that the applied force equals the frictional force. Also, the slope of the graph represents the coefficient of friction, μ, for the two surfaces involved.

❏ Exercises 2 and 3 provide practice finding equations of least-squares lines and using them to make predictions.

Exercise 4 asks students to investigate the relationship between the diameter of a circle and its circumference. If the data are accurate, the slope of the least-squares line should be close to π. If students are asked to think about the formula that relates the diameter and the circumference, $C = \pi d$, they should recognize that π is the slope of the line.

Exercise 5 returns to students' data-driven models from Discovery 3.1 and asks them to make predictions outside the range of the data. Data for four years after the original data is then supplied. Reiterate the use of caution when extrapolating from data.

Exercises 7–14 provide practice with skills and concepts introduced in the lesson.

❏ Exercises 15 and 16 use technology to determine the equation of the least-squares line.

Section 3.4

The material in this section can be divided into two one-day lessons. If you choose to split the lesson into two parts, the logical break occurs just prior to Discovery 3.2. The first part of the section discusses the modeling process, residuals, and residual plots. The second part of the section, which includes Discovery 3.2, discusses making predictions from two or more models. The correlation coefficient is introduced after the discovery. If you choose to divide the section, any of the following exercises are appropriate for assignment after the first day: 2, 7, 8, 9, 10, 11, 12, 13, 14, 17, and 18.

The Modeling Process

Point out to students that the modeling process does not stop when a model is found. This process continues until the model yields results that are accurate enough for the situation involved.

Assessing the Quality of Fit

Examination of residuals can help us make decisions as to whether our model adequately describes the relationship we are studying. Make sure students continue to ask themselves both of the following questions when they are looking at the residuals: Are the residuals relatively small? Are they randomly scattered above and below the line?

The light bulb activity leads students through the process of using calculators to make scatter plots, determining the least-squares equation, calculating the residuals, and creating a residual plot.

Discovery 3.2

Discovery 3.2 can be used as an in-class activity or as an individual homework assignment.

Correlation Coefficient

The correlation coefficient, r, is mentioned in this section because for some calculators it will appear when students do a linear regression. This value can be helpful in assessing the goodness of fit, but as Exercise 1 will demonstrate, equal r-values do not necessarily indicate equally good fits.

Special Notes on Exercises

$\Rightarrow$ Exercise 2 provides an opportunity for students to apply the modeling process. In this exercise, they are asked to determine a model, examine it, decide it is not as good as it could be, and then refine the model. Most likely, students will need to refer to their calculator manual to find how to graph a piecewise function.

$\Rightarrow$ Exercise 3 introduces the term *outlier*. This exercise should be completed before Exercises 4, 15, or 16 are attempted.

Exercise 19 provides data that are definitely nonlinear. Students should see a definite pattern in the residual plot. This exercise should lead students to wonder what can be done to refine the model.

Chapter Review

For instructors who use only parts of this chapter, the breakdown of the exercises in the Chapter Review by section is:

Section 3.1   Exercises 2 and 3

Section 3.2 Part I   Exercises 4–8, 10–12

Section 3.2 Part II   Exercises 9 (a)–(b), 13 (a)–(d), 14

Section 3.3   Exercises 9 (c), 13 (e)–(f)

Instructor Notes

Chapter 4 Polynomials and Exponents

Goals of the Chapter

- To recognize and use polynomials to model situations and solve problems
- To perform operations with polynomials
- To use properties of exponents to simplify expressions

What You Will Learn

Section 4.1

- To model a real-world situation with a polynomial

Section 4.2

- To use the properties of exponents to simplify expressions containing exponents
- To multiply and divide numbers expressed in scientific notation

Section 4.3

- To recognize a polynomial expression
- To add, subtract, and multiply polynomial expressions
- To divide a polynomial expression by a monomial

Section 4.4

- To factor polynomial expressions
- To recognize prime numbers and prime polynomial expressions

Section 4.5

- To model some situations with polynomial functions
- To graph polynomial functions
- To solve equations containing factorable polynomials

What You Need to Know

Section 4.1

- How to use percents in calculations

Section 4.2

- How to evaluate an expression containing exponents
- How to express large numbers using scientific notation

Section 4.3

- How to use the properties of exponents to simplify expressions containing exponents
- How to combine like terms

Section 4.4

- How to add, subtract, and multiply polynomials
- How to apply the properties of exponents

Section 4.5

- How to graph a linear function
- How to evaluate polynomial expressions

Instructor Notes for Chapter 4

Introduction to Chapter 4

This chapter introduces properties of exponents and provides a first detailed look at a class of nonlinear functions, the polynomials. Polynomial arithmetic, factoring, and solving factorable equations are included.

After a brief discussion of real-world situations that can be described by polynomials, the chapter begins with a simplified modeling activity (Section 4.1) based on the important environmental problem of hazardous waste cleanup. Students write a one-term polynomial function to model the dilution of a contaminant. The cost of environmental cleanup leads to a discussion of properties of exponents in Section 4.2, followed by the definition of a polynomial and by operations with polynomials in Section 4.3. The need for solving polynomial equations motivates factoring in Section 4.4, and the chapter concludes with an examination of a variety of polynomial models.

The polynomial model in the initial environmental cleanup activity is used in Exercise 7 of Section 4.2 in a different context (caffeine elimination by the human body). Then in Exercise 1 of Section 4.5, the environmental context is revisited with a graphical exploration of polynomial models.

Preparation Reading

This reading gives a brief introduction to polynomials and their graphs. It also provides a connection to previous chapters and examines the use of polynomials in today's world.

Section 4.1

This section can be completed in one day. It contains an activity in which students add a "contaminant" to a fixed volume of water. They then physically model an environmental cleanup process through successive dilutions of the contaminated water. By constructing a table of the dilution values, they are led to find a pattern that enables them to eventually write a simple one-term polynomial expression to model the process. Notice that a similar development could be used to introduce exponential functions by focusing on the exponent as the variable. But here the student is asked (item 11) to consider the base to be the variable, making the expression a one-term polynomial.

The "dyed liquid" that represents contaminant can be created by adding roughly one or two drops of food coloring to 200 milliliters of water. This should enable students to observe a change in color as the dilution process occurs. The term "dyed liquid" is used in the activity to avoid confusion that might occur if students worry about the total amount of water involved if a water solution is added.

Metric units are used in the activity to make it easier for students to do the calculations.

If students have trouble writing the table entries for the fourth and fifth flushings (item 6), encourage them to model each step physically with their liquid.

The nature of a polynomial expression is introduced informally at the end of the activity. A more formal definition is presented in Section 4.3, after students are more familiar with exponents.

The sidebar in the introductory discussion for this section refers to "hydrocarbons" as groundwater contaminants. This is a general term for organic chemicals based on hydrogen and carbon and includes such compounds as toluene, trichloroethylene (TCE), polyvinyl chlorides (PVCs), and polychlorinated biphenyls (PCBs). More information about the EPA and Superfund can be found at www.epa.gov/superfund/.

Section 4.2

This section can be completed in one day.

This section begins by returning to our context from Section 4.1. The problem posed requires division of two numbers written in scientific notation. The solution to the problem appears later in the section after students have explored multiplication and division of exponents.

Discovery 4.1

This discovery reminds students of the meaning of an exponent and helps them develop the properties (rules) for multiplying and dividing powers of like bases. The meanings of zero and negative exponents are also explored. Make sure students can generalize the properties and definition in items 2, 5, and 6. The last item in the discovery (item 11) asks students to summarize their findings.

Examples 1 and 2

Examples 1 and 2 show students that often more than one method can be used to evaluate expressions that contain exponents. Remind students of the cautionary note in the sidebar in Discovery 4.1. Failure to distinguish between -3^2 and $(-3)^2$ creates problems for many students.

Example 4

Example 4 shows how these rules apply to numbers written in scientific notation.

Negative Exponents and Scientific Notation

This section returns to our original discussion of scientific notation from Chapter 1. Now that the students have been introduced to negative exponents, we can use scientific notation to express small numbers.

More Exponent Properties

Properties for finding the power of a product, power of a power, and power of a quotient are given to the student and examples are shown. Continue to point out that if the rules are forgotten or if students get confused, they can always use the meaning of an exponent to redevelop the property.

Special Notes on Exercises

Exercises 1–5 provide a review of scientific notation and contextual practice multiplying and dividing numbers in scientific notation. With regard to Exercise 5, pictures made by the Galileo spacecraft of Jupiter and its moons can be viewed on the NASA Web site (www.nasa.gov).

⇒ Exercise 6 discusses problems that arise when the denominators of fractions are zero. Although not mentioned in the text, the expression 0^0 can sometimes come about in certain ways that do allow for a reasonable numerical interpretation, usually involving calculus. In such contexts, forms like 0^0 are referred to as "indeterminate."

Exercise 7 provides a contextual variation on Activity 4.1. In (d), students are asked to write a polynomial that models introducing more contaminant (in this case, coffee) at some point in time during the dilution or kidney-cleansing process. If students experience difficulty with this part of the exercise, suggest they make a table as in (a).

❑ The objective of the group activity in Exercise 8 is for students to use the CBL and light probe to verify the theory that if l is the fraction of the light that passes through 1 filter, then $(l)^n$ is the fraction of the light that passes through n filters. Directions for the data collection are provided; (c) is most important. To find the fraction of the light that passes through 1 filter, divide the amount of light that passes through 1 filter by the amount of light that passes through 0 filters. If these two measurements are off, the remaining data could deviate considerably from the predictions. One hint is to make sure that it is as dark as possible when measurements are taken.

Exercises 9 and 10 are contextual, while 11–37 provide drill in simplifying expressions that contain exponents.

Exercises 38–52 provide practice with scientific notation.

Section 4.3

This section can be completed in one day.

Polynomials were defined informally in Section 4.1. The definition is formalized in this section. The formal definition may look intimidating to students. Taking a few minutes of class time to explain its meaning could be worthwhile.

Discovery 4.2

As most instructors have experienced, students often attempt to add unlike terms when simplifying polynomial expressions. Discovery 4.2 provides an opportunity for students to examine geometric representations of like and unlike terms in hopes that this error in thinking can be avoided.

Examples of subtracting (Example 11), multiplying a polynomial by a monomial (Examples 12 and 13), and dividing a polynomial by a monomial (Example 14) are given.

Multiplying a Binomial by a Binomial

Students are then shown two methods for multiplying two binomials. Allow students to use whichever method is most comfortable for them. Eventually all should see that the "horizontal" method is most efficient.

Special Notes on Exercises

Exercise 1(a): A brief review of surface area may be needed here. If that is the case, you may want to mention that surface area can be thought of as the amount of paint needed to paint the outside of a cube or the amount of cardboard it would take to make a box of this same size and shape.

Exercise 1(b): Watch for students who include the two faces that are inside the solid when they are expressing surface area. If students do not combine like terms when writing the expression for the surface area, ask if their expression can be simplified by adding. This exercise and others about area and volume are much easier if students have physical cubes to use as they reason through the problem.

Exercise 1(c): If students do not simplify the volume to $4x^2y$, take time to discuss this. Physical objects are useful here. Cuisenaire rods are helpful in building the shapes. Show the specific volumes in the figure. What does x^2y look like? What does x^2 look like in the figure? What does xy look like? Are they alike?

❏ In Exercises 2 and 3, students create polynomial expressions and then evaluate them.

⇒ Exercise 4 demonstrates how area models can be used to multiply numbers and asks students to expand this thinking into multiplying binomials. This model is then used in Exercise 5 to show the various allele combinations in offspring of a population.

⇒ In Exercise 6, students notice that not only are the coefficients the same as the numbers in Pascal's triangle, but also that there is a pattern within the expanded binomial itself. When $(a + b)$ is raised to the fourth power, have students look at the variables from left to right: The exponent of a decreases by 1 as the exponent of b increases by 1. Also, the sum of the exponents of the variables in each term is always 4, the power to which you are raising the binomial.

Exercises 7–10 provide practice writing polynomial expressions along with practice finding areas of plane figures.

Exercises 11–21 provide practice identifying polynomials and writing polynomials that fit a particular description.

Exercises 22–49 provide practice adding, subtracting, and multiplying polynomials.

Exercises 50 and 51 provide practice cubing a binomial.

Section 4.4

This section may take more than one day, depending on students' prior experiences with factoring.

The section opens with a problem for which an algebraic model is given. Students are told that the problem can be solved by setting the function equal to zero and factoring it. Factoring is introduced in this section, and solving polynomial equations is explored in Section 4.5. The solution to the problem is given in Section 4.5, Example 22.

Have students pay close attention to the sidebars, as they all provide important information.

Prior to Discovery 4.3, students are shown how to factor polynomials that have a common factor in each term.

Discovery 4.3

The focus of this discovery is finding patterns to factor trinomials with leading coefficients of 1. Remind students that any time they propose a factored form of a polynomial, they should multiply the factors to check their work.

After the discovery is completed, factoring trinomial squares and the difference of two squares is presented. The section ends with a summary of factoring procedures.

Special Notes on Exercises

⇒ Exercise 1 presents the trial-and-error method of factoring trinomials with leading coefficients not equal to 1. It is up to you, the instructor, as to whether you wish to introduce this procedure or not.

Exercise 3 yields a surprise to most students. After investigating the area of a square field covered with water by one large circle, students examine the area covered by four smaller circles. The surprise: both arrangements water the same fractional part of the field.

In Exercises 4 and 5, students explore a series of divisibility rules and prime factorization that could be helpful to them when factoring. If time is at a premium, these exercises can be skipped.

Exercise 7: A possible Web site for the Mersenne prime search is www.mersenne.org/prime.htm.

Exercises 8–45 provide practice in factoring. Two of the contextual exercises (17 and 44) could present a challenge for students.

Section 4.5

This section can be completed in one day. A typical homework assignment might include choosing 2–3 problems from among Exercises 1, 2, 3, and 5. Assign Exercises 4 and 6 if students have graphing calculators. Also assign several problems from the Additional Practice section.

Discovery 4.4

This culminating section to the chapter begins with a discovery that revisits a problem examined originally in Chapter 1. In so doing, concepts such as ways to represent a function (table, equation, graph) and problem domain are reviewed. Pay special attention to feasible values for x.

Example 20

This particular example shows a cubic model that serves as an approximation of drug concentration in the bloodstream. It is used here to point out the need for careful examination of the problem domain.

Make sure students understand the zero product property. Examples 21, 22, and 23 use this property to solve polynomial equations. Example 22 solves the problem that was initially posed at the beginning of Section 4.4.

The section ends with a summary of the relationships among the zeros of a polynomial function, the solutions to a polynomial equation, and the factors of a polynomial. This connection sets the stage for using the graphing calculator to help factor polynomials (Exercise 4).

Special Notes on Exercises

❑ Exercise 1 returns to the original context introduced at the beginning of this chapter. In this exercise, students are asked to develop a function that models the dilution process. But this time, they are asked to find the fractional part that remains when given a specific desired remaining amount of contaminate. To find an approximate value, students are asked to solve the equation graphically.

Exercises 2, 3, and 5 provide students with real-world examples of polynomial functions.

❑ Exercise 4 explores the use of the graphing calculator in factoring. Remind students that the ZOOM feature on their calculator is helpful in finding the value of y when $x = 0$. Some calculators have a CALCULATE menu in which there is a zero feature that will find the zeros of a function for you. Some instructors may wish to explore this technique further with their students.

Exercise 6: Information about icebergs and how they are monitored can be found on the NOAA Web site at www.natice.noaa.gov.

⇒ The purpose of Exercise 7 is to encourage students to compare models for given data. It is intended to be only an introduction to nonlinear regression. This exercise draws on students' previous experiences, such as in Chapter 3, Section 3.4, Exercise 19, which provided a problem involving nonlinear data. In this exercise, students are asked to read data from a given graph, make a table, and explore three types of polynomial regression looking for a function that seems to fit the data. It may be worth noting that a fourth-degree model based on all the data predicts an ozone level of 75 DU for the year 2000. Students could be encouraged to search out more recent data to find which model actually resulted in the better prediction. Caution regarding extrapolating too far beyond known data can be brought up here.

⇒ Exercise 8: This exercise is a follow-up to Exercise 8 from Section 2.5 on finding graphical solutions to systems of equations. If you did not do that exercise, you may wish to skip this one. If this exercise is assigned, it may be worth mentioning that because of the complexity of the functions involved, it is not possible to perform an algebraic solution of this problem, as was done in Exercise 8 of Section 2.5.

Exercise 9: To learn more about the satellite images of fires, try this Web site: http://fermi.jhuapl.edu/avhrr/.

Exercise 10 provides a business context for students who are interested.

Exercises 11–37 provide practice solving polynomial equations.

Chapter Summary and Review

For instructors who use only parts of this chapter, the Chapter 4 Review exercises break down in the following manner:

Chapter Summary	Exercise 1
Sections 4.1 and 4.2	Exercises 2–8
Section 4.3	Exercises 9–19
Section 4.4	Exercises 20–25
Section 4.5	Exercises 26–34

Chapter 1—Measurement

Goals of the Chapter

- To accurately express and compute with measured quantities
- To determine geometrical properties of two- and three-dimensional figures
- To describe one-variable data numerically and graphically
- To begin to create and use mathematical models

Preparation Reading

An architect makes a scale drawing when designing a building. An automotive engineer creates a three-dimensional computer image to test a new idea. A newspaper uses a graph to display economic trends. Scale drawings, computer images, and graphs are a few examples of what we call a **model.** (See **Figure 1.1.**)

A model gives people valuable information about a particular real-world situation. The automotive engineer can examine the airflow around a newly designed car before actually building it.

Figure 1.1

In an attempt to explain why things happen the way they do or to make predictions about something in the future, people sometimes create **mathematical models.** A mathematical model can take the form of an equation, a table of information, a graph, a diagram, a verbal rule, or sometimes a combination of all these.

In this book we will examine specific types of models that are used by people in their work. We will focus much of our attention on learning the mathematics needed to create such models.

The following section contains an activity in which we begin examining and creating models to help us solve the kinds of problems that people face in the real world.

Section 1.1 Measuring Length

What You Need to Know

- How to perform basic arithmetic operations

- How to round numbers

- How to identify basic polygon shapes

What You Will Learn

- To estimate lengths of objects using various units

- To state the precision of a measuring instrument

- To express the accuracy of a measurement

- To compute perimeters of some two-dimensional figures

Materials

- Meter sticks or yardsticks

Measurements of various kinds are a necessary and routine part of many occupations. Some measurements must be very precise. Others can be approximate. And there are times when rough estimates are good enough.

Thoughtforms Corporation is a company that does custom home building and renovations. The materials used are frequently expensive and in limited supply. Therefore, it is important to order just the right amount for some jobs. For example, if too little custom tile is ordered for a bathroom, the project may be delayed or an exact match may be impossible. On the other hand, an overestimate of dimensions by just a few inches could result in hundreds of dollars of unneeded tiles being purchased.

The construction industry is particularly dependent on measurements of size. In order to predict the cost of a construction project, estimates of amounts of concrete, steel, and lumber are needed. These estimates are frequently based on total floor space. To build a house, such things as the length of a gutter or the surface area of a roof or kitchen counter are required.

For budgeting purposes, estimates within 5% or 10% of the actual cost may be sufficient. When ordering materials, greater accuracy is necessary. But the survey that establishes lot boundaries and a carpenter's framing measurements must be made with a high degree of precision.

In job-related tasks that involve quantitative data, clearly expressing accuracy is crucial. In the following activity and throughout the chapter, we will explore ways of determining and communicating the accuracy of measurements.

Activity 1.1 Finding the Dimensions of a Room *(SE pages 3–4)*

Suppose that your classroom is going to be carpeted and repainted. It's also going to get a new heating and air conditioning system. In order to make important and informed decisions about these improvements, measurements must be made.

1. Use a metric ruler or meter stick to measure as accurately as possible the width of a piece of notebook paper.

1. **Answers will vary, but a piece of standard notebook paper is approximately 21.6 cm wide.**

2. Since *all* measurements are approximate, the *exact* width of your paper cannot be measured. But the more precise your measuring instrument, the closer your measurements are to being exact.

    To determine the **precision** of a ruler or meter stick, look at the smallest markings on it. As an example, if you were using a foot-long ruler marked off in sixteenths of an inch, the precision of the ruler would be $\frac{1}{16}$ of an inch. What is the precision of your metric ruler or meter stick?

2. **The smallest division on a standard meter stick is one millimeter (with each centimeter being numbered). So a meter stick has a precision of 1 mm.**

3. You can indicate the accuracy of a measurement by showing the **maximum likely error** when you write the measurement. To do so, write your result followed by a ± symbol followed by half the precision amount. For example, for a ruler with a precision of $\frac{1}{16}$ of an inch, a measurement might be written as $7\frac{5}{16}$ inches $\pm \frac{1}{32}$ inch. This indicates that the actual length is somewhere between $\left(7\frac{5}{16}\text{ inches} + \frac{1}{32}\text{ inch}\right)$ and $\left(7\frac{5}{16}\text{ inches} - \frac{1}{32}\text{ inch}\right)$.

    Did you measure the width of the paper using the full precision of the meter stick? If not, do so now. Write the width of your notebook paper with an appropriate indication of accuracy.

3. **Possible answers: 21.6 cm ± 0.05 cm, 21.6 cm ± 1/20 cm, 216 mm ± 0.5 mm, 21.6 cm ± 0.5 mm.**

4. Now look across your classroom from left to right. Have each person in your group estimate the width of the room in meters. (You may want to examine a meter stick before making your estimate.) How close do you think your estimate might be to the real width of the room?

4. **Dimensions of most classrooms are approximately 6–12 meters. A typical estimate might be to the nearest meter.**

5. Now measure the room's width using the full precision of the meter stick. Write your result along with an indication of the maximum likely error in the measuring process.

5. **Sample answer: For a classroom with a measured width of 11.324 m, the measurement could be written as 11.324 m ± 0.0005 m.**

Units larger or smaller than a meter (or any other metric unit) are indicated with **prefixes** attached to the front of the word. Some of the most common prefixes used in length measurement are listed in **Table 1.1.**

Prefix	Meaning	Unit of Length
kilo-	thousands	1 kilometer = 1 thousand meters
centi-	hundredths	1 centimeter = 1 hundredth of a meter
milli-	thousandths	1 millimeter = 1 thousandth of a meter
micro-	millionths	1 micrometer = 1 millionth of a meter
nano-	billionths	1 nanometer = 1 billionth of a meter

Table 1.1

Sometimes (although rarely) these prefixes are used with non-metric units. Structural engineers often calculate force loads on beams and columns in terms of kilopounds, or thousands of pounds, which are abbreviated kips. And the thickness of a sheet of paper or plastic may be given in mils, which are thousandths of an inch.

6. Measure the width of the room three more times. Are the four measurements all the same? Explain.

6. **Sample answer: 11.324 m, 11.330 m, 11.326 m, and 11.432 m. Even if measurements were carefully made, they may not be the same. This could happen if the room's width is not perfectly constant. No matter how careful the measuring, there is usually some variability in the dimensions of the room itself, so it would not be surprising if your four width measurements were slightly different. (Of course, a large discrepancy would suggest that there might be an error in one of the measurements.)**

7. Now examine your group's results. Your four measurements form a **sample data set.** Calculate the **sample mean** (average) width by dividing the sum of all the sample data by the number of measurements in the sample.

7. **Sample answer: For a sample data set of 11.324 m, 11.330 m, 11.326 m, and 11.432 m, the mean is (11.324 + 11.330 + 11.326 + 11.432)/4 = 11.353 m.**

What would you call the front-to-back dimension of your room?

It is worth noting that some people might refer to this dimension as length, and others might call it depth. Depending on the particular room involved, the terms *length* and *width* might even be interchanged.

Although we often think of the length of a rectangle as being longer than the width, there could be situations where it is more convenient or appropriate to call the shorter dimension length. Think of a glider or sailplane that has a very large wingspan compared to its nose-to-tail distance, which would still be called its length. An Unmanned Aerial Vehicle used by the military for surveillance purposes has a wingspan (or width) of 9 meters but a length of only 7 meters.

8. In a similar manner, determine the front-to-back dimension of the classroom. Find the sample mean for this dimension.

8. **Depth (front-to-back) data for the sample room: 7.085 m, 7.088 m, 7.091 m, 7.080 m. The sample mean is 7.086 m.**

9. Create a geometric model of the floor of your room by making a sketch of the floor and labeling the dimensions with the sample mean length and width.

9. Sample answer:

7.086 m

11.353 m

10. One possible direct use of the linear measurements you have made would be in determining the length of floor molding necessary to cover the edges where the floor meets the walls. Using your sample mean dimensions for the room, calculate the total length of floor molding needed.

10. For the sample data from previous items, the total length of the molding needed is 2(11.353 m) + 2(7.086 m) = 36.878 m.

The name of the geometrical property you have just determined is the **perimeter** of the floor, which means the distance around any plane surface (although you may have subtracted doorway widths from your perimeter to find floor-molding length). Since perimeter is a measure of length, it is measured in linear units such as inches, feet, yards, miles, centimeters, and meters.

11. In your own words, write a rule for determining the perimeter of any two-dimensional figure.

11. To determine the perimeter of any two-dimensional figure, add the lengths of all of the sides.

12. When finding the perimeter of a figure that you know is a rectangle, explain why it is unnecessary to measure all four sides.

12. Sample answer: Since a rectangle has two pairs of equal sides, you only need to measure the length and the width.

13. In your own words, write a rule for determining the perimeter of a rectangle.

13. Sample answers: To find the perimeter of a rectangle, multiple the width by two, multiple the length by two, and add the results. Or add the length and width, then multiply by two.

14. When finding the perimeter of a figure that you know is a square, will the rule for finding the perimeter of a rectangle work? Explain. Write a simpler rule for finding the perimeter of a square.

14. Yes, a square is a special kind of rectangle. And since all four sides of a square are equal in length, a simpler rule would be to multiply the length of one side by four.

Extend the Activity *(SE pages 5–6)*

15. For each length, (a) state the precision with which the measurement was made and (b) write the length with an appropriate indication of accuracy.

    i. 14.25 m

    ii. $3\frac{7}{16}$ in

    iii. 86 cm

    iv. 42.9 mm

    v. 181.2 mi

15. i) a) 0.01 m b) 14.25 m ± 0.005 m; ii) a) $\frac{1}{16}$ in b) $3\frac{7}{16}$ in ± $\frac{1}{32}$ in; iii) a) 1 cm b) 86 cm ± 0.5 cm; iv) a) 0.1 mm b) 42.9 mm ± 0.05 mm; v) a) 0.1 mi b) 181.2 mi ± 0.05 mi

16. Three students used the same meter stick to measure the length of a wire. They reported the following measurements: 0.6 m, 0.60 m, 0.600 m. Using what you know about precision, explain the meaning of each measurement.

16. The precision of the first measurement (0.6 m) is 0.1 m; the precision of the second measurement (0.60 m) is 0.01 m; the precision of the third measurement (0.600 m) is 0.001 m. The first student measured to the nearest tenth of a meter, the second to the nearest hundredth of a meter, and the third to the nearest thousandth of a meter.

17. A common way of describing measurement error is to express the error as a percentage of the measured value. If a carpenter's tape measure marked off in $\frac{1}{32}$ of an inch is used to measure a 2-inch length, then the built-in error due to the precision of the tape measure is $\frac{1}{64}$ of an inch. The ratio of this error to the measured length is $\left(\dfrac{\frac{1}{64}\ \text{in}}{2\ \text{in}}\right) = \dfrac{1}{128}$. We could say that the error is 1 part in 128.

    The **percent error** in the measurement is found by determining another fraction that is equal to $\frac{1}{128}$ but that has a denominator of 100. (Percent means, literally, per hundred.) To do so, we write a **proportion,** or a mathematical statement that two ratios or fractions are equal: $\dfrac{1}{128} = \dfrac{\text{Percent error}}{100}$. If both sides of this proportion are multiplied by 100, then the right-hand side will just be the percent error, since $\dfrac{100}{100}$ equals 1.

The left-hand side becomes $(100)\left(\dfrac{1}{128}\right) \approx 0.78$. Therefore, the percent error is 0.78%.

As a general rule, we can simplify this process and directly calculate the percent error as follows: Percent error $= \left(\dfrac{\text{actual error}}{\text{length measured}}\right)(100)$.

a) If the same tape measure is used to measure a 70-inch length, determine the percent error in the measurement.

17. a) Percent error $= \left(\dfrac{\dfrac{1}{64}\text{ in}}{70\text{ in}}\right)(100) \approx 0.02\%$. This is much lower than the

percent error for the 2-inch measurement, even though the absolute error is the same in both cases.

b) If a surveyor makes an error of 0.32 meters in measuring an 84-meter distance, what is the percent error in the measurement?

b) Percent error $= \left(\dfrac{0.32\text{ m}}{84\text{ m}}\right)(100) \approx 0.38\%$.

c) The Universal Transverse Mercator (UTM) is one type of global positioning system. Originally developed by the military, it is separated into 60 zones around the earth, 11 of which cover the United States. At the edges of each zone, the accuracy of this GPS system is 1 part in 2500. What percent error does this correspond to?

c) Percent error $= \left(\dfrac{1}{2500}\right)(100) \approx 0.04\%$.

d) A new type of measuring device uses ultrasonic waves to measure distances. Devices of this type are accurate to 2 inches when used to measure a distance of 50 feet (600 inches). Determine the percent error in this measurement.

d) Percent error $= \left(\dfrac{2}{600}\right)(100) \approx 0.33\%$.

e) Determine the inherent percent error in the measurements of the width of your classroom (item 5 of the activity) due to the precision of the measuring device you used.

e) Assuming meter sticks accurate to millimeters were used, the percent error can be no better than half a millimeter expressed as a percent of the value of the measured dimension. So for a room 11.324 meters wide, the percent error is $\left(\dfrac{0.0005\text{ m}}{11.324\text{ m}}\right)(100) \approx 0.004\%$.

18. a) Try to estimate (from memory) the dimensions of the room where you sleep. Write down your estimates both in meters and in feet. Then measure the actual dimensions and compare them to your estimates. Did you find that your estimates were generally too high or too low? To improve your ability to make geometrical estimates, try this with other rooms and see if your accuracy increases.

   a) Answers will vary with room size and estimation skills.

   b) Try estimating things like the number of teaspoons in a cup of water. Check to see how close your estimate comes to the correct number.

   b) There are 48 teaspoons in a cup of water.

   c) Estimate how many cars, sitting end to end, would reach the length of a mile. Then measure the length of a typical car and check your estimate.

   c) A Toyota Camry sedan (a typical mid-sized car) is 187.8 inches long, so the number that would stretch a mile would be

   $$\left(\frac{1 \text{ mi}}{187.8 \text{ in / car}}\right)\left(\frac{5280 \text{ ft}}{1 \text{ mi}}\right)\left(\frac{12 \text{ in}}{1 \text{ ft}}\right) = 337.38... \approx 337 \text{ cars.}$$

19. Finding the length of floor molding needed for the classroom was mentioned as a reason for determining lengths. Surveyors must make very accurate measurements of property dimensions, since their results are the basis for legal descriptions of lot boundaries. Officials of cities and towns that have ocean borders need to know the lengths of shoreline for which they are responsible. List other jobs that require detailed knowledge of length measurements (including perimeters). Also, identify the kind of accuracy that may be required in each case.

   19. There are many possible answers, such as fencing contractors (need nearest foot accuracy for property perimeter), highway engineers and contractors (need nearest tenth of a mile, or 0.1 km, estimate of road length), U.S. Coast Guard (needs nearest mile estimate of coastline), and manufacturing technicians (need as much as nearest 0.01 mm accuracy for part specifications).

Section 1.2 Linear Measurement and the Pythagorean Theorem

What You Need to Know

- How to perform basic arithmetic operations, including powers and square roots

- How to multiply numerical fractions

- How to identify place value of a digit in a number

- How to round numbers

What You Will Learn

- To change the units of a measured or computed quantity

- To use the Pythagorean theorem to compute certain distances

- To use the correct order of operations

- To use arrow diagrams to help identify correct order of operations

- To use formulas to find perimeters of two-dimensional figures

Materials

- None

The sketch you drew in item 9 of Activity 1.1 provides a **geometric model** of your classroom. In items 11, 13, and 14 you created another kind of model by writing rules for finding perimeters of figures. This kind of model is called a **verbal model** because it consists of words. In this section we will examine two additional kinds of models.

Writing Geometry Formulas

When finding the perimeter of a rectangle, we can represent the length and width by the symbols l and w. (See **Figure 1.2.**) The **formula** $P = 2l + 2w$ uses symbols to show a mathematical relationship between the perimeter of a rectangle and its length and width.

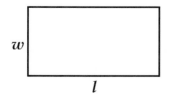

Figure 1.2

In the perimeter formula, when we write $2l$, it is understood that the length is to be multiplied by 2 because the 2 and the l are written next to each other. (This is referred to as **implied multiplication.**) The notation $P = 2l + 2w$ means the same as $P = 2 \cdot l + 2 \cdot w$ or $P = 2(l) + 2(w)$, and all three stand for the sentence "The perimeter of a rectangle equals the sum of twice the length and twice the width." (Multiplication is the only operation for which the operational symbol can be omitted. Symbols must always be used for addition, subtraction, or division.)

In the formula, l and w are referred to as **variables** because the values of l and w vary for different rectangles. But the steps for computing perimeter remain the same. That is, the formula $P = 2l + 2w$ always gives the correct perimeter value for a rectangle if its length and width are substituted for l and w. This formula is an **algebraic model** for the perimeter of a rectangle.

Order of Operations and Arrow Diagrams

When using formulas, it is important to identify which operation is performed first. For example, unless we agree on specific guidelines, the value of $3 + 4 \cdot 5$ can be interpreted in two different ways. If the 3 and 4 are added first, the result is 35. But if the 4 and 5 are multiplied first, the result is 23. Which answer is correct and why?

To avoid confusion in situations such as this, order of operations guidelines have been established that tell us the order in which mathematical operations must be performed.

Order of Operations Guidelines

To evaluate an expression containing more than one operation, the following order is used:

1. Perform the operations within the grouping symbols such as parentheses ( ), brackets [ ], braces { }, and the fraction bar.

2. Raise numbers to powers.

3. Perform multiplications and divisions from left to right.

4. Finally, perform additions and subtractions from left to right.

So to answer the question about the value of $3 + 4 \cdot 5$, the guidelines indicate that multiplication must be performed before addition. Hence, $3 + 4 \cdot 5 = 3 + 20 = 23$.

In **Figure 1.3,** an **arrow diagram** is used to help us analyze and communicate the order in which the operations are performed in evaluating the expression $3 + 4 \cdot 5$.

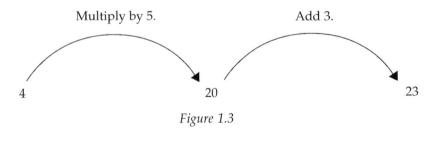

Figure 1.3

Example 1

Perform the indicated operations in proper order.

a) $3 \cdot 20 - 9 \div 3$

b) $2 \cdot 4^2 + 6 - 3 \cdot 2$

c) $\dfrac{12}{2+4}$

Solution:

a) $3 \cdot 20 - 9 \div 3 = 60 - 3$ Multiply and divide from left to right.

           $= 57$ Subtract.

b) $2 \cdot 4^2 + 6 - 3 \cdot 2 = 2 \cdot 16 + 6 - 3 \cdot 2$ Raise numbers to powers.

           $= 32 + 6 - 6$ Multiply from left to right.

           $= 32$ Add and subtract from left to right.

c)   The fraction bar acts as a grouping symbol, so the operations above and below the bar are performed before the division.

     $\dfrac{12}{2+4} = \dfrac{12}{6}$ Perform the operations in the grouping symbols.

         $= 2$ Divide.

When using a formula like $P = 2l + 2w$, we notice two operations, addition and multiplication. From the order of operations guidelines, we know that the multiplication in the formula is done before the addition. An arrow diagram showing the order of operations for the perimeter of a rectangle is shown in **Figure 1.4.**

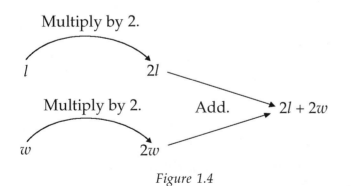

Figure 1.4

Example 2

A rectangular picture frame with dimensions of 6 inches and 4 inches is designed to hold a standard-sized photograph. (See **Figure 1.5.**) Use the formula for the perimeter of a rectangle to find the perimeter of the frame.

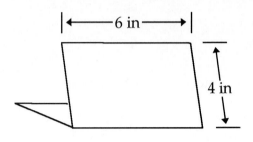

Figure 1.5

Solution:

Substitute the dimensions for l and w in the perimeter formula.

$P = 2l + 2w$

$ = 2(6 \text{ in}) + 2(4 \text{ in})$

$ = 20 \text{ in.}$

Example 3

The formula $P = 2a + b$ can be used to find the perimeter of the isosceles triangle in **Figure 1.6.** Draw an arrow diagram that illustrates this formula.

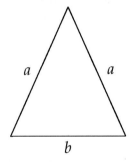

Figure 1.6

Solution:

Since multiplication is a higher priority operation than addition, the first arrow shows multiplication by 2. (See **Figure 1.7.**)

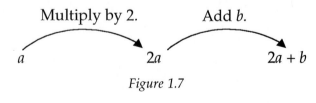

Figure 1.7

Perimeters of Two-Dimensional Figures

The perimeter of any two-dimensional figure can always be found by adding the lengths of all the sides of the figure. But we can find the perimeters of some shapes by using formulas that reflect special properties of the figures. (See **Figures 1.8–1.10.**)

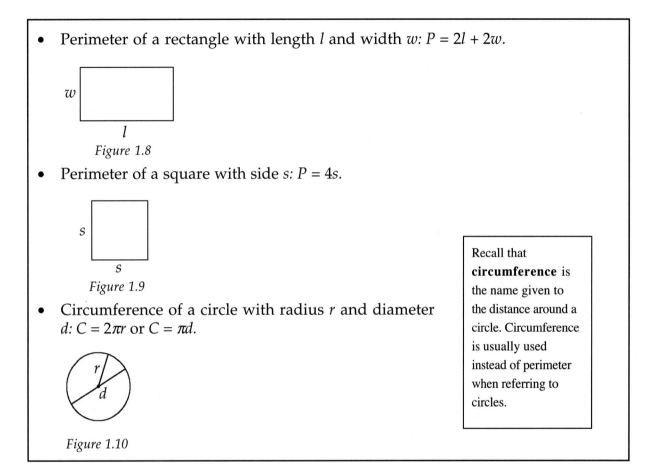

- Perimeter of a rectangle with length l and width w: $P = 2l + 2w$.

  w l

  Figure 1.8

- Perimeter of a square with side s: $P = 4s$.

  s s

  Figure 1.9

- Circumference of a circle with radius r and diameter d: $C = 2\pi r$ or $C = \pi d$.

  Figure 1.10

  > Recall that **circumference** is the name given to the distance around a circle. Circumference is usually used instead of perimeter when referring to circles.

Example 4

Find the perimeter of the square in **Figure 1.11**.

2.74 cm

Figure 1.11

Solution:

$P = 4s$

$ = 4(2.74\ \text{cm})$

$ = 10.96\ \text{cm}.$

Example 5

The Tevatron at Fermilab in Batavia, Illinois, is the highest energy particle accelerator in the world. It has a circular shape with a radius of 0.68 miles. What is the circumference of the Tevatron?

Solution:

$C = 2\pi r$

$\quad = 2\pi(0.68 \text{ mi})$

$\quad = 4.2725... \approx 4.27 \text{ mi.}$

Example 6

Find the perimeter of the irregular plot of land shown in **Figure 1.12**.

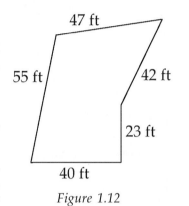

Figure 1.12

Solution:

The perimeter equals the sum of the lengths of the sides of the figure.

$P = 55 \text{ ft} + 47 \text{ ft} + 42 \text{ ft} + 23 \text{ ft} + 40 \text{ ft}$

$\quad = 207 \text{ ft.}$

Other Linear Measurements

In Activity 1.1, we found the perimeter of the classroom in order to determine how much floor molding to install. An additional linear measurement that might be needed in other applications is the length of the **diagonal** of a rectangle.

For example, in order to provide bracing to a vertical structure, it may be necessary to use diagonal supports. One dramatic example of such bracing is provided by the John Hancock Tower in Chicago. As we can see in **Figure 1.13,** the sides of this structure are not exactly rectangular, since they taper inward from ground to roof. Notice that the building is stabilized by diagonal external cross braces.

Figure 1.13

For a rectangle, a diagonal is actually the hypotenuse of a right triangle formed by any two adjacent sides of the rectangle. (See **Figure 1.14.**) (Remember that the **hypotenuse** of a right triangle is always the longest of the three sides and is opposite the right angle.)

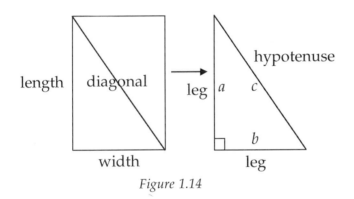

Figure 1.14

In a right triangle, the relationship among the lengths of the sides is given by the **Pythagorean theorem:**

The Pythagorean Theorem

In a right triangle with a hypotenuse of length c and legs of lengths a and b, the square of the length of the hypotenuse equals the sum of the squares of the lengths of the legs. That is, $c^2 = a^2 + b^2$. (See **Figure 1.15.**)

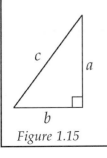

Figure 1.15

The hypotenuse can be found by using a different form of the Pythagorean theorem formula.

Finding the Hypotenuse
The length c of the hypotenuse of a right triangle having legs of known lengths a and b can be found from $c = \sqrt{a^2 + b^2}$.

Example 7
Find the hypotenuse of a right triangle with legs $a = 67$ cm and $b = 42$ cm.

Solution:

The length of the hypotenuse is $c = \sqrt{a^2 + b^2} =$
$\sqrt{(67 \text{ cm})^2 + (42 \text{ cm})^2} = \sqrt{4489 \text{ cm}^2 + 1764 \text{ cm}^2} = \sqrt{6253 \text{ cm}^2} = 79.0759... \approx 79$ cm.

Example 8
Figure 1.16 shows a computer monitor screen with dimensions 12 in x 9 in. Find the diagonal measurement of the screen.

Figure 1.16

Solution:

The length of the diagonal is
$\sqrt{(9 \text{ in})^2 + (12 \text{ in})^2} = \sqrt{81 \text{ in}^2 + 144 \text{ in}^2} = \sqrt{225 \text{ in}^2} = 15$ in.

If the hypotenuse of a right triangle is known, the length of one of the other sides can be found by using yet another form of the Pythagorean theorem.

Finding a Leg
The length of one leg b of a right triangle having another leg of known length a and a hypotenuse of known length c can be found from $b = \sqrt{c^2 - a^2}$.

Example 9

For a right triangle with a hypotenuse of 45.2 cm and one leg of length 29.7 cm, find the length of the other leg.

Solution: $b = \sqrt{c^2 - a^2} = \sqrt{(45.2 \text{ cm})^2 - (29.7 \text{ cm})^2} = 34.1$ cm.

Unit Conversions

If your classroom is in the United States, items related to construction are usually measured in feet and inches rather than in meters and centimeters. Although we have been using metric units up to this point, we can convert any of these results to feet and inches.

When converting units, it is helpful to use a systematic method in order to avoid making a mistake by dividing when we should multiply, or vice versa. Since 3.281 feet equals approximately 1 meter, the ratio $\left(\dfrac{3.281 \text{ ft}}{1 \text{ m}}\right)$ is a ratio of equal size measurements. So even though it is not *numerically* equal to 1, it is *physically* equal to 1. If a length of 24 meters is multiplied by this ratio, it has the effect of changing the numerical value and units without changing the physical length. Notice that the units of meters can be thought of as "reducing to one" in the same way as equal numbers would, leaving an equivalent length measured in feet:

$(24 \text{ m})\left(\dfrac{3.281 \text{ ft}}{1 \text{ m}}\right) = 78.744$ ft, or about 79 ft.

Example 10

A classroom has a perimeter of 36.8 meters. What is its perimeter measured in feet?

Solution:

Use a conversion ratio that has units of meters in the denominator.

$(36.8 \text{ m})\left(\dfrac{3.281 \text{ ft}}{1 \text{ m}}\right) = 120.7408... \approx 120$ ft.

Example 11

The St. Louis Gateway Arch is 630 feet high. How high is the arch measured in meters?

Solution:

Use a conversion ratio that has units of feet in the denominator.

$(630 \text{ ft})\left(\dfrac{1 \text{ m}}{3.281 \text{ ft}}\right) = 192.014... \approx 192$ m.

Example 12

How many meters are there in 541 centimeters?

Solution:

Use a conversion ratio that has units of centimeters in the denominator.

$$(541 \text{ cm})\left(\frac{1 \text{ m}}{100 \text{ cm}}\right) = 5.41 \text{ m}.$$

Conversions for many kinds of units are provided in the Appendix.

Exercises 1.2

I. Investigations *(SE pages 17–20)*

1. When we measured the width of a piece of notebook paper in Activity 1.1, we used the notation 21.6 cm ± 0.05 cm to indicate the measurement's maximum likely error. For single measurements, this is a good way to clearly indicate accuracy.

   However, when we make several measurements on a real object, we often find that the measurements vary. This might be due to irregularities in the shape of the object. Variability can also occur when we measure similar dimensions of manufactured objects that are supposed to be identical.

   Sometimes this variability keeps us from using the full precision of the measuring instrument. For example, assume that a quality control inspection is made on the diameters of five automobile pistons. The following values are found using an instrument with a precision of 0.001 cm:

   9.235 cm, 9.262 cm, 9.217 cm, 9.241 cm, 9.283 cm

   The sample mean of these data is 9.2476 cm. But in reporting this value, we must be careful. If we report the mean as 9.2476 cm, we would be indicating that the piston diameters are accurate to 0.0001 cm, which is untrue.

   Engineers have guidelines for rounding off sample mean values. They suggest that we round the mean to the first place value in which the data show significant variation. In our example, variation is seen in the hundredths place. So we would round our mean value to hundredths of a centimeter and write the result as 9.25 cm.

   a) The following data are measurements of room width:

   5.34 m, 5.37 m, 5.29 m, 5.31 m, 5.40 m

   What would be the best way to write the sample mean of the data?

1. **a) (5.34 + 5.37 + 5.29 + 5.31 + 5.40)/5 = 5.342. Since variability in the data occurs in the tenths place, the mean would be written as 5.3 m.**

   b) The following data are the result of weighing several packing crates containing large commercial heating and air conditioning units:

   471.4 lb, 470.6 lb, 472.8 lb, 471.3 lb, 469.1 lb, 471.5 lb, 472.9 lb

   What would be the best way to write the sample mean of the data?

   b) 471 lb. Computation of the mean results in a numerical value of 471.3714286..., but since the data vary in the ones place, the result should be rounded to ones in order to give the best indication of average weight.

2. In Exercise 1 we found that the sample mean for the diameter of five pistons was best written as 9.25 cm.

   a) Express 9.25 cm as millimeters and as meters.

2. **a)** **9.25 cm = 92.5 mm; 9.25 cm = 0.0925 m.**

Notice that it does not matter whether you write the measurement in centimeters, millimeters, or meters, the precision is equivalent to 0.01 cm. Also notice that the number of nonzero digits remains at three (the 9, the 2, and the 5).

We say that the measurement contains three **significant figures.** The term *significant figures* refers to the number of digits in a result that actually give measurement information. In the various expressions for piston diameter, the zeros serve as placeholders that help locate the decimal point.

b) For i–vii, write the number of significant figures in each measurement.

  i.   78.045 kilograms

  ii. 93,000,000 miles

  iii. 3451 pounds per square inch

  iv. 0.0024 seconds

  v.   210.8 degrees

  vi. 72 mph

  vii. 1000.03 liters

b) (i) 5; (ii) 2, the zeros are just placeholders and not significant; (iii) 4; (iv) 2, the zeros are placeholders; (v) 4; (vi) 2; (vii) 6, all zeros are significant.

3. Consider the three lengths of plastic pipe in **Figure 1.17.** If the pipes are joined end to end, the total length is 16.946 inches. To decide whether this is the best way to express the total length, consider the length of the shortest pipe. When we write its length as 4.3 inches, we imply a precision of only 0.1 inches. That is, the pipe's length is somewhere between 4.25 and 4.35 inches.

Since there is a slight inaccuracy in the tenths place in the measurement for the shortest pipe, any numbers in the hundredths or thousandths place for the total length are certainly meaningless. Hence, it would be misleading to include them. Therefore, round off the total length to 16.9 inches.

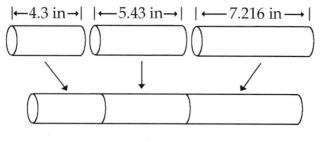

Figure 1.17

For (a)–(e), find the sum of the measurements and round the total appropriately.

a) 23.45 cm + 31.8956 cm + 50.032 cm

3. a) 105.3776 ≈ 105.38 cm.

b) 311.6 lb + 120.89 lb + 438 lb

b) 870.49 ≈ 870 lb.

c) 1.0038 g + 0.994 g – 0.83127 g + 0.0153 g

c) 1.18183 ≈ 1.182 g.

d) The diagram in **Figure 1.18** is called a *schematic* of part of an electrical circuit. The schematic shows three resistors connected end to end in "series." Note that different numerical **subscripts** are used to distinguish the three values of resistance.

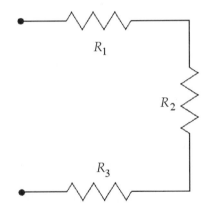

Figure 1.18

The total resistance of the circuit can be computed by adding the values of the individual resistances. If the measured values of R_1, R_2, and R_3 are 0.715 ohms, 0.532 ohms, and 0.64 ohms, respectively, what is the best value to report for R_{total}?

d) 1.887 ≈ 1.89 ohms.

e) The top part of the window shown in **Figure 1.19** is semicircular. Find the length of molding needed to go around the window.

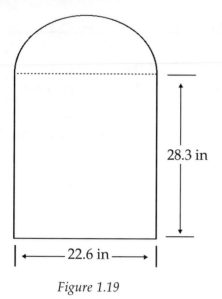

28.3 in

22.6 in

Figure 1.19

e) Total length = length of semicircle + lengths of the three straight sides

$$= (1/2)\pi(22.6) + 22.6 + 28.3 + 28.3$$

$$= 35.4999... + 22.6 + 28.3 + 28.3$$

$$= 114.6999... \approx 114.7 \text{ in.}$$

4. Measure the dimensions (width and height) of a computer monitor screen. Use the Pythagorean theorem to compute the length of the screen diagonal. Then measure the diagonal to see if its length agrees with your calculated result. Compare these values with the manufacturer's specifications for the monitor screen size.

4. **Computer monitor sizes, as most televisions, are described in terms of the length of the screen diagonal. However, the diagonal of the viewable area may be shorter than the actual screen diagonal; a 17-inch monitor may have as small as a 16-inch diagonal measurement for the viewable area, the border area of the screen being black.**

5. A common scale used in architectural drawings is $\frac{1}{16}$ in = 1 ft. This means that every $\frac{1}{16}$ of an inch on the drawing is equivalent to 1 foot in the actual structure. Conversions from plan dimensions to actual dimensions can be made by using a proportion based on the scale ratio of $\left(\dfrac{1 \text{ ft}}{\frac{1}{16} \text{ in}}\right)$. For example, suppose that one side of a building on a drawing measures 4 inches. If we represent the actual length of the side by L, we can write $\left(\dfrac{1 \text{ ft}}{\frac{1}{16} \text{ in}}\right) = \left(\dfrac{L \text{ ft}}{4 \text{ in}}\right)$.

Multiplying both equal ratios in this proportion by 4 in, we find that

$$(4\text{ in})\left(\frac{1\text{ ft}}{\frac{1}{16}\text{ in}}\right) = L, \text{ which means the same as } L = (4\text{ in})\left(\frac{1\text{ ft}}{\frac{1}{16}\text{ in}}\right) = 64\text{ ft.}$$

a) If the length of a room is indicated on such a plan by a line that is $1\frac{1}{2}$ inches long, use a proportion to find the actual length of the room.

5. a) $\left(\frac{1\text{ ft}}{\frac{1}{16}\text{ in}}\right) = \left(\frac{L\text{ ft}}{1.5\text{ in}}\right)$, so $L = (1.5\text{ in})\left(\frac{1\text{ ft}}{\frac{1}{16}\text{ in}}\right) = 24$ ft.

b) If the width of the same room measures $1\frac{1}{8}$ in, what is the actual area of the room?

b) $\left(\frac{1\text{ ft}}{\frac{1}{16}\text{ in}}\right) = \left(\frac{W\text{ ft}}{1.125\text{ in}}\right)$, $W = (1.125\text{ in})\left(\frac{1\text{ ft}}{\frac{1}{16}\text{ in}}\right) = 18$ ft. Area =

(24 ft)(18 ft) = 432 ft². **(Considering plan accuracy, 430 ft² is probably a better answer, accurate to only about the nearest 10 ft².) Architects use "architect's scales," which are rulers calibrated in such a way as to allow reading of actual dimensions from drawings.**

c) New York City has a unique map called NYCMap (pronounced "nice map"). This accurate map consists of the entire city and everything in it. It has been called "the most complicated and detailed urban map ever created." The map has a scale of 1 in = 100 ft. How large would a side of a square telephone booth be if the length of one of its sides on the map is $\frac{1}{32}$ in?

c) $\left(\frac{100\text{ ft}}{1\text{ in}}\right) = \left(\frac{M\text{ ft}}{\frac{1}{32}\text{ in}}\right)$, $M = 3.125$ ft.

II. Projects and Group Activities *(SE page 21)*

6. Learn to use calculator lists, or a spreadsheet, to perform computations efficiently on a large quantity of data. The calculator screens in **Figures 1.20** and **1.21** show converting four measurements from meters to feet.

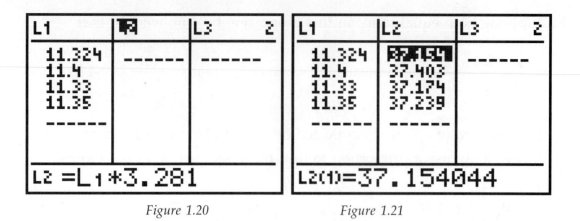

Figure 1.20   Figure 1.21

Enter your group's data values for classroom length in one list or column, and convert all of the measurements to other units of measurement by entering a formula in an adjacent list or column. (Although many calculators will automatically convert the entire list, a spreadsheet requires a two-step process: first enter the appropriate formula in one cell, then copy that cell into the entire column of target cells.) Practice using the lists by converting all the measurements into feet, centimeters, and millimeters.

6. **Texas Instruments calculators allow formula entry into a list if the cursor is placed on the list name in the editor and the "Enter" key is pressed. The variable in the formula must be the name of the list where the data is located, just as a cell label acts as a variable in a computer spreadsheet.**

7. The U.S. Postal Service sets limits on the dimensions of packages that it will deliver. Find out how these limits are specified and, in particular, how the specifications are related to the concept of perimeter.

7. **The U.S. Postal Service requires that length plus girth (distance around, or perimeter of the cross section) be no more than 108 inches. This could be stated as $L + 2W + 2H \leq 108$, although it is not expected that students would write such an inequality statement at this point.**

III. Additional Practice *(SE pages 21–27)*

For 8–13, (a) state the precision with which the measurement was made and (b) write the measurement with an appropriate indication of accuracy.

8. 147.21 mm

8. **a) 0.01 mm; b) 147.21 mm $\pm$ 0.005 mm**

9. 12.8 miles

9. **a) 0.1 mi; b) 12.8 mi $\pm$ 0.05 mi**

10. $2\frac{3}{4}$ yards

10. **a) $\frac{1}{4}$ yd; b) $2\frac{3}{4}$ yd $\pm$ $\frac{1}{8}$ yd**

11. $25\dfrac{5}{16}$ inch

11. a) $\dfrac{1}{16}$ **in; b)** $25\dfrac{5}{16}$ **in** $\pm$ $\dfrac{1}{32}$ **in**

12. 43.7 miles per hour

12. a) 0.1 mph; b) 43.7 mph ± 0.05 mph

13. 73 degrees

13. a) 1 degree; b) 73 degrees ± 0.5 degrees

14. **Figure 1.22** shows a meter stick next to a block of wood.

Figure 1.22

a) How far apart are the numbered divisions?

14. a) 1 cm or 0.01 m

b) What is the precision of the meter stick? (Hint: Note that the meter stick is more precise than the numbered divisions in (a).)

b) 0.1 cm or 1 mm or 001 m

c) What is the maximum likely error in any measurement made with this instrument?

c) ± 0.05 cm or 0.5 mm or 0.0005 m

d) How wide is the block of wood? (Notice that the edge of the block is not placed at 0 on the meter stick.)

d) 5.6 cm or 0.056 m

e) Express the width of the block using an appropriate indication of accuracy.

e) 5.6 cm ± 0.05 cm or 5.6 cm ± 0.5 mm or 0.056 m ± 0.0005 m

15. **Figure 1.23** shows a portion of a thermometer calibrated in degrees Celsius (°C).

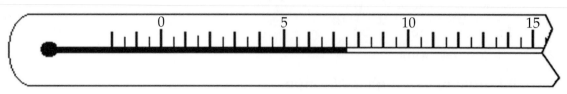

Figure 1.23

a) What is the precision of the thermometer?

15. a) 0.5°C or $\frac{1}{2}$°C (smallest division on the scale)

b) What is the maximum likely error in any measurement made with this instrument?

b) 0.025°C or $\frac{1}{4}$°C (half the smallest division)

c) What is the temperature reading on the thermometer?

c) 7.5°C

d) Express the temperature using an appropriate indication of accuracy.

d) 7.5°C ± 0.025°C

For 16–18, round off your answers appropriately.

16. Find the sample mean of the following measurements of ball bearing diameters: 0.357 cm, 0.349 cm, 0.355 cm, 0.350 cm, 0.352 cm.

16. Sample mean = (1.763 cm/5) = 0.3526 ≈ 0.353 cm.

17. Find the sample mean of the following lengths of logs in a log moisture content study: 15.6 in, 13.1 in, 20.2 in, 12.9 in, 16.4 in, 13.8 in, 15.3 in.

17. Sample mean = (107.3 in/7) = 15.3285... ≈ 15.3 in.

18. Find the sample mean of the following measurements on the elevation of a mountain made with a global positioning system (GPS): 14,523 ft, 14,527 ft, 14,522 ft, 14,523 ft.

18. Sample mean = (58,095 ft/4) = 14,523.75 ≈ 14,524 ft.

19. The Grollo Tower being built in Melbourne, Australia, will be the world's tallest building when it is finished during the first decade of the 21st century. Its projected height has been listed as 1700 feet. How tall will the Grollo Tower be in meters and in kilometers?

19. (1700 ft)$\left(\dfrac{1\ m}{3.281\ ft}\right)$ = 518 m; (518 m)$\left(\dfrac{1\ km}{1000\ m}\right)$ = 0.518 km.

20. The recently completed Akashi Kaikyo Bridge linking the Japanese islands of Honshu and Awaji is the longest suspension bridge in the world at 3910 m.

a) How long is the bridge in kilometers, in feet, and in miles?

20. a) $(3910 \text{ m})\left(\dfrac{1 \text{ km}}{1000 \text{ m}}\right) = 3.91 \text{ km}$; $(3910 \text{ m})\left(\dfrac{3.281 \text{ ft}}{1 \text{ m}}\right) = 12{,}829 \text{ ft}$;

$(12{,}829 \text{ ft})\left(\dfrac{1 \text{ mi}}{5280 \text{ ft}}\right) = 2.42967... \approx 2.43 \text{ mi.}$

b) The bridge is designed for eight lanes of traffic. Approximately how many cars might fit on the bridge at any time? (Assume that approximately 337 cars will stretch for a distance of about 1 mile.)

b) Since about 337 cars will stretch for a distance of 1 mile, the eight lanes of the bridge could hold (8)(2.43 mi)(337 cars/mi) ≈ 6550 cars.

21. a) Wires in integrated circuits are typically 0.00000025 m thick (about 400 times thinner than a human hair). Write this thickness in millimeters (mm), in micrometers (μm), and in nanometers (nm).

21. a) $(0.00000025 \text{ m})\left(\dfrac{1000 \text{ mm}}{1 \text{ m}}\right) = 0.00025 \text{ mm}$; $(0.00000025 \text{ m})\left(\dfrac{1{,}000{,}000 \ \mu\text{m}}{1 \text{ m}}\right) =$

$0.25 \ \mu\text{m}$; $(0.00000025 \text{ m})\left(\dfrac{1{,}000{,}000{,}000 \text{ nm}}{1 \text{ m}}\right) = 250 \text{ nm.}$

b) It has recently been hypothesized that one day it might be possible to use strands of DNA for wiring in some computer and other electronics applications. A typical strand of a DNA molecule is two-billionths of a meter wide. Write this width as a decimal dimension, using an appropriate metric prefix.

b) 0.000000002 m = 2 nm.

22. A particular radial tire has a width of 205 mm. What is its width measured in inches?

22. $(205 \text{ mm})\left(\dfrac{1 \text{ cm}}{10 \text{ mm}}\right)\left(\dfrac{1 \text{ in}}{2.54 \text{ cm}}\right) = 8.07 \text{ in.}$

For 23–34, express each of the lengths as indicated.

23. 32 miles as feet

23. $(32 \text{ mi})\left(\dfrac{5280 \text{ ft}}{1 \text{ mi}}\right) = 168{,}960 \text{ ft} \approx 170{,}000 \text{ ft.}$

24. 102 inches as feet

24. $(102 \text{ in})\left(\dfrac{1 \text{ ft}}{12 \text{ in}}\right) = 8.5 \text{ ft.}$

25. 3.7 yards as inches

25. $(3.7 \text{ yd})\left(\dfrac{36 \text{ in}}{1 \text{ yd}}\right) = 133.2 \approx 130 \text{ in.}$

26. $1\dfrac{3}{4}$ feet as inches

26. $\left(1\frac{3}{4}\text{ ft}\right)\left(\dfrac{12\text{ in}}{1\text{ ft}}\right) = \left(\dfrac{7}{4}\text{ ft}\right)\left(\dfrac{12\text{ in}}{1\text{ ft}}\right) = 21$ in.

27. 27.5 feet as yards

27. $\left(27.5\text{ ft}\right)\left(\dfrac{1\text{ yd}}{3\text{ ft}}\right) = 9.166\ldots$ yd ≈ 9.17 yd.

28. 10,327 feet as miles

28. $\left(10,327\text{ ft}\right)\left(\dfrac{1\text{ mi}}{5280\text{ ft}}\right) = 1.95587\ldots$ mi ≈ 1.9559 mi.

29. 90.01 meters as millimeters

29. $\left(90.01\text{ m}\right)\left(\dfrac{1000\text{ mm}}{1\text{ m}}\right) = 90,010$ mm.

30. 438 centimeters as meters

30. $\left(438\text{ cm}\right)\left(\dfrac{1\text{ m}}{100\text{ cm}}\right) = 4.38$ m.

31. 14.5 inches as centimeters

31. $\left(14.5\text{ in}\right)\left(\dfrac{2.54\text{ cm}}{1\text{ in}}\right) = 36.83$ cm $\approx 36.8.$

32. 120.3 centimeters as inches

32. $\left(120.3\text{ cm}\right)\left(\dfrac{1\text{ in}}{2.54\text{ cm}}\right) = 47.3622\ldots$ in ≈ 47.36 in.

33. 42.25 feet as meters

33. $\left(42.25\text{ ft}\right)\left(\dfrac{1\text{ m}}{3.281\text{ ft}}\right) = 12.8771\ldots$ m ≈ 12.88 m.

34. 4.2 meters as feet

34. $\left(4.2\text{ m}\right)\left(\dfrac{3.281\text{ ft}}{1\text{ m}}\right) = 13.7802 \approx 14$ m.

For 35–37, draw an arrow diagram that illustrates the formula.

35. $P = 4s$ (perimeter of a square).

35.

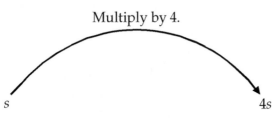

Multiply by 4.

s $4s$

36. $C = \pi d$ (circumference of a circle).

36.

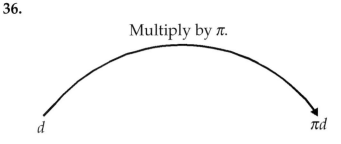

Multiply by π.

d πd

37. $d = \sqrt{l^2 + w^2}$ (diagonal of a rectangle).

37.

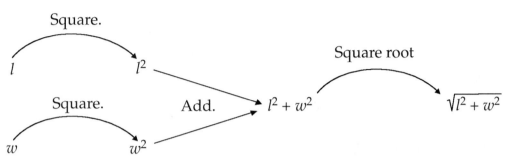

Square.

l l^2

Square root

Square.   Add. $l^2 + w^2$ $\sqrt{l^2 + w^2}$

w w^2

For 38–41, perform the indicated operations in proper order.

38. $2 + 3(7)$

38. $2 + 3(7) = 2 + 21 = 23$.

39. $4(5) + 2(3) \div 6$

39. $4(5) + 2(3) \div 6 = 20 + 6 \div 6 = 20 + 1 = 21$.

40. $7(5) - 2$

40. $7(5) - 2 = 35 - 2 = 33$.

41. $7(5 - 2)$

41. $7(5 - 2) = 7(3) = 21$.

42. Find the perimeter of the quadrilateral shown in **Figure 1.24**.

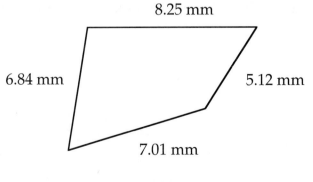

8.25 mm

6.84 mm   5.12 mm

7.01 mm

Figure 1.24

42. $8.25 + 5.12 + 7.01 + 6.84 = 27.22$ mm.

43. Find the perimeter of the polygon shown in **Figure 1.25.**

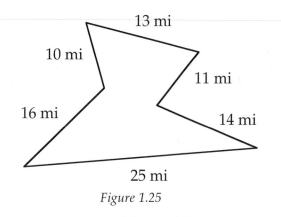

Figure 1.25

43. 13 + 11 + 14 + 25 + 16 + 10 = 89 mi.

For 44–47, use an appropriate formula to find the perimeter of the figure that is described.

44. An 80 ft × 115 ft rectangular house lot.

44. $P = 2l + 2w$; $P = 2(115 \text{ ft}) + 2(80 \text{ ft}) = 390$ ft.

45. A rectangular strip of sheet metal that has the dimensions 3.4 cm × 7 mm.

45. $P = 2l + 2w$; $P = 2(3.4 \text{ cm}) + 2(0.7 \text{ cm}) = 8.2$ cm or 82 mm.

46. A $3\frac{1}{2}$ in × $5\frac{1}{2}$ in rectangular picture frame.

46. $P = 2l + 2w$; $P = 2\left(5\frac{1}{2}\right) + 2\left(3\frac{1}{2}\right) = 2\left(\frac{11}{2}\right) + 2\left(\frac{7}{2}\right) = 11 + 7 = 18$ in.

47. A 1.76 m square mirror.

47. $P = 4s$; $P = 4(1.76) = 7.04$ m.

48. A square field that is 736 m on each side.

48. $P = 4s$; $P = 4(736) = 2944$ m.

For 49–52, use an appropriate formula to find the circumference of the figure that is described.

49. See **Figure 1.26.**

Figure 1.26

49. $C = \pi d$; $C = \pi(4.2) = 13.1946\ldots \approx 13.2$ cm.

50. See **Figure 1.27.**

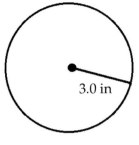

Figure 1.27

50. $C = 2\pi r$; $C = 2\pi(3.0) = 18.8495\ldots \approx 18.9$ in.

51. A circular swimming pool that is 25 ft in diameter.

51. $C = \pi d$; $C = \pi(25 \text{ ft}) = 78.5$ ft.

52. A circular gasket with a radius of 2.13 cm.

52. $C = 2\pi r$; $C = 2\pi(2.13 \text{ cm}) = 13.4$ cm.

53. For (a)–(d), use **Figure 1.28.**

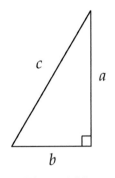

Figure 1.28

a) Find the length of side c if $a = 10$ in and $b = 13$ in.

53. a) $c = \sqrt{10^2 + 13^2} = 16.401$ in ≈ 16 in.

b) Find the length of side b if $c = 15.1$ cm and $a = 2.5$ cm.

b) $b = \sqrt{(15.1)^2 - (2.5)^2} = 14.891$ cm ≈ 14.9 cm.

c) Find the length of side a if $b = 1.02$ m and $c = 3.71$ m.

c) $a = \sqrt{(3.71)^2 - (1.02)^2} = 3.5670$ m ≈ 3.57 m.

d) Find the length of side c if $a = 4$ yd and $b = 11$ yd.

d) $c = \sqrt{4^2 + 11^2} = 11.7047$ yd ≈ 11.7 yd.

For 54–57, find the length of the diagonal of the figure that is described.

54. See **Figure 1.29.**

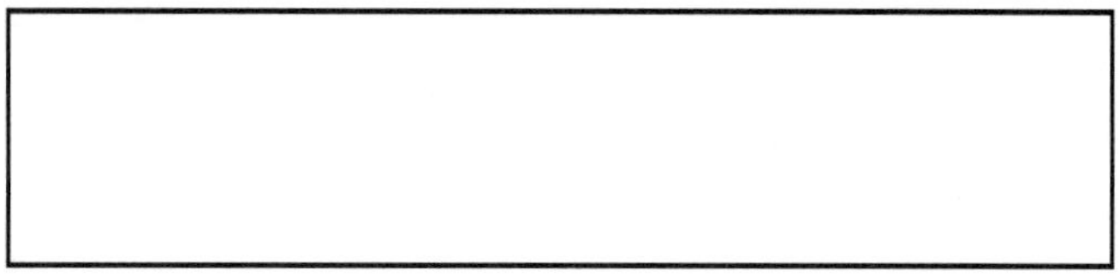

9 yd

3 yd

Figure 1.29

54. $\sqrt{(9)^2 + (3)^2} \approx 9.5$ **yd.**

55. A square that is 23.8 in on a side.

55. $\sqrt{(23.8 \text{ in})^2 + (23.8 \text{ in})^2} \approx 33.7$ **in.**

56. A square that is 1 cm on a side.

56. $\sqrt{(1 \text{ cm})^2 + (1 \text{ cm})^2} = \sqrt{2} = 1.414...$ **cm** ≈ 1.4 **cm.**

57. A 4.6 m × 6.1 m rectangle.

57. $\sqrt{(4.6 \text{ m})^2 + (6.1 \text{ m})^2} \approx 7.6$ **m.**

58. Find the perimeter of the right triangle in **Figure 1.30.**

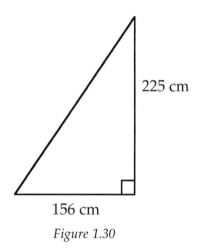

225 cm

156 cm

Figure 1.30

58. Length of hypotenuse is $\sqrt{(225 \text{ cm})^2 + (156 \text{ cm})^2} = 274$ **cm, so perimeter is** **225 cm + 156 cm + 274 cm = 655 cm.**

59. A computer monitor has a 20-inch diagonal rectangular screen. If the height of the screen is 12.5 inches, what is its width?

59. $w = \sqrt{(20 \text{ in})^2 - (12.5 \text{ in})^2} = 15.6$ **in.**

60. A doorway is 78 inches high and 28 inches wide. Will a 7 ft × 8 ft panel fit through the doorway? Explain.

60. No, the diagonal of the doorway is $\sqrt{(78 \text{ in})^2 + (28 \text{ in})^2} = 83$ **in, one inch too short for the 7-foot dimension.**

61. If a 2-meter-long pole is leaned against a wall with its lower end 1 meter from the wall, how high up the wall will the upper end reach?

61. $\sqrt{(2\text{ m})^2 - (1\text{ m})^2} = \sqrt{3}$ **m ≈ 1.7 m.**

62. A coil of wire in an automobile fuel injector control is 6.0 mm in diameter and contains 300 turns. How long is the wire in the coil?

62. Each loop is $C = \pi d = \pi(6.0\text{ mm})$ in circumference, so the total length of wire is $300\pi(6.0\text{ mm}) = 5655\text{ mm}\left(\dfrac{1\text{ m}}{1000\text{ mm}}\right) = 5.655 \approx 5.7$ m.

63. The Pentagon in Alexandria, Virginia, occupies a ground space that is a regular pentagon with five equal sidewalls, each 921 feet in length.

   a) What is the perimeter of the Pentagon?

63. a) 5(921 ft) = 4605 ft.

   b) Approximately how long do you think it would take to run around the Pentagon?

b) 4605 feet is almost a mile. The world record for running a mile is just under 4 minutes, so most people would take significantly longer, somewhere in the vicinity of 10 minutes.

64. **Figure 1.31** represents a top view of a drain line.

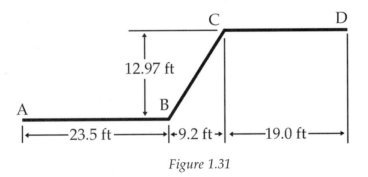

Figure 1.31

   a) How much pipe is needed to construct the drain line?

64. a) BC $= \sqrt{(9.2)^2 + (12.97)^2} \approx 15.9$ ft; the length of the pipe = 23.5 ft + 15.9 ft + 19.0 ft = 58.4 ft.

   b) If it were possible to connect A and D with a straight pipe, how much less pipe would be needed?

b) A straight run would be the hypotenuse of a right triangle with legs of 51.7 ft and 12.97 ft, or $\sqrt{(51.7\text{ ft})^2 + (12.97\text{ ft})^2} = 53.3$ ft. The savings would be 58.4 ft − 53.3 ft = 5.1 ft.

65. In determining the impedance Z of a series circuit, an impedance triangle is sometimes used. The resistance R forms one leg of the right triangle. The reactance X (which depends on any capacitors and inductors present in the circuit) forms the other. The length of the hypotenuse of the triangle equals the impedance of the circuit. For the impedance triangle in **Figure 1.32**, find the value of the impedance.

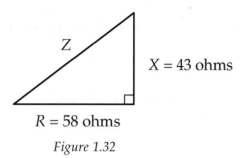

$X = 43$ ohms

$R = 58$ ohms

Figure 1.32

65. $Z = \sqrt{(43 \text{ ohms})^2 + (58 \text{ ohms})^2} = 72$ ohms.

Section 1.3 Describing the Results of Measurement

What You Need to Know

- How to plot numbers on a number line

What You Will Learn

- To compute the mean, median, mode, and range of a data sample
- To use inequality symbols to indicate relative sizes of quantities
- To construct a dot plot of a data set
- To construct a frequency histogram from a data set
- To use technology to create histograms

Materials

- None

How can we make sense of data that have been collected?

What is the best way to communicate results of measurement to others?

How are measured data used to predict what may happen in other situations?

The branch of mathematics called **statistics** provides the answers to these questions. Statistics refers to the many different methods for obtaining and using data. These methods include collecting data, organizing data, analyzing the data for patterns, and going beyond the data to make general conclusions and predictions.

In this section we will consider some of the common techniques of **descriptive statistics,** which means organizing and summarizing data in numerical and graphical forms. For now, only data measuring the value of a single quantity will be discussed. In Chapter 3 we will explore data that suggest relationships between two different quantities and their use in prediction.

A Formula for the Sample Mean

In Activity 1.1 we found sample means for our width and length data. We calculated the mean by adding the measurements and dividing the sum by the number of measurements.

A convenient way of writing a formula for calculating the sample mean for a variable called x is $\bar{x} = \dfrac{\Sigma x_i}{n}$. In this formula, $\bar{x}$ is a symbol denoting the sample mean, and x_i stands for any particular one of the measured values of the variable. The Greek symbol *sigma* Σ indicates a sum, in this case the sum of all the values of x, and n is the total number of values that were measured. The subscript i is called an *index*, which can take on any of the values from 1 to n.

Note that this is another way of using subscripts. In Exercise 3(d) of Section 1.2, subscripts were used to distinguish different *quantities* (resistances R_1, R_2, and R_3), whereas here x_1, x_2, etc., refer to different *specific values* of the same variable x.

Example 13

The data in **Table 1.2** represent the diameters of metal rods measured with a micrometer as part of a quality control inspection.

Length (mm)	4.523	4.541	4.507	4.529	4.518

Table 1.2

Find the sample mean.

Solution:

Here x_1 = 4.523 mm, x_2 = 4.541 mm, etc., and n = 5.

$$\bar{x} = \frac{(4.523 + 4.541 + 4.507 + 4.529 + 4.518)}{5} = 4.5236 \text{ mm, which is rounded to}$$

4.52 mm, since significant variation begins to occur in the hundredths place.

Discovery 1.1 Summarizing Data (*SE pages 29–30*)

The sample mean is probably the most common single statistic used to represent a data set. But there are other ways of representing data. In this discovery we will explore some of the ways data can be summarized.

1. To begin summarizing the class data, share your group's four measurements of room width with all the other groups in the class. Then find the sample mean for the data set.

1. **A typical sample of 11 measurements might be: 11.324 m, 11.330 m, 11.352 m, 11.318 m, 11.347 m, 11.321 m, 11.332 m, 11.321 m, 11.339 m, 11.328 m, 11.325 m. The mean of these data is 11.330636... ≈ 11.33.**

> The median is often used in describing such things as educational statistics, where it may be referred to as the "50th percentile." This means that 50% (or half) of a group of test scores or other data are below the median.

2. The **median** is another statistic that is frequently used to represent data. When a data set contains an odd number of data values and is arranged in either increasing or decreasing order, the median is the middle value.

    A data set with an even number of values has no middle value. In such cases the median is equal to the mean of the two central values of the ordered data set. For the numbers 23, 34, 42, 45, 51, 57, 60, 62, the median is 48, since it is the mean of 45 and 51. Notice that in this case the median does not actually appear in the data.

    Arrange your room width data in order from the largest to the smallest value. Then find the median of the data.

2. **Sample answer: 11.352 m, 11.357 m, 11.339 m, 11.332 m, 11.330 m, 11.328 m, 11.325 m, 11.324 m, 11.321 m, 11.321 m, 11.318 m; the median is 11.328 m.**

3. Find the median of the following set of numbers, which represent the response times (in milliseconds) for data retrieval from a computer CD drive: 11, 18, 13, 24, 20, 17, 10, 14, 13, 21, 18.

3. **In increasing order, the data are 10, 11, 13, 13, 14, 17, 20, 21, 24, and 26. There are 10 values in the data set. The two middle values are 17 and 20, which have a mean of 18.5. The median response time is 18.5 milliseconds.**

> Not all data sets have a single mode. It is not uncommon for data to be **bimodal,** with two different values being "tied" for the greatest frequency. Sometimes there may even be more than two modes, and the data is then called *multimodal.*

4. A third number that is sometimes used to summarize data is the **mode.** The mode is the number that occurs with the greatest frequency in the data set. For example, the mode of the data set consisting of 12, 14, 9, 10, 14, 11, 9, 14 is 14 because it occurs more than any other value. Find the mode of your room width data.

4. **Sample answer: The only value that appears more than once in the sample data is 11.321 m, so it is the mode.**

5. When describing data, it is also helpful to indicate the variability in the data. One way to indicate how much your room width measurements vary is to calculate the difference between the largest and the smallest measurement. This difference is called the **range** of the data. Find the range of your class data.

5. **Sample answer: The range of the sample data from item 1 is 11.352 m – 11.318 m = 0.034 m, or 3.4 cm.**

6. Share your group's four measurements for room length. Find the sample mean, median, mode, and range for the class's length data.

6. **A typical sample for 10 measurements might be 7.083 m, 7.087 m, 7.092 m, 7.082 m, 7.060 m, 7.095 m, 7.083 m, 7.081 m, 7.086 m, 7.063 m. The mean is 7.0812 ≈ 7.08 m; the median is 7.083 m; the mode is 7.083 m; and the range is 7.095 – 7.060 = 0.035 m.**

7. It is possible for two data sets to have the same mean but quite different ranges. Find the mean and range of each of the following data sets: {7, 8, 7, 7, 6} and {2, 8, 9, 5, 11}.

7. **For {7, 8, 7, 7, 6}, the mean is 7 and the range is 2. For {2, 8, 9, 5, 11}, the mean is 7 and the range is 9.**

Describing a data set using the range can give a better sense of whether the data are consistent. For this reason we frequently summarize data with two statistics. One is the mean, the median, or occasionally the mode. The other is a measure of variability. The range is not the only measure of variability, but it is often used because it is so easy to identify.

Choosing among the Mean, Median, and Mode

The mean and median of the classroom width data are probably very similar. This is usually the case for data resulting from measurement on a single quantity. But when one or two values are significantly higher or lower than the rest of the data set, the mean and median may be quite different.

For example, if average home prices in cities are being compared, a few very expensive homes can produce a significant effect on the mean home price, even if the vast majority of homes are worth much less. In such cases the median provides a better summary of the data.

Consider the following small random sample of home prices in one city: $145,000; $305,000; $230,000; $1,450,000; $265,000; $178,000; $130,000.

The mean of this sample is about $386,000. But notice that this value is higher than all but one individual price. The median is $230,000 and is much more representative of how affordable the city is with regard to home ownership.

When identifying the mode of a data set, a **frequency table** such as **Table 1.3** is helpful. In a frequency table, the number of times a value occurs is written next to the corresponding value.

Example 14

A company that manufactures tires for cars might assemble data on wheel rim sizes for tires bought in a particular region's tire stores in one month, resulting in data like those in **Table 1.3.** Find the mode of the data.

Rim Diameter (inches)	Frequency of Purchase
13	62
14	117
15	316
16	124

Table 1.3

Solution:
The mode of these data is 15 inches because that is the most common value of rim diameter. This would suggest to the manufacturer that production efforts should emphasize tires for 15-inch rims.

The mode is usually important only when data are **discrete,** which means that only certain values (often integers) are possible for the data. The wheel rim data can only take on whole number values because wheel rims are only made with these sizes. However, the computer response times in item 3 of Discovery 1.1 are **continuous** data, meaning that the actual values could be anywhere in the data range, including all fractional and decimal values. An exact mode is usually not of interest for continuous data.

Using Inequalities to Compare Two Sample Means

Knowledge of sample means provides a simple way of comparing two data sets that measure the same kind of property.

Suppose that two groups of people with chronic arthritic pain were treated with different pain medications. Each time interval before pain relief was recorded. These data are shown in **Table 1.4.**

Medication A Times (min)	Medication B Times (min)
13	10
17	11
14	10
14	10
15	9
19	11
15	11
16	10
13	9

Table 1.4

It would be reasonable to report the experimental results as $\bar{t}_A = 15.111... \approx$ 15 min, and $\bar{t}_B = 10.111... \approx 10$ min. Thus, there appears to be a difference in the times of action of the two medications. Symbolically, we could write $\bar{t}_B < \bar{t}_A$. This means, "The average time of action of medication B is *less than* that of medication A." Or we could write $\bar{t}_A > \bar{t}_B$, which means, "The average time of action of medication A is *greater than* that of medication B."

The use of the inequality symbols < and > provides a convenient notation for indicating whether one quantity is larger or smaller than another. The open end of each symbol is closer to the larger quantity, and the symbol becomes narrower as it approaches the smaller quantity.

Other symbols that are used to indicate relations between the sizes of things are the familiar =, meaning that two quantities are equal, and ≠, meaning that two quantities are not equal. We use the ≠ symbol when we want to indicate that two values are different, but we are not concerned with which one is larger.

When combining the equality and inequality symbols, we use ≥ to stand for "greater than or equal to" and ≤ to mean "less than or equal to." We can interpret the ≥ symbol as "at least as large as" and the ≤ symbol as "no larger than." For example, some amusement park rides require that a rider's height h be at least 48 inches, which might be symbolized $h \geq 48$ inches.

A **one-dimensional axis** or number line can be helpful in graphically depicting inequality relationships. On such a line, the value of the variable is customarily shown as increasing toward the right. Therefore, any number on the line has a greater value than all numbers to its left.

The interval $h \geq 48$ inches is graphed in **Figure 1.33.** The solid circle at $h = 48$ is an indication that the value of 48 inches is included in the interval.

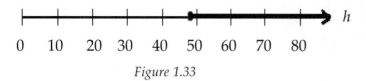

Figure 1.33

If a boundary of an interval is not included, the graph is drawn with an open circle instead of a solid one. **Figure 1.34** shows a graph of the inequality $h > 48$.

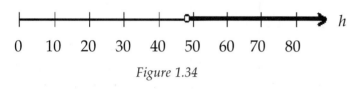

Figure 1.34

Example 15

A town requires that the area of a house lot cannot be smaller than one-half acre in size. Write an inequality that expresses this requirement, using the symbol A to represent area.

Solution:

$$A \geq \frac{1}{2}$$

Example 16

The freezing point of water is 0°C. Write an inequality that expresses what must be true of the outdoor temperature T in the winter if the water on the surface of a pond is to remain in a liquid state.

Solution:

$$T > 0$$

Example 17

The boiling point of water is 100°C. Express the *complete range* of temperatures over which water will remain in the liquid state using inequalities.

Solution:

Since there are both an upper and a lower limit to this range, two inequalities are needed. The temperature must satisfy two inequalities, $T > 0$ *and* $T < 100$. This can also be expressed as the compound inequality $0 < T < 100$.

Example 18

A particular motor occasionally vibrates excessively but only when its rotational frequency f is 500 rpm (revolutions per minute). Write an expression that represents the frequencies for which such vibrations will *not* occur.

Solution:

$f \neq 500$. Or two inequalities could be used, as in $f < 500$ or $f > 500$. Notice that this pair of inequalities cannot be expressed as a compound inequality. The inequality $500 < f < 500$ is meaningless, because there is no single number that can be both greater than 500 *and* less than 500.

Example 19

If the data for classroom dimensions in Discovery 1.1 contain a minimum value of 11.328 m and a maximum value of 11.352 m, the range is 0.024 m. Another way to indicate the variability is to state the compound inequality $11.328 \leq w \leq 11.352$, where w represents the width of the classroom in meters.

Show this inequality on a number line.

Solution:

Since the endpoints of the interval are included, solid circles are placed at width values of 11.328 and 11.352. (See **Figure 1.35**.)

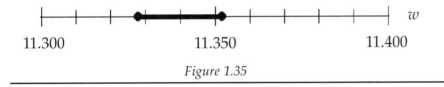

$$11.300 \qquad 11.350 \qquad 11.400$$

Figure 1.35

Making Decisions Based on Sample Means

In analyzing the data in Table 1.4, the correct determination of which pain medication works faster would have been made even if only one trial of each had been performed. This is true in this case because the data from the two experiments are clearly separated. But there are times that we can't draw conclusions based on a single measurement. Example 20 shows one such possibility.

Example 20

Two different mixtures of concrete exhibit the compressive strength data (measured in pounds per square inch) given in **Table 1.5.**

Concrete A Strength (psi)	Concrete B Strength (psi)
3446	3290
3517	3627
3172	3108
3408	3541
3313	3589
3025	3376

Table 1.5

How do the strengths compare?

Solution:

There is enough overlap of the strength data from the two mixtures that a comparison based only on a single measurement of each formulation might have suggested that formulation A has a greater strength than formulation B. However, the opposite is true, as can be seen by comparing the sample mean strengths:

$$\overline{S}_A = 3313.5 \approx 3300 \text{ psi}, \ \overline{S}_B = 3421.8333... \approx 3400 \text{ psi, so } \overline{S}_A < \overline{S}_B.$$

Visual Models of Data Sets

Although the sample mean, median, and mode provide simple ways to describe the result of a group of measurements, it is often useful to know more information about a set of data. A graph, which is a visual model, provides a look at all the data at once. Graphs help us process the information in a way that can reveal aspects of the data that might be obscured in a list or table. Patterns in the data are often easier to see when presented in graphical form.

While there are many types of data graphs, we will examine two here and a few more in the exercises. Still others will be examined in later chapters.

Dot Plots

When the number of measurements is fairly small and we want only a quick, informal picture of how the data are distributed, a **dot plot** may be a good choice. A dot plot involves spreading out data values along a single scale and stacking dots for repeated values.

For example, if the weight gains of 10 laboratory mice fed a certain diet rich in the amino acid lysine were (in grams) 80, 100, 120, 150, 110, 130, 100, 140, 130, 110, the data could be arranged in a dot plot. (See **Figure 1.36.**)

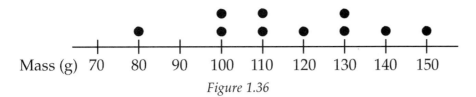

Mass (g) 70   80   90   100 110 120 130 140 150

Figure 1.36

Notice that the mode and range of the data are clearly visible in a dot plot.

Frequency Histograms

Dot plots have the advantage of being easy and quick to make, but they can become difficult to create with large data sets. In such cases a particular kind of bar graph called a **histogram** can give a better look at the data.

Consider the following data on major earthquakes (**Table 1.6**). For each of the hundred years from 1900 to 1999, the number of earthquakes of Richter magnitude 7.0 or greater has been recorded. The yearly totals are:

13	14	8	10	17	26	32	27	18	32
36	34	32	33	32	18	26	21	21	14
8	11	14	23	18	17	19	20	22	19
13	26	13	14	22	24	21	22	26	21
23	24	27	41	31	27	35	26	28	36
39	21	17	22	17	19	15	34	10	15
22	18	15	20	15	22	19	16	30	27
29	23	20	16	21	21	25	16	18	15
18	14	10	15	8	15	6	11	8	7
13	10	23	16	15	25	22	20	16	11

Table 1.6 (Source: U.S. Geological Survey)

Of course, the mean value would summarize the data with a single number. But in order to present the data that shows the entire data set in a more easily understood way, we can first group the data into **classes.** Each class should contain a range of earthquake occurrences such as from 0 to 4 major earthquakes per year, from 5 to 9 major earthquakes per year, etc. Such a **grouped frequency table** for these data would look like **Table 1.7.**

Number of Earthquakes per Year	Frequency
0–4	0
5–9	6
10–14	16
15–19	27
20–24	24
25–29	13
30–34	9
35–39	4
40–44	1

Table 1.7

The table reveals some information that cannot be easily seen in the raw data list. For instance, a typical year has approximately 20 major earthquakes. But we also see that it is relatively rare for either fewer than 10 or more than 34 major quakes to occur in a single year.

Figure 1.37 shows a histogram of the grouped frequency data. It shows each class as a bar. In this histogram the bars are vertical, but some histograms have horizontal bars. Since the class width is 5, the width of the bar is equal to 5. The length or height of the bar is measured on a scale that shows the frequency of the number of observations in each class.

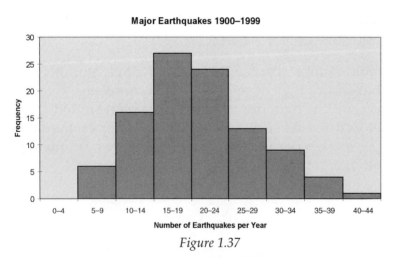

Figure 1.37

Although it would be extremely difficult to look at the original data for this situation and make any real sense of it, the histogram provides a visual summary of the entire data set. Its one disadvantage is that sorting the data into groups results in a loss of the individual measurements. This disadvantage is usually far outweighed by the added clarity and ease of finding patterns in the data.

Much of the information contained in the original data set can be found by reading the histogram. For example:

- The total number of years of data involved can be determined by adding the total of all the bar heights.

- In most years there have been from 10 to 29 major earthquakes.

- The number of years in which there have been fewer than 15 major earthquakes can be found by adding the heights of the first two bars, giving a total of 22 years.

However, it is not possible to determine in how many years there have been more than 32 earthquakes. This is because a single bar includes 30, 31, 32, 33, and 34 earthquakes per year, and it is *not* possible to distinguish the frequencies of individual values. It *is* possible to determine that there were 14 years with *at least* 30 major earthquakes by totaling the heights of the last three bars ($9 + 4 + 1 = 14$ years).

A histogram can be created on a calculator by first entering grouped data and frequencies into lists (**Figure 1.38**) and then producing a plot based on those lists (**Figure 1.39**).

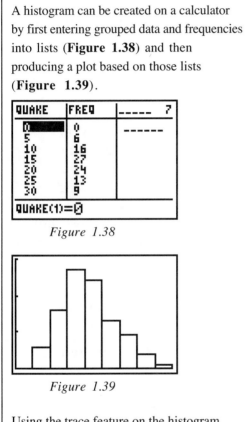

Figure 1.38

Figure 1.39

Using the trace feature on the histogram (**Figure 1.40**) allows direct examination of both the frequency and the class width. Note that the calculator clearly distinguishes the exact data interval contained in the selected bar.

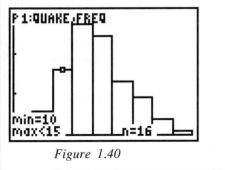

Figure 1.40

Exercises 1.3

I. Investigations *(SE pages 39–45)*

1. As we saw in this section, a sample mean can be distorted if one or two of the values are much larger or smaller than most of the data.

   The data in **Table 1.8** show the results of a physics experiment where a ball was dropped from a fixed height and the time (in seconds) it took for the ball to fall to the floor was measured.

Time (seconds)	0.476	0.482	0.481	2.349	0.478	0.480

   Table 1.8

   a) Find the mean of the data in Table 1.8.

1. a) Mean: 0.791 s.

> Trimmed means are regularly used in averaging judges' marks in international sporting events such as gymnastics, figure skating, and diving. This helps prevent national prejudices from affecting the scores of individual athletes.

Upon careful observation of the data, it is obvious that something unusual happened to produce the 2.349 time value. It would be an acceptable practice just to discard that reading from the data set. However, to avoid having to make subjective decisions about whether data are too extreme, sometimes we decide in advance of the experiment to use a **trimmed mean** calculation.

To calculate a trimmed mean, first discard the largest and the smallest observations. Then calculate the mean of the remaining data.

   b) In calculating a trimmed mean for the data in Table 1.8, which two data values should be discarded?

b) Drop 2.349 and 0.476.

   c) Calculate the trimmed mean for the data in Table 1.8, and compare it to the mean of the untrimmed data.

c) The trimmed mean is 0.48025 ≈ 0.480 s. The trimmed mean is less than the untrimmed mean, which is 0.791 s.

   d) The data in **Table 1.9** represent measurements of DDT residues in riverbank soil samples from the vicinity of a chemical plant. All measurements are in parts per billion (ppb). Calculate both the trimmed mean and the untrimmed mean.

> The manufacture of DDT, an insecticide found to cause serious environmental problems, was banned in the United States in 1973. However, traces of DDT are still found in most inland bodies of water. Even on the level of "parts per billion" concentrations, DDT can adversely affect the ability of fish to survive.

Residue (ppb)	34	21	42	18	56	48	30	87	28	43	62	39

Table 1.9

d) Trimmed mean: 40.3 ppb; untrimmed mean: 42.333... ≈ 42.3 ppb.

2. Another variation on sample mean calculations involves determining a **weighted mean.** This is used when we want to give greater emphasis to particular values in the data set.

Consider a case when one of your instructors decides to count the final exam as double the weight of any of the other three tests in the course. If your scores on the first three exams are 80, 72, and 92 and your score on the final exam is 93, your final average would be $\dfrac{(80 + 72 + 92 + 2 \cdot 93)}{5} = 86$, even though the unweighted average is 84.25.

When managers of large projects use modern quantitative techniques to predict how long a project will last, they sometimes try to estimate the length of each project activity using the following three separate time estimates:

- The time the activity should usually take under normal circumstances, or the *modal time* t_M

- The shortest time in which the activity could possibly be done, t_{min}

- The longest time it might take if things get delayed, t_{max}

The modal time is then weighted four times as much as each of the other time estimates in order to calculate a weighted mean, or expected, time for the activity.

Consider a (simplified) project to test-market a new razor. Assume the project consists of only three tasks, which must be performed in order: (1) design a prototype, (2) produce the prototype, and (3) do market research.

Suppose that you, as project manager, have made the following estimates of time required for the three tasks (**Table 1.10**):

Activity	Minimum Time	Modal Time	Maximum Time
Design prototype	3 months	5 months	9 months
Produce prototype	1.5 months	3 months	4 months
Market research	2 months	4 months	7 months

Table 1.10

a) Calculate the weighted mean time (expected time) for each activity.

2. **a) For each activity, expected time is $\dfrac{t_{min} + 4t_M + t_{max}}{6}$. Results are 5.3333... ≈ 5.3 months, 2.91666... ≈ 2.9 months, and 4.1666... ≈ 4.2 months.**

b) Add the expected activity times to find a prediction for how long the project can be expected to take.

b) Expected project completion time is the sum of the individual weighted mean times, 5.3 + 2.9 + 4.2 = 12.4 months.

3. Some data sets consist of what are called categorical data. That is, the data do not measure numerical values, but named categories or qualities. Such data are often pictured as a simple bar graph, which is different from a histogram in that the widths of the bars have no quantitative meaning. **Figure 1.41** is an example that shows the variety of birds observed in the rocky areas of Joshua Tree National Park in California.

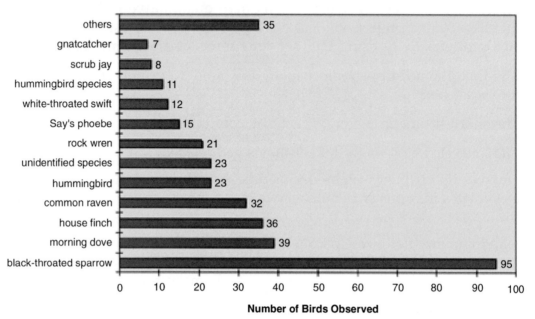

Bird Varieties in Joshua Tree Park

Figure 1.41 (Source: American Scientist, *September–October 1999)*

Bar graphs are also used to show how some quantity of interest has changed from year to year (or month to month, etc.). The graph in **Figure 1.42** shows the change in U.S. sales of diet supplements such as vitamins, minerals, and herbal substances.

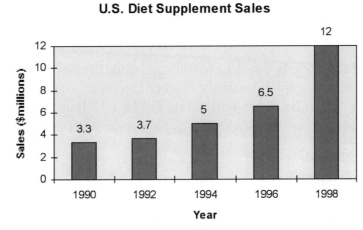

U.S. Diet Supplement Sales

Figure 1.42 (Source: Science, September 1999)

Such data, if they show a clear trend, can be the basis for establishing an equation that may allow forecasting of future expected results, as we will see in Chapter 3.

Table 1.11 shows the number of biotechnology companies located in six different midwestern states.

State	Number of Companies
Illinois	27
Iowa	23
Michigan	23
Minnesota	21
Ohio	26
Wisconsin	33

Table 1.11

Construct a bar graph of the data.

3.

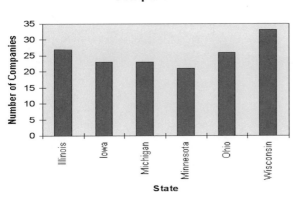

4. A **Pareto diagram** is a bar graph arranged to show categories in order of decreasing frequency. That is, the mode of the data set leads off the graph. This graphical display helps emphasize the most common category.

Pareto analysis in manufacturing is used to list all possible causes of quality problems and to prioritize them by frequency of occurrence so that the most critical or influential causes can be dealt with first. **Table 1.12** lists causes of circuit board failures from an electronics company's production run.

Cause	Number of Occurrences
Component failure	14
Wrong component	6
Solder defect	12
Contact resistance	20
Wrong polarity	8
Loose connection	5
Others	7

Vilfredo Pareto was a 19th century Italian economist who studied the distribution of wealth among different population groups. Joseph Juran, who coined the term "Pareto Analysis," applied similar principles to manufacturing processes in 1950.

Table 1.12

Figure 1.43 shows the corresponding Pareto diagram.

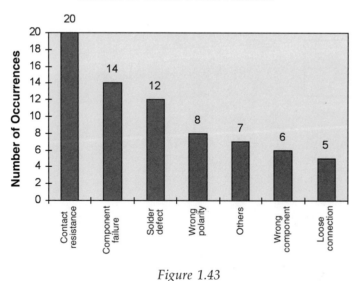

Causes of Circuit Board Failures

Figure 1.43

Table 1.13 shows the percentages of delayed flights at 10 major U.S. airports during 2000.

Airport	Delayed Flights (%)
Atlanta	3
Boston	5
Chicago	6
Dallas	2
La Guardia	16
Los Angeles	2
Newark	8
Philadelphia	5
Phoenix	2
San Francisco	6

Table 1.13 (Source: Newsweek, *4/23/01)*

Construct a Pareto diagram for the data.

4.

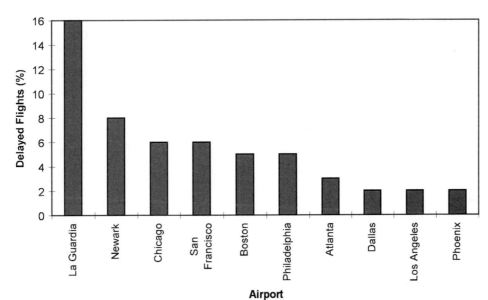

5. The data concerning frequency of major earthquakes presented in this section can also be graphed in a **relative frequency histogram.** Such a graph would differ from the one in Figure 1.37 only in the treatment of the frequencies on the vertical scale. A relative frequency or fraction of the total number of observations would replace each of the group frequencies.

The first nonzero class, containing years when from 5 to 9 major earthquakes occurred, would have a relative frequency of $\frac{6}{100} = 0.06$, since there were 100 total yearly observations included. These numbers would usually be expressed as percentages.

Recall that the percentage is just the numerator of the fraction that represents the ratio of actual frequencies to the total number of observations, *provided that the denominator is written as 100*. There were from 5 to 9 major earthquakes recorded in 6% of the years between 1900 and 1999. The relative frequency histogram would look like **Figure 1.44.**

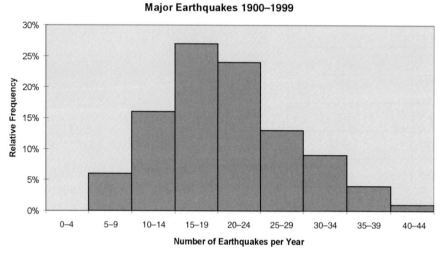

Figure 1.44

The data in **Table 1.14** shows the undercounts of black males in the 1990 census.

Age	Undercount Amount
20–24	78,000
25–29	192,000
30–34	207,000
35–39	148,000
40–44	103,000
45–49	87,000
50–54	72,000
55–59	63,000
60–64	48,000

Table 1.14 (Source: U.S. Census Bureau)

a) Complete Table 1.14 by calculating the relative frequency for each group to the nearest percent.

a)

Age	Undercount Amount	Relative Frequency (%)
20–24	78,000	8
25–29	192,000	19
30–34	207,000	21
35–39	148,000	15
40–44	103,000	10
45–49	87,000	9
50–54	72,000	7
55–59	63,000	6
60–64	48,000	5

b) Create a relative frequency histogram for the data in Table 1.14.

b)

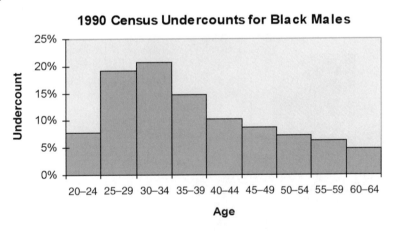

II. Projects and Group Activities *(SE pages 45–48)*

6. The purpose of a histogram usually is to convey a maximum amount of information about the distribution of a set of measurements with a minimum of numerical detail. However, for this to occur, the following guidelines for histogram construction should be followed:

- Most histograms should contain from 5 to 20 groups, depending on the size of the data set. If there are too few groups, any pattern in the data will be lost, whereas too many groups leads to too much fluctuation in bar height, defeating the purpose of the graph. A rule of thumb that is often used sets the number of groups at approximately the value of the square root of the number of values in the data set.

- The width of each group (i.e., the range of values contained in the group) should be the same as for all other groups. Otherwise, the pictorial information will be distorted.

- Labeling the data scale on the graph should make it clear where each bar of the histogram starts and stops. In the example on earthquake data (Figure 1.37), there is no question the 30–34 group overlaps the 35–39 group. However, some people might label this histogram differently, as shown in **Figure 1.45,** in order to simplify the data scale and make it appear less cluttered. In this case it is not clear which group contains a value of exactly 40, since it is at the boundary of two different groups: 40 appears to be the upper limit of one group and the lower limit of another. When histograms are labeled this way, it is a good idea to include a note of explanation, such as, "Lower limits are included in each group." The labeling of histograms created with computer spreadsheets or calculators is often done automatically, and it may not be clear exactly how the labeling is related to the group data. Caution should be exercised when interpreting such graphs.

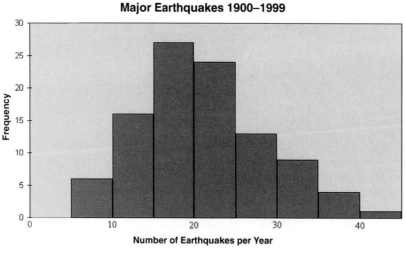

Figure 1.45

The data in **Table 1.15** represent the numbers of employees at each of the top 76 fastest-growing home-building companies in the United States from 1996 to 1998 (based on percent increase in revenue):

100	15	66	14	14	80	12	28	350	3
50	11	2	3	4	16	2852	10	20	65
4	30	15	40	38	24	1111	16	4	9
70	1190	24	20	2	55	68	2	35	92
6	29	363	80	45	304	1690	634	4	31
400	66	82	350	611	40	7	110	27	35
10	60	75	12	744	100	1583	35	93	101
42	22	23	220	45	240				

Table 1.15 (Source: Builder, *September 1999)*

Use the given guidelines to create a grouped frequency table and histogram of these data. (Hint: Since most of the firms have fewer than 1000 employees, but there are some very large firms included in the sample, you can use a common technique for dealing with such data sets and include one class for all companies with over 1000 employees as the last bar on your histogram.)

6.

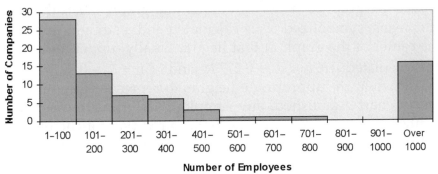

Sizes of Fastest-Growing Builders

7. An important use of mathematics in manufacturing occurs in *statistical quality control*. This involves using statistical methods to monitor the consistency of production, allowing quality control technicians to spot problems when they begin to occur. Then corrective action can be taken with a minimum of waste. Early adoption of such methods by Japanese automakers was one factor that helped them make large inroads into the American auto market during the 1970s.

A key ingredient of statistical quality control is the *control chart*, which involves graphing sample mean values for small inspection samples taken at regular intervals from a production line. A typical *x*-bar chart, or $\bar{x}$-chart, is shown in **Figure 1.46**.

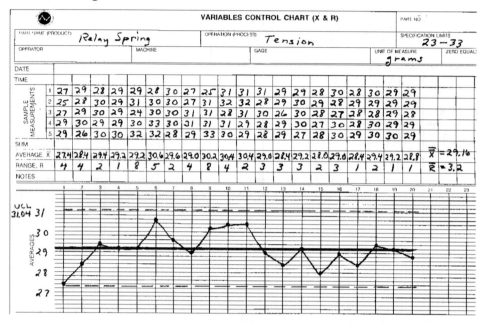

Figure 1.46

Each quality control sample consists of five measurements of the tension of a relay spring in a control system. These are all listed below the date the sample was taken. The sample mean $\bar{x}$ and average range $\bar{R}$ are both calculated, and sample mean values are graphed as a continuous line graph. Then the mean of all the sample means, symbolized $\bar{\bar{x}}$, is calculated and a straight line is drawn across the center of the graph at that height. Finally, upper and lower control limits are calculated: $UCL = \bar{\bar{x}} + 0.577\,\bar{R}$, and $LCL = \bar{\bar{x}} - 0.577\,\bar{R}$. Dashed lines are drawn at the appropriate heights to represent these limits. With such a control chart established, any sample mean measurement that falls outside of either of the control limits becomes a red flag for the quality control inspector. A process that consistently wanders outside of these limits is said to be "out of control" and requires corrective action.

Data are shown in the chart in **Figure 1.47** for quality control samples of the breakpoints of fuses (i.e., the current level measured in amperes at which the fuses blow). Create an $\bar{x}$-chart for these data, and draw in the centerline and upper and lower control limits. Does the process ever go out of control?

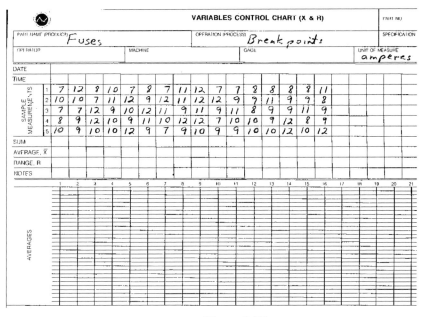

Figure 1.47

7. **Sample means and ranges are shown in the chart. The mean of the sample means is 9.625 amperes, and the mean range is 3.7 amperes. Therefore, the UCL is 9.625 + 0.577(3.7) = 11.76 amperes, and the LCL is 9.625 − 0.577(3.7) = 7.49 amperes. The process never goes out of control in this chart, since no sample means are outside of the control limits.**

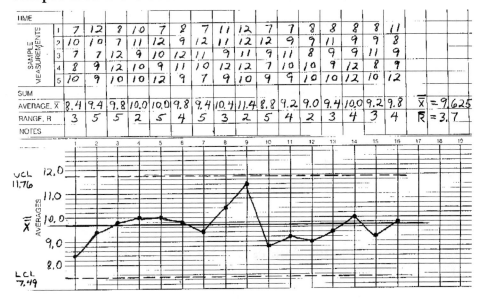

III. Additional Practice (*SE pages 48–54*)

8. **Table 1.16** indicates the high temperatures for the first week in May in Denver, Colorado.

Day of the Week	Sun	Mon	Tues	Wed	Thurs	Fri	Sat
Temperature (°F)	56	58	89	61	57	51	58

Table 1.16

Find the mean, median, mode, and range of these data.

8. **Mean: 61.428… ≈ 61 degrees; Median: 58 degrees; Mode: 58 degrees; Range: 89–51 = 38 degrees.**

9. The amount of energy that is produced when wood is burned depends on the type of wood used. **Table 1.17** indicates the number of cords of wood required to replace 2500 gallons of fuel oil.

Tree	Amount of Wood (Cords)
Hickory	17
White Oak	19
Beech	19
Yellow birch	20
Hard maple	20
Ash	21
Soft maple	23
Paper birch	23
Elm	25
White pine	32
Aspen	34

Table 1.17 (Source: Boston Globe/Forest & Wood Products Institute)

Find the mean, median, mode, and range of these data.

9. **Mean: 23 cords; Median: 21 cords; Modes: 19, 20, and 23 cords; Range: 34 – 17 = 17 cords.**

10. Create a data set of the weights of eight adults so that the mean weight is 160 pounds and the median weight is 180 pounds.

10. **Sample answer: 100 lb, 105 lb, 135 lb, 175 lb, 185 lb, 185 lb, 195 lb, 200 lb**

11. Create a data set of the weights of eight adults so that the median weight is 160 pounds and the mean weight is 180 pounds.

11. Sample answer: 135 lb, 140 lb, 145 lb, 150 lb, 170 lb, 200 lb, 240 lb, 260 lb

12. A small charter school consists of 1 administrator and 9 instructors. The administrator makes $500,000 a year. The local paper published an article stating that the mean salary for the school was $70,800. Is the mean a good indicator of the salary for all 10 personnel? Explain.

12. No, if the mean salary for 10 people is $70,800, the total salary for all 10 people is 10($70,800) = $708,000. The 9 instructors have a total salary of $708,000 – $500,000 = $208,000. Their average salary is 208,000/9, or approximately $23,000, which is far below the reported mean of $70,800.

13. Find the mean, median, mode, and range of the earthquake data shown in Table 1.6. Use a calculator list or spreadsheet to do the computations.

13. Mean = 20.35 ≈ 20; Median = 20; Mode = 15; Range = 41 – 6 = 35.

14. **Table 1.18** lists the ages at inauguration of all of the first 43 presidents of the United States.

57	61	57	57	58	57	61	54	68	51
49	64	50	48	65	52	56	46	54	49
50	47	55	55	54	42	51	56	55	51
54	51	60	62	43	55	56	61	52	69
64	46	54							

Table 1.18

Find the mean, median, mode, and range of these data.

14. Mean ≈ 54.81 years; Median = 55 years; Range = 69 – 42 = 27 years.

15. **Table 1.19** lists 20 measurements of the strength (modulus of elasticity) of a polypropylene plastic (in units of pounds per square inch (psi)).

35,600	30,444	34,304	28,138	35,235
29,949	28,993	32,000	34,327	34,380
33,939	36,056	37,463	26,619	35,107
33,481	35,142	28,915	30,495	33,106

Table 1.19

Find the mean, median, and range of these data.

15. Mean ≈ 32,685 psi; Median = (33,939 psi + 33,481 psi)/2 = 33,710 psi; Range = 37,463 psi – 26,619 psi = 10,844 psi.

16. In order to determine the oxygen content of water in a lake in Minnesota, 55 dissolved oxygen measurements were made. The data (in units of milligrams per liter) are shown in **Table 1.20.**

9.8	10.0	10.6	9.6	10.7	10.4	9.3	9.6	10.4	9.8	10.6
10.5	9.9	10.3	9.4	9.4	10.5	9.6	9.2	9.6	9.7	10.6
10.5	9.9	9.7	10.9	9.6	9.8	10.5	10.0	9.7	10.8	10.6
9.5	10.4	10.8	9.7	10.3	9.7	10.7	10.4	9.9	9.5	9.5
9.6	9.6	10.7	10.5	10.3	9.4	9.6	10.9	10.2	10.6	10.1

Table 1.20

Find the mean, median, and range of these data.

16. Mean ≈ 10.06 mg/l; Median = 10.0 mg/l; Range = 10.9 mg/l − 9.2 mg/l = 1.7 mg/l.

17. Copper communication cables can transmit signals no farther than 1.2 miles without further processing or amplification. For fiber optical cables, the equivalent limit is 100 kilometers.

a) Write an inequality that expresses the distances D_C over which signals can be transmitted without further processing using copper cables.

17. a) $D_C \leq 1.2$ and $D_C > 0$, which can also be written $0 < D_C \leq 1.2$.

b) Write an inequality that expresses the distances D_F over which signals can be transmitted without further processing using fiber optical cables.

b) $D_F \leq 100$ and $D_F > 0$, which can also be written $0 < D_F \leq 100$.

c) Write an inequality that expresses the relationship between the maximum distances of transmission using the two types of cables.

c) Since the maximum fiber optical distance is $(100 \text{ km})\left(\dfrac{1 \text{ mi}}{1.609 \text{ km}}\right) = 62 \text{ mi}$, D_F is greater than D_C, or $D_F > D_C$.

18. The U.S. Postal Service will not accept a package for mailing if the sum of its length L and its girth G (distance around) is greater than 108 inches. Write an inequality expressing the possible sizes of packages that *will* be accepted for mailing.

18. $L + G \leq 108$, or $0 < L + G \leq 108$.

19. One type of reinforced concrete application limits allowable applied compressive stress S to no more than 1350 psi. Write an inequality that indicates stress values that would *not* be acceptable.

19. $S > 1350$.

20. According to the National Cholesterol Education Program's guidelines, a low-density blood cholesterol level in the interval from 130 to 159 milligrams per deciliter is considered borderline high. Write a compound inequality that expresses the cholesterol level C that is considered borderline high.

20. $130 \le C \le 159$.

21. Write an inequality expressing the interval shown in **Figure 1.48**.

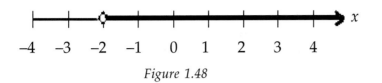

Figure 1.48

21. $x > -2$.

22. Write an inequality expressing the interval shown in **Figure 1.49**.

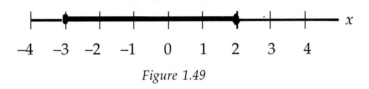

Figure 1.49

22. $-3 \le x \le 2$.

23. Draw on a number line a representation of the inequality $x \le 3$.

23.

24. Draw on a number line a representation of the inequality $-1 < x < 4$.

24.

25. Ten measurements of relative humidity at different randomly sampled locations within an old growth forest are given in **Table 1.21**.

Location	1	2	3	4	5	6	7	8	9	10
Rel. Hum. (%)	78	83	85	69	76	74	80	72	76	73

Table 1.21

a) Construct a dot plot for these data.

25. a)

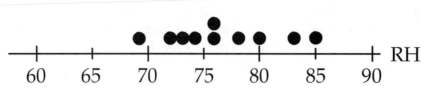

b) Use the dot plot to find the range and mode for the data.

b) Range: 85 – 69 = 16%; Mode: 76%.

26. **Table 1.22** lists the weights of babies at birth for two groups of babies. The first group had mothers who never smoked. The second group had mothers who smoked at least 10 cigarettes per day.

Never Smoked	6.3	7.3	8.2	7.1	7.8	9.7	6.1	9.6	7.4	7.8	9.4	7.6
Smoked 10 or More a Day	6.3	6.4	4.2	9.4	7.1	5.9	6.8	8.2	7.8	5.9	5.4	6.3

Table 1.22

a) One good way to compare these groups is to graph both sets of data on the same dot plot. Construct a dot plot for these data. Use a single axis, and indicate the two groups by using different symbols for each set.

26. a)

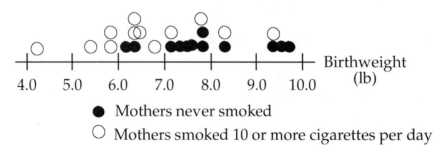

● Mothers never smoked
○ Mothers smoked 10 or more cigarettes per day

b) Use the dot plot to make a statement about the influence of smoking on a baby's birthweight.

b) It appears that babies whose mothers never smoked tended to have higher birthweights than those whose mothers smoked 10 or more cigarettes per day.

27. **Table 1.23** lists grouped frequencies for the data on presidents' ages given in Exercise 14. Construct a well-labeled frequency histogram of the data.

Age (years)	Frequency
40–44	2
45–49	8
50–54	15
55–59	9
60–64	7
65–69	2

Table 1.23

27.

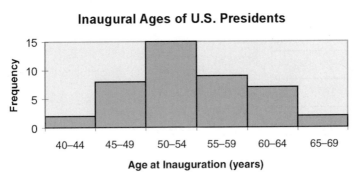

28. **Table 1.24** lists grouped frequencies for the plastic strength data given in Exercise 15. Construct a well-labeled frequency histogram of the data.

Strength (psi)	Frequency
26,000–under 28,000	1
28,000–under 30,000	4
30,000–under 32,000	5
32,000–under 34,000	4
34,000–under 36,000	4
36,000–under 38,000	2

Table 1.24

28.

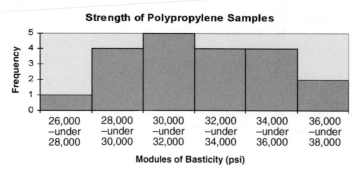

29. **Table 1.25** lists grouped frequencies for the dissolved oxygen data given in Exercise 16.

O_2 Concentration (mg/l)	Frequency
9.0–9.2	1
9.3–9.5	7
9.6–9.8	16
9.9–10.1	6
10.2–10.4	8
10.5–10.7	13
10.8–11.0	4

Table 1.25

a) Construct a well-labeled frequency histogram of the data.

29. a)

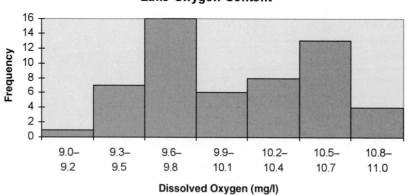

b) The histogram you have constructed shows a data pattern that is sometimes referred to as bimodal. Even though the dissolved oxygen measurements are continuous data, there are clearly two different regions of the graph in which the data are clustered. Give a possible explanation for this particular bimodal behavior.

b) Sample answer: It's possible that there are two regions of the lake that are partially separate (e.g., there might be a large bay in one section of the lake) and have different dissolved oxygen characteristics due to different vegetation patterns or some other cause.

30. **Figure 1.50** is a histogram of measured times for computer systems to boot up after being turned on.

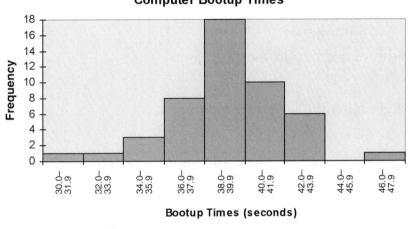

Figure 1.50

a) How many computers were tested?

30. a) Total heights of columns = 48.

b) What is the width of a group in the histogram?

b) 2.0 seconds

c) Which interval contains the largest fraction of bootup times?

c) 38.0–39.9 seconds

d) What percent of the sample took at least 40.0 seconds to boot up?

d) $\dfrac{10+6+0+1}{48} = \dfrac{17}{48}; \left(\dfrac{17}{48}\right)(100) = 35.4\%.$

31. **Figure 1.51** is a histogram of scores on an exam for a college mathematics class.

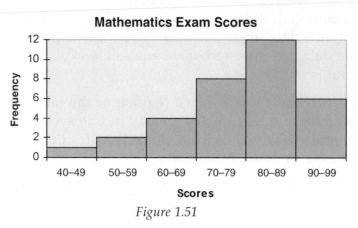

Mathematics Exam Scores

Figure 1.51

a) How many students took the exam?

31. a) Total heights of columns = 33.

b) What is the width of a group in the histogram?

b) 10 points

c) Which interval contains the largest fraction of scores?

c) 80–89

d) If a score of 60 is the lowest passing score, how many students failed the exam?

d) (2 + 1) = 3.

Section 1.4 Measuring a Surface: Area

What You Need to Know

- How to compute perimeters of plane figures

What You Will Learn

- To compute areas of some plane figures

- To use formulas to compute areas

- To change units of area

- To distinguish between the quantities perimeter and area

Materials

- None

The measurements made and discussed in the first section of this chapter were all one-dimensional and measured in units of length such as meters, centimeters, feet, and inches. Even though perimeter is a property of two-dimensional objects, it is essentially a one-dimensional quantity.

In order to understand this better, imagine an intelligent inchworm slowly working its way around the perimeter of the floor of the classroom. It would have no sense of the space taken up by the floor surface. Instead, it would just be aware of a long journey along a line that happens to have a few turns in it. To have a real grasp of the concept of the area of a surface, it is necessary to be able to rise above the surface.

The 19th century English author Edwin Abbott imagined a world of only two dimensions. He investigated what it might be like if it were impossible to move off of a surface to see the shapes on it. His book *Flatland* takes a look at what it is like to live in a two-dimensional world. It also examines the meaning of a fourth dimension.

Since a unit of length like a meter has no width, we must find another kind of unit to measure the area of a figure on a flat surface (or **plane**). There are several simple geometrical shapes, such as triangles, squares, rectangles, and hexagons, that can fill the space on a plane without any gaps. (See **Figure 1.52.**) This means we could measure the area of a floor in triangular units, square units, rectangular units, or even hexagonal units. The most common units used are square units.

Figure 1.52

Consider the 3 cm x 7 cm rectangle in **Figure 1.53.** We can think of its area as the space it takes up on the plane surface of this page. Notice that the number of 1 cm squares is (3)(7) = 21. We therefore say that the area of the rectangle is 21 square centimeters. This can be written as 21 sq cm, or we can use the exponent symbol for squaring and write 21 cm^2.

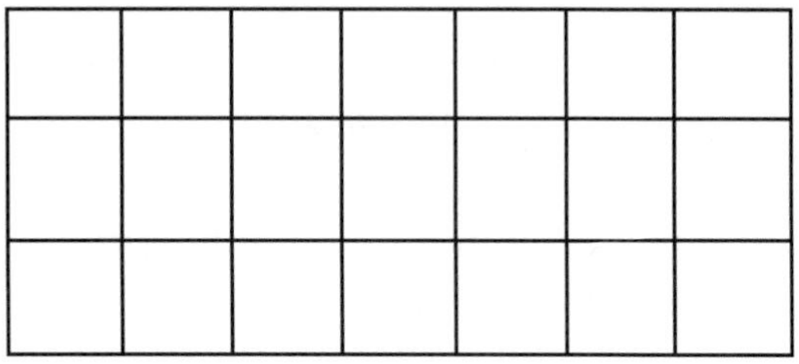

It is also possible to "tile the plane" with other kinds of shapes. Artists and designers make use of this fact to create interesting—and sometimes rather bizarre—patterns in paintings, fabrics, and floors. Many such tilings were explored by the artist M. C. Escher, who incorporated mathematical principles into the design of his drawings and sculptures.

Figure 1.53

Example 21

Find the area of a rectangular lot with dimensions 72 ft x 115 ft.

Solution:

The area is (72 ft)(115 ft) = 8280 ft^2.

Converting Units of Area

It is worth noting here that unit conversions involving squared units must be treated with special care. Consider the square represented in **Figure 1.54,** 1 foot long on each side. It has an area of 1 square foot (1 ft^2). But how many square inches are in 1 square foot?

It is a common mistake to assume that since there are 12 inches in a foot, there are also 12 square inches in a square foot. But just a glance at the figure shows that there are many more than 12 squares, each 1 inch on a side, that fit in the 1 square foot area. In fact, the large square contains 12 rows of 12 one-inch squares each, so 1 square foot must contain (12 in)(12 in) = 144 sq in.

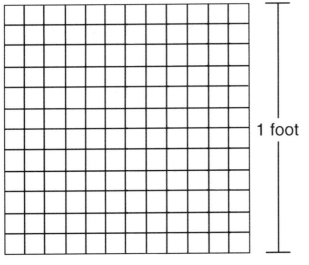

Figure 1.54

In making a conversion from square feet to square inches, we use the same conversion fraction described in Section 1.2 $\left(\dfrac{12 \text{ in}}{1 \text{ ft}}\right)$, but this fraction must be squared to produce the correct conversion. For example, to convert 25 square feet to an equivalent number of square inches, write:

$$(25 \text{ ft}^2)\left(\frac{12 \text{ in}}{1 \text{ ft}}\right)^2 = \frac{(25 \text{ ft}^2)(144 \text{ in}^2)}{1 \text{ ft}^2} = 3600 \text{ in}^2.$$

Example 22

Convert 50.7 square centimeters to an equivalent number of square inches. (Use the conversion 1 in = 2.54 cm.)

Solution:

$$(50.7 \text{ cm}^2)\left(\frac{1 \text{ in}}{2.54 \text{ cm}}\right)^2 = \frac{(50.7 \text{ cm}^2)(1 \text{ in}^2)}{6.4516 \text{ cm}^2} \approx 7.86 \text{ in}^2.$$

Discovery 1.2 Calculating Floor Area (SE pages 57–58)

1. As in Activity 1.1, in which you measured the dimensions of your classroom, estimate the number of square meters of area taken up by the floor.

1. **Estimates will vary depending on the size of the room.**

2. Now use the class sample mean values for the length and width of the room (items 1 and 6 of Discovery 1.1, Section 1.3) to calculate the area of the floor. (Round the area to the nearest thousandth of a square meter.) Was your estimate from item 1 close to the actual value?

2. **Sample answer: Using the sample mean dimensions length = 11.33 m and width = 7.08 m, the area is (11.33 m)(7.08 m) ≈ 80.216 m². Estimates within 10 m² of this value might be possible.**

3. The value you found for the floor area of the room is based on a computation that used measured dimensions. Since the measurements themselves can never be exact, it is worth considering how accurate your area value might be.

For example, if you were to give your area figure to a company that will be laying tile or carpet in the classroom, it would be important for them to know the possible error in the area. That way, they would know how much floor-covering material might be needed.

a) You can get a good sense of the maximum possible error in your area result by looking at the original class data for length and width measurements. Examine your class data set for the room length. Find the smallest measurement in the set. Also find the shortest width reported. Find the product of these two values. This should give a reasonable lower limit for the actual area of the floor.

3. a) Sample answer using a shortest width of 11.318 m and a shortest length of 7.060 m: The lower limit for the actual area is (11.318 m)(7.060 m) = 79.905 m².

b) Similarly, find the largest reported values for room length and width. Find the product of these two values. This gives you an upper limit for the actual room area.

b) Sample answer using a longest width of 11.352 m and a longest length of 7.095 m: The upper limit on the actual room area is (11.352 m)(7.095 m) = 80.542 m².

c) Now calculate the difference between each of these limits and the mean area, as computed from the mean length and width (item 2). Whichever difference is larger (in absolute value) can then be called the maximum likely error in the area. Find the maximum likely error for your mean area value.

c) Sample answer assuming the mean area is 80.216: The upper limit is farthest from the mean, with a difference of about 0.336 m². So the maximum likely error is 0.336 m².

Maximum likely error can often be estimated even when single measurements are made of quantities that are to be multiplied. If a rectangular field has measured dimensions 124 ft X 217 ft, but each dimension has a possible error of ±2 ft, then the area would be calculated in the usual way as (124 ft)(217 ft) = 26,908 ft². However, there is **uncertainty** about the actual area value due to the measurement error.

The actual dimensions of the field could be as small as 122 ft and 215 ft, which would give a minimum possible field area of 26,230 ft². Similarly, the actual dimensions could be as large as 126 ft and 219 ft, giving a maximum possible field area of 27,594 ft².

The value of the field area could then be reported as between 26,230 ft² and 27,594 ft², or 26,908 ft² ± 686 ft². Or as an alternative, it may be clearer to report the area simply as 27,000 ft², where it would have to be understood that the value is correct only to the nearest 1000 ft². (See Exercise 6 in this section.)

d) Report your mean floor area as a numerical average plus or minus the maximum likely error.

d) Sample answer: The area can be reported as 80.215 m^2 ± 0.336 m^2. A better form is 80.2 m^2 ± 0.3 m^2 due to the irrelevance of the last two or three digits.

4. To conclude the area measurement work, remember that most people in the United States whose work involves construction or renovations of the kind discussed here measure lengths in feet and inches instead of metric units. Convert your area from square meters to square feet.

4. Sample answer: $(80.215 \text{ m}^2)\left(\dfrac{3.281 \text{ ft}}{1 \text{ mi}}\right)^2 = 863.5113... \approx 863.5 \text{ ft}^2.$

5. List several kinds of jobs people do that require the calculation of rectangular areas.

5. Any kind of design work, from interior to industrial to mechanical design, as well as surveying, forest, and agricultural management.

Area Formulas

As we have seen in this section, we can calculate the area A of any rectangle by multiplying the length l of the rectangle by its width w. To show this relationship, we can use the formula $A = lw$. Recall that when we write l and w next to each other, multiplication is implied. This notation means the same as $A = l \cdot w$ or $A = (l)(w)$.

Example 23

31.7 cm

18.4 cm

Figure 1.55

Find the area of the rectangular piece of sheet metal in **Figure 1.55.**

Solution:

Substitute 31.7 cm for the length l in the area formula and 18.4 cm for the width w:

$A = lw$

$\quad = (31.7 \text{ cm})(18.4 \text{ cm})$

$\quad = 583.8 \text{ cm}^2$

Example 24

A computer monitor has screen dimensions 13 in x $9\frac{1}{2}$ in. Use the area formula to find the area of the computer screen.

Solution:

In order to use the width measurement easily in computation, it is more convenient to write it as 9.5 in. Then using the formula for the area of a rectangle:

$A = lw$

$\quad = (13 \text{ in})(9.5 \text{ in})$

$\quad = 123.5 \text{ in}^2$

In a formula such as $A = lw$, the value of one variable quantity (in this case, area) depends on the values of other quantities. For this reason, the variables are referred to as either **dependent variables** or **independent variables.** In the area formula, the dependent variable (area) depends on the values of two independent variables (length and width). We often say that area is a **function** of the length and width.

A square is a special rectangle where the length and width are equal in length. If s represents the side of a square, we can write the formula for its area as $A = (s)(s)$ or $A = s^2$. In this case we say the area A depends on only one variable, the length of the side s. Hence, A is a function of the single variable s.

The following formulas are useful when calculating areas.

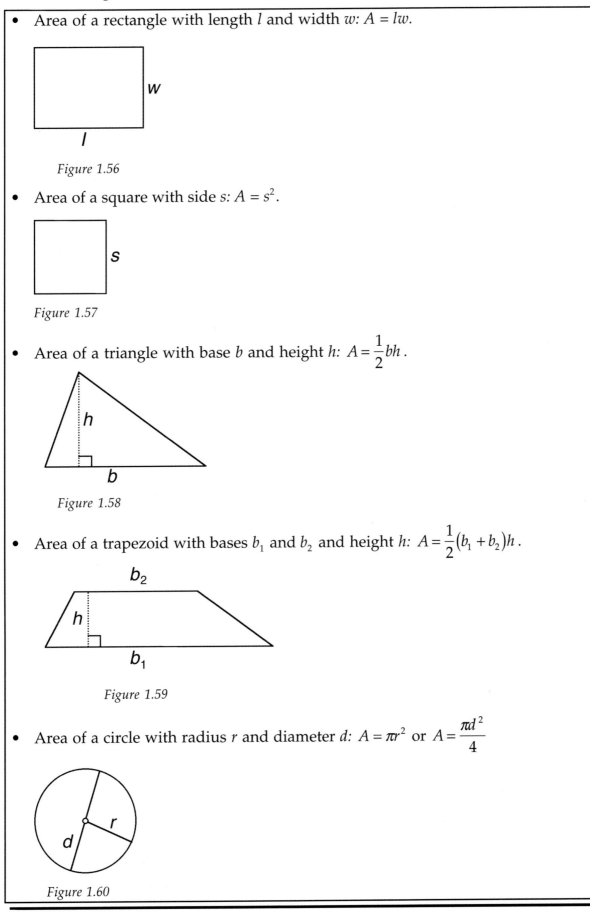

- Area of a rectangle with length l and width w: $A = lw$.

Figure 1.56

- Area of a square with side s: $A = s^2$.

Figure 1.57

- Area of a triangle with base b and height h: $A = \frac{1}{2}bh$.

Figure 1.58

- Area of a trapezoid with bases b_1 and b_2 and height h: $A = \frac{1}{2}(b_1 + b_2)h$.

Figure 1.59

- Area of a circle with radius r and diameter d: $A = \pi r^2$ or $A = \frac{\pi d^2}{4}$

Figure 1.60

Example 25

Find the area of the trapezoidal corner brace in **Figure 1.61.**

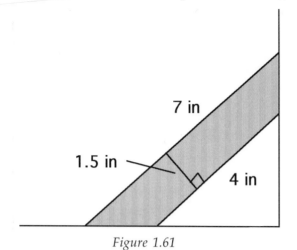

Figure 1.61

Solution:

The brace is in the shape of a trapezoid.

$$A = \frac{1}{2}(b_1 + b_2)h$$

$$= \frac{1}{2}(7 \text{ in} + 4 \text{ in})(1.5 \text{ in})$$

$$= 8.25 \text{ in}^2.$$

If a figure is too involved to deal with by using a single formula, divide it into simpler figures. Calculate the areas of the simpler figures. Then find the sum of the individual areas.

Example 26

Figure 1.62 is an outline of a Norman window, which consists of a semicircle on top of a rectangle. Find its area.

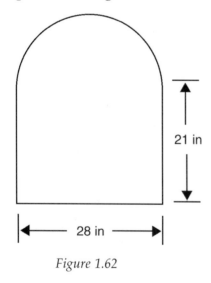

Figure 1.62

Solution:

Divide the figure into a semicircle with radius 14 inches and a rectangle with dimensions 28 in x 21 in as shown in **Figure 1.63.**

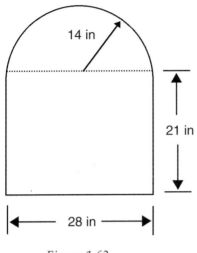

14 in

21 in

28 in

Figure 1.63

Find the area of the semicircle and the rectangle, then add the individual areas.

$$A_{\text{total}} = A_{\text{semicircle}} + A_{\text{rectangle}}$$

$$= \frac{1}{2}\pi r^2 + lw$$

$$= \frac{1}{2}\pi(14 \text{ in})^2 + (28 \text{ in})(21 \text{ in})$$

$$= \frac{1}{2}\pi(196 \text{ in}^2) + (588 \text{ in}^2)$$

$$= 307.876 \text{ in}^2 + 588 \text{ in}^2$$

$$= 895.876 \approx 896 \text{ in}^2.$$

Example 27

Figure 1.64 shows the cross section (slice) of a round peg in a square container. In the cross section, find the area of the space between the peg and the container if the radius of the peg is 3.0 inches.

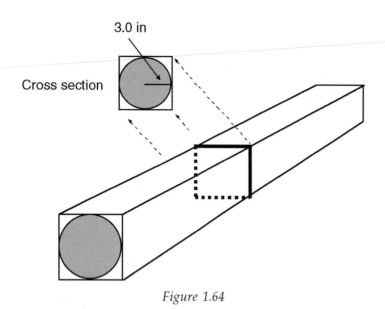

3.0 in

Cross section

Figure 1.64

Solution:

Since the radius of the circle is 3.0 inches, the side of the square is 6.0 inches.

$$A_{between} = A_{square} - A_{circle}$$

$$= s^2 - \pi r^2$$

$$= (6.0 \text{ in})^2 - \pi (3.0 \text{ in})^2$$

$$= 36 - (\pi)(9) \approx 7.7 \text{ in}^2.$$

Exercises 1.4

I. Investigations *(SE pages 64–67)*

1. Rather than reporting a nonmetric measurement in units such as feet in decimal form, it is customary to report it in feet and inches. (But keep in mind, when using such measurements for calculation, it is easiest to use the decimal representation.)

   To change 37.16 feet to feet and inches, change the fractional portion of the measurement (0.16 feet) to inches:

   $$(0.16 \text{ ft})\left(\frac{12 \text{ in}}{1 \text{ ft}}\right) = 1.92 \text{ in} \approx 2 \text{ in. So } 37.16 \text{ ft is approximately } 37 \text{ ft } 2 \text{ in.}$$

   a) Change 4.76 feet to feet and inches.

1. a) $(0.76 \text{ ft})\left(\dfrac{12 \text{ in}}{1 \text{ ft}}\right) = 9.21 \text{ in} \approx 9 \text{ in. So } 4.76 \text{ ft} \approx 4 \text{ ft } 9 \text{ in.}$

   b) Change 24.08 feet to feet and inches.

   b) $(0.08 \text{ ft})\left(\dfrac{12 \text{ in}}{1 \text{ ft}}\right) = 0.96 \text{ in} \approx 1 \text{ in. So } 24.08 \text{ ft} \approx 24 \text{ ft } 1 \text{ in.}$

   c) Change 7.63 yards to yards, feet, and inches.

   c) $(0.63 \text{ yd})\left(\dfrac{3 \text{ ft}}{1 \text{ yd}}\right) = 1.89 \text{ ft. So } 7.63 \text{ yd} = 7 \text{ yd } 1.89 \text{ ft.}$

   $(0.89 \text{ ft})\left(\dfrac{12 \text{ in}}{1 \text{ ft}}\right) = 10.68 \text{ in} \approx 11 \text{ in. Therefore, } 7.63 \text{ yd} \approx 7 \text{ yd } 1 \text{ ft } 11 \text{ in.}$

2. A regular polygon is a polygon with all sides equal and all angles equal. Such a figure can be inscribed in a circle, like the regular pentagon shown in **Figure 1.65.** Notice that every vertex of the pentagon is a distance r (the radius of the circle) from the center of the pentagon.

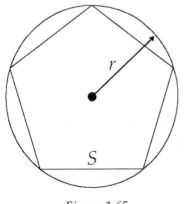

Figure 1.65

Suppose that the pentagon represents the common area of an apartment building and that the distance r is 25 ft 6 in (or 25.5 ft) and the distance S is 30 ft 0 in.

To calculate the area of the pentagon, first divide the pentagon into five congruent triangles. (One of the triangles, ΔABC, is shown in **Figure 1.66.**)

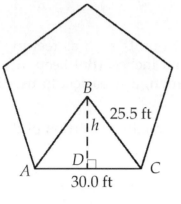

Figure 1.66

ΔABC is **isosceles,** meaning that two of its sides are of equal length. If a perpendicular line from B to the side AC is drawn, it divides side AC into two equal segments.

a) Line segment $\overline{BD}$ is the height of ΔABC. Find the length of $\overline{BD}$.

2. a) $\overline{BD} = \sqrt{(25.5)^2 - (15.0)^2} \approx 20.6$ ft.

b) Find the area of ΔABC.

b) $A = \left(\dfrac{1}{2}\right)bh = \left(\dfrac{1}{2}\right)(30.0)(20.6) = 309$ ft^2.

c) Find the area of the entire pentagon.

c) $A = 5(309) = 1545$ ft^2.

d) Use a similar method to determine the area of a regular octagonal window that is 2 ft 0 in on each side and 5.2 ft across (from vertex to opposite vertex).

d) **The "radius" of the octagon is 2.6 ft. If divided into eight isosceles triangles, each triangle will have an area of** $\left(\dfrac{1}{2}\right)(2.0)\left(\sqrt{(2.6)^2 - (1.0)^2}\right) =$ $\left(\dfrac{1}{2}\right)(2.0)(2.4) = 2.4$ **ft^2. The entire window has an area of** 8(2.4 ft^2) = **19.2 ft^2.**

3. The formula for the area of a circle can be stated in two different ways: as a function of radius, the area is $A = \pi r^2$; as a function of diameter, the area is $A = \pi d^2/4$. Why do you think most engineers generally use the latter formula?

3. **It is difficult to measure the radius of most objects, such as rods and spheres. Using calipers or other tools, diameter is easier to determine accurately.**

4. **Figure 1.67** shows a house with a *hip roof*. Although the roof is actually a three-dimensional figure, its **surface area** is still essentially a two-dimensional quantity. (The surface area of a three-dimensional object is the sum of the areas of all the object's surfaces.)

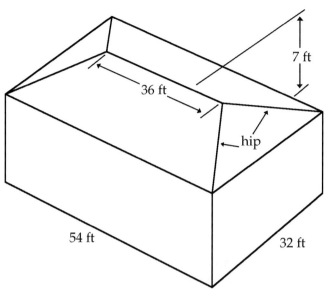

Figure 1.67

a) Look carefully at the roof in the figure. What are the shapes of the four surfaces that must be shingled?

4. **a) Two are triangles and two are trapezoids.**

To find the area of each of the four surfaces, we must know the height of each figure.

b) We know from the drawing that the centerline of the roof is 7 feet above the elevation of the edge of the roof. Use the Pythagorean theorem to find the slant height of each of the long sides of the roof.

b) $\sqrt{(7 \text{ ft})^2 + (16 \text{ ft})^2} \approx 17.46$ **ft.**

c) Find the area of each of the long sides of the roof.

c) Each of the long sides is a trapezoid with area (1/2)(36 ft + 54 ft)(17.46 ft) ≈ 786 ft².

d) Use the Pythagorean theorem to find the slant height of each of the ends of the roof.

d) The slant height of the ends of the roof will be $\sqrt{(7 \text{ ft})^2 + (9 \text{ ft})^2} \approx 11.4$ **ft.**

e) Find the area of each of the ends of the roof.

e) The area of each triangular end is (1/2)(32 ft)(11.4 ft) = 182.4 ft².

f) Find the total surface area of the roof.

f) **The total surface area of the roof is then 2(786 ft²) + 2(182.4 ft²) = 1937 ft².
(The accuracy of this result depends on the accuracy of the dimensions,
which is not apparent from the figure.)**

5. Examine the formula for finding the area of a rectangle.

   a) What would happen to the area of a rectangle if each dimension were
   doubled?

5. a) $A = (2l)(2w) = 4lw$, so area is multiplied by 4.

   b) What if the dimensions were tripled?

b) $A = (3l)(3w) = 9lw$, so area is multiplied by 9.

   c) Can you make a generalization about what would happen if each
   dimension were multiplied by any constant factor?

c) Area would be multiplied by the square of the factor.

   d) What if the length of the rectangle were tripled and the width cut in half?

d) $A = (3l)(w/2) = 1.5(lw)$, so area is increased by 50%.

6. In Exercise 3 of Section 1.2, we examined how to treat the outcome of addition
   and subtraction with measured quantities. When measured numbers are
   multiplied or divided, the results are handled differently.

   One way to deal with uncertainty in these computations was discussed in
   Discovery 1.2 with regard to the area of a field. There the measurement error
   in the dimensions was explicitly stated. A similar method can be used to
   decide where to round off a result even when no error measurement is
   given.

   Consider the rectangular metal plate in **Figure 1.68.**

10.3 cm

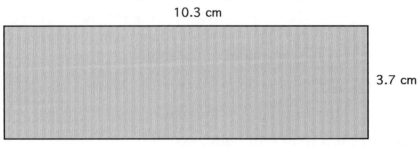

3.7 cm

Figure 1.68

Without other information, we would assume that both dimensions are
accurate to the nearest 0.1 cm. (Their precision is 0.1 cm.) This implies a
maximum error in each dimension of ±0.05 cm.

If we need to find the plate's area, the calculated result is 38.11 cm². However,
the true area of the plate could be as small as (10.25 cm)(3.65 cm) = 37.4125 cm²
and as large as (10.35 cm)(3.75 cm) = 38.8125 cm².

When we say that the area is 38.11 cm², it implies more accuracy than can be
justified by the measured data. It would be less misleading to state that the
area is between 37.4125 cm² and 38.8125 cm². To avoid the need for these

multiple calculations, we can report the area as 38 cm². This indicates that the measurement is accurate only to the nearest cm².

As with addition and subtraction, we can state a general guideline:

> For multiplication or division of measured numbers, round off results of computations to the fewest significant figures contained in any of the data.

Notice that with addition and subtraction, the number of decimal places was important, but here it is only the total number of significant figures in the least accurate number, regardless of decimal position.

Powers and roots are essentially similar to multiplication and division, so these operations follow the same guideline for rounding. When combinations of several operations are involved, it is impossible to state a general rule. The most important thing to remember is that the calculator will generally display computed results with many more digits than are necessary to convey the true accuracy of the quantity being computed. Therefore, it is up to us to determine the best way of expressing such results.

For (a)–(e), assume that the quantities in the calculations are measured. Write each result with an appropriate number of figures.

a) (0.47 cm)(5.475 cm)

6. a) 2.57325 ≈ 2.6 cm².

b) $\dfrac{345.8 \text{ ft}^2}{27 \text{ ft}}$

b) 12.8074074... ≈ 13 ft.

c) $\dfrac{(25 \text{ m})(0.9297 \text{ m})}{0.0102 \text{ m}}$

c) 2278.67647059... ≈ 2300 m. (The zeros are not significant.)

d) 2.9 in)(3.57 in + 10.28 in)

d) (2.9 in)(13.85 in) = 40.165 ≈ 40 in². (Here the zero *is* significant.)

e) What would be the best way to record the area of the Norman window in Example 26?

e) Since the given dimensions are accurate presumably to only two significant figures, the total area can be accurate to only two significant figures, so round off to the nearest 10 in², or 900 in². (Here the first zero is significant, but the second is not.) Most people would still round to the nearest integer, writing 896 in², even though this implies more accuracy than actually exists.

II. Projects and Group Activities *(SE pages 67–69)*

7. Suppose that a very large rectangular area needs to be fenced off in order to allow cattle to graze. Assume that 1800 feet of fencing is available.

   a) If one dimension of the field were 800 feet, what would the other dimension be? (Remember that the perimeter must be 1800 feet.)

7. a) For a perimeter of 1800 feet, the other dimension would have to be 100 feet.

   b) The theoretical minimum value for a dimension of the field is 0 feet. What is the theoretical maximum dimension?

b) 900 feet

   c) Complete **Table 1.26** with possible dimensions for the field. The first column lists some possible values for one of the dimensions, ranging from the minimum to the maximum possible. In the second column, determine what the second dimension would be for each value in the first column.

First Dimension (ft)	Second Dimension (ft)
0	
100	
200	
300	
400	
500	
600	
700	
800	
900	

Table 1.26

c)

First Dimension (ft)	Second Dimension (ft)
0	900
100	800
200	700
300	600
400	500
500	400
600	300
700	200
800	100
900	0

d) Now add a third column to your table from (c). Label the column "Area (ft^2)." Calculate the area for each set of dimensions.

d)

First Dimension (ft)	Second Dimension (ft)	Area (ft^2)
0	900	0
100	800	80,000
200	700	140,000
300	600	180,000
400	500	200,000
500	400	200,000
600	300	180,000
700	200	140,000
800	100	80,000
900	0	0

e) Examine your table, noting the relationships among the dimensions and the size of the area. What generalizations or conclusions can you draw from your analysis?

e) Sample answer: As the field becomes more "squarelike," the area gets larger.

f) Use a spreadsheet or calculator to investigate in more detail how changing the dimensions of the rectangle affects the area.

f) **Sample answer: Area is maximized for a square field with sides of 450 feet.**

g) For a variation on this kind of problem, imagine that a company wants to build a rectangular storage yard alongside its main warehouse, using an existing 160-foot-long wall of the warehouse as one of the sides of the yard. If 140 feet of fence is available, investigate some possible dimensions, and again determine how to obtain maximum area.

g) **Area is maximized if the length is twice the width. Dimensions are 70 ft x 35 ft.**

8. **Figure 1.69** shows a plan for the basement and foundation of a house. What is the total ground area taken up by the foundation?

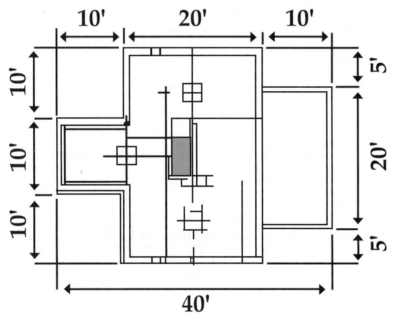

Figure 1.69

8. **The foundation consists of a square 10 ft on a side and two rectangles, one 20 ft x 30 ft and the other 10 ft x 20 ft. The total area is (10 ft)² + (20 ft)(30 ft) + (10 ft)(20 ft) = 900 ft².**

III. Additional Practice *(SE pages 69–75)*

9. Find the area and perimeter of the square in **Figure 1.70** if it is $3\frac{1}{2}$ inches on a side.

Figure 1.70

9. $A = (3.5 \text{ in})^2 = 12.25$ or $12\frac{1}{4}$ in²; $P = 4(3.5 \text{ in}) = 14$ in.

10. Find the area and perimeter of the triangle in **Figure 1.71.**

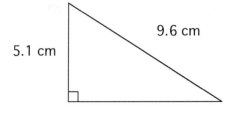

9.6 cm

5.1 cm

Figure 1.71

10. Length of base = $\sqrt{(9.6 \text{ cm})^2 - (5.1 \text{ cm})^2}$ = 8.1333 cm.
A = (1/2)(8.1333 cm)(5.1 cm) = 20.7398 cm^2 ≈ 21 cm^2;
P = 5.1 + 9.6 + 8.1 = 22.8 cm.

11. Find the area and perimeter of the rectangle in **Figure 1.72.**

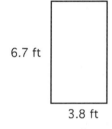

6.7 ft

3.8 ft

Figure 1.72

11. A = (6.7 ft)(3.8 ft) = 25.46 ft^2 ≈ 25 ft^2;
P = 2(6.7) + 2(3.8) = 21 ft.

12. Find the area of the triangle in **Figure 1.73.**

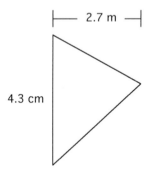

2.7 m

4.3 cm

Figure 1.73

12. A = (1/2)(4.3 m)(2.7 m) = 5.8050 m^2 ≈ 5.8 m^2.

13. Find the area of the trapezoid in **Figure 1.74.**

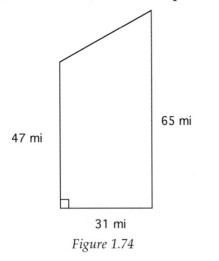

65 mi

47 mi

31 mi

Figure 1.74

13. $A = 1/2(47 + 65)(31) = 1736$ **mi**$^2 \approx 1700$ **mi**^{2}.

14. Find the area and circumference of a circle with a radius of 17.2 ft.

14. $A = \pi(17.2)^2 \approx 929$ **ft**^{2}; $C = 2\pi(17.2) \approx 108$ **ft.**

15. Find the area and circumference of a circle with a diameter of 8.3 cm.

15. $A = \dfrac{\pi(8.3)^2}{4} \approx 54$ **cm**^{2}; $C = \pi(8.3) \approx 26$ **cm.**

For 16–24, express each of the areas as indicated.

16. 42.0 ft^2 as in^2

16. $42.0 \text{ ft}^2 \left(\dfrac{12 \text{ in}}{1 \text{ ft}}\right)^2 \approx 6050 \text{ in}^2.$

17. 16,238 in^2 as ft^2

17. $16{,}238 \text{ in}^2 \left(\dfrac{1 \text{ ft}}{12 \text{ in}}\right)^2 \approx 112.76 \text{ ft}^2.$

18. 86 yd^2 as ft^2

18. $86 \text{ yd}^2 \left(\dfrac{3 \text{ ft}}{1 \text{ yd}}\right)^2 \approx 770 \text{ in}^2.$

19. 2.5 acres as ft^2 (1 acre = 43,560 ft^2)

19. $2.50 \text{ acres} \left(\dfrac{43{,}560 \text{ ft}^2}{1 \text{ acre}}\right) \approx 109{,}000 \text{ ft}^2.$

20. 1.75 mi^2 as ft^2

20. 1.75 mi^2 $\left(\dfrac{5280 \text{ ft}}{1 \text{ mi}}\right)^2 \approx$ 48,800,000 ft^2.

21. 7.88 ft^2 as yd^2

21. 7.88 ft^2 $\left(\dfrac{1 \text{ yd}}{3 \text{ ft}}\right)^2 \approx$ 0.875 yd^2.

22. 2 m^2 as cm^2

22. 2 m^2 $\left(\dfrac{100 \text{ cm}}{1 \text{ m}}\right)^2 =$ 20,000 cm^2.

23. 87,000 mm^2 as cm^2

23. 87000 mm^2 $\left(\dfrac{1 \text{ cm}}{10 \text{ mm}}\right)^2 =$ 870 cm^2.

24. 95 km^2 as m^2

24. 95 km^2 $\left(\dfrac{1000 \text{ m}}{1 \text{ km}}\right)^2 \approx$ 95,000,000 m^2.

25. a) A rectangular integrated circuit chip on the motherboard of a computer has dimensions 2.74 cm x 1.95 cm. Find its area.

25. a) 5.34 cm^2

b) What is the area in m^2? Try a direct conversion from cm^2 to m^2, and then check your result by first converting the dimensions to meters before multiplying to find the area.

b) (5.34 cm^2) $\left(\dfrac{1 \text{ m}}{100 \text{ cm}}\right)^2 =$ 0.000534 m^2; also (0.0274 m)(0.0195 m) = 0.000534 m^2.

c) What is the area in mm^2?

c) (5.34 cm^2) $\left(\dfrac{10 \text{ mm}}{1 \text{ cm}}\right)^2 =$ 534 mm^2.

26. The northern spotted owl has been an endangered species for some time. A detailed study was made of its behavior and habitat over an area of 1474 km^2 in Oregon.

a) What is the study area measured in square miles? (1 mi = 1.609 km.)

26. a) (1474 km^2) $\left(\dfrac{1 \text{ mi}}{1.609 \text{ km}}\right)^2 =$ 569.3580 $\approx$ 569.4 mi^2.

b) What is the area in acres? (1 acre = 43,560 ft^2.)

b) (569.4 mi^2) $\left(\dfrac{5280 \text{ ft}}{1 \text{ mi}}\right)^2 \left(\dfrac{1 \text{ acre}}{43,560 \text{ ft}^2}\right)$ **= 364,416 ≈ 364,400 acres.**

27. The Akashi Kaikyo Bridge is built on steel caissons, sunk into the sea floor. These caissons are shaped like cylinders and are 80 meters in diameter. Find the circular cross-sectional area of one of these caissons?

27. $A = \dfrac{\pi(80)^2}{4} \approx 5027 \text{ m}^2.$

28. A large tire manufacturing plant in South Carolina has a floor area of 1,400,000 ft^2. If the plant were square in shape, how long would a side of the square be? (Hint: Since the area of a square is given by $A = s^2$, the length of a side of a square with known area can be found from $s = \sqrt{A}$.)

28. $s = \sqrt{1,400,000 \text{ ft}^2} = 1183 \approx 1200 \text{ ft.}$

29. If an 8.6-inch-diameter log has a bark layer 0.5 inches thick, what is the cross-sectional area of the bark layer? (Hint: Make a drawing of the circular cross section.)

29. **Circular cross-sectional area of entire log is $\pi(8.6 \text{ in})^2/4 \approx 58 \text{ in}^2$. Area of wood inside the bark is $\pi(7.6 \text{ in})^2/4 \approx 45 \text{ in}^2$. Bark area is therefore (58 in^2 − 45 in^2) = 13 in^2.**

30. Find the area of the template in **Figure 1.75.**

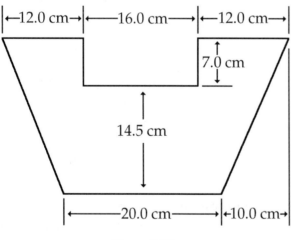

Figure 1.75

30. **There are several approaches to this problem. One is to treat the figure as a large rectangle with one small rectangular and two triangular cutouts: (40.0 cm)(21.5 cm) − 2(1/2)(10.0 cm)(21.5 cm) − (7.0 cm)(16.0 cm) = 533 cm^2.**

31. What is the cross-sectional area of the piece of wood molding in **Figure 1.76?** (Hint: Think of the ends as semicircles.)

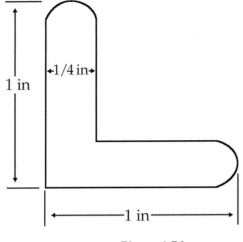

Figure 1.76

31. The semicircles on the ends taken together form a circle with a diameter of 1/4 inch and area $= \pi(1/4 \text{ in})^2/4 = 0.0491 \text{ in}^2$. This leaves two rectangles, one 7/8 in long and the other 5/8 in long and both 1/4 in wide, with total area 3/8 (or 0.375) in^2. 0.0491 in^2 + 0.375 in^2 ≈ 0.424 in^2.

32. Find the area of the floor plan in **Figure 1.77,** assuming all dimensions are accurate to the nearest inch.

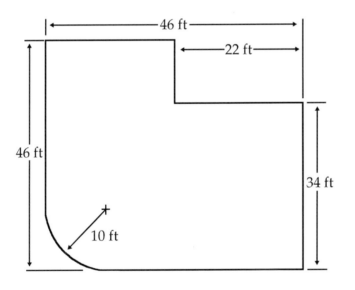

Figure 1.77

32. If we divide the plan horizontally at the center of the quarter circle, the entire figure can be treated as two rectangles above that line, with a third rectangle and the quarter circle below:
(36 ft)(24 ft) + (24 ft)(22 ft) + (36 ft)(10 ft) + (1/4)π(10 ft)^2 = 1830.539... ≈ 1830ft^2.
(Dimensions are accurate to the nearest inch, which is approximately 0.1 ft, so three significant figures are appropriate.)

33. **Figure 1.78** shows the cross section of a uniform width concrete T section. Find its area.

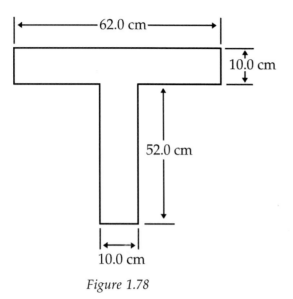

62.0 cm

10.0 cm

52.0 cm

10.0 cm

Figure 1.78

33. A = (62.0 cm)(10.0 cm) + (52.0 cm)(10.0 cm) = 1140 cm².

34. Find the cross-sectional area of the 14WF wide-flange steel beam shown in **Figure 1.79.**

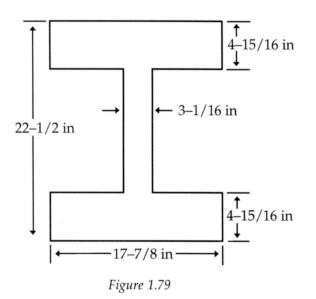

4–15/16 in

3–1/16 in

22–1/2 in

4–15/16 in

17–7/8 in

Figure 1.79

34. A = 2(17-7/8 in)(4-15/16 in) + (12-5/8 in)(3-1/16 in) = 215.1796... ≈ 215 in².

35. A 52 ft x 40 ft house sits on a lot that is 90 ft x 120 ft. How many bags of grass seed would it take to cover the lawn, which includes the entire area of the lot except where the house stands, if one bag is advertised as covering 800 ft²?

35. (90 ft)(120 ft) − (52 ft)(40 ft) = 8720 ft², and $(8720 \text{ ft}^2)\left(\dfrac{1 \text{ bag}}{800 \text{ ft}^2}\right) = 10.9 ≈$

11 bags.

36. **Figure 1.80** is a diagram of the flag of Kuwait. Find the area taken up by each color on a 1.80 m × 2.70 m display flag if all of the color bars are of equal width. (Hint: Look for trapezoids.)

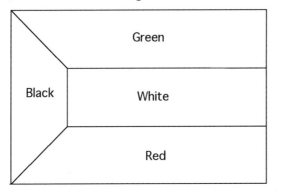

Figure 1.80

36. **Each bar will be (1.80 m)/3 = 0.60 m wide. The white region is a rectangle, and the others are trapezoids, with $A = (1/2)(b_1 + b_2)h$. The white region has an area of (2.10 m)(0.60 m) = 1.26 m². The black region has an area of (1/2)(1.80 m + 0.60 m)(0.60 m) = 0.72 m². The red and green regions are each (1/2)(2.70 m + 2.10 m)(0.60 m) = 1.44 m².**

37. **Figure 1.81** shows the packing of 6.6 cm diameter cans in a typical 12-pack carton.

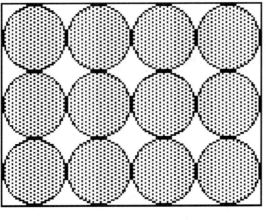

Figure 1.81

a) What is the area of the base of the carton?

37. **a) Length of carton = 4(6.6 cm) = 26.4 cm; width is 3(6.6 cm) = 19.8 cm. Area of bottom of carton = (26.4 cm)(19.8 cm) = 522.72 cm² ≈ 523 cm².**

b) What is the total area that is shaded by the cans?

b) $12\left(\dfrac{\pi(6.6)^2}{4}\right) = 410.54 \text{ cm}^2 \approx 411 \text{ cm}^2.$

c) The efficiency of a package is defined as the percent of the total base area that is occupied by the cans. Find the efficiency of this package.

c) The efficiency is $= \left(\dfrac{410.543 \text{ cm}^2}{522.72 \text{ cm}^2} \right)(100) = 78.53... \approx 78.5\%.$

38. **Figure 1.82** shows the cross-sectional pattern of wires in a strand of wire rope of the type used in suspension cables of timber bridges such as those found in the Clearwater National Forest in Idaho. The seven wires are wound in a helix, and then several strands are wound into a cable. If the strand pictured here has an overall diameter of 1 cm, what is the total area of the solid part of the cross section?

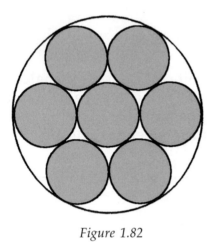

Figure 1.82

38. **Diameter of one wire is one-third the diameter of the overall strand diameter, or 1/3 cm. Total cross-sectional area is**

$$7\left(\dfrac{\pi \left(\dfrac{1}{3} \right)^2}{4} \right) = 0.61086... \approx 0.611 \text{ cm}^2.$$

39. Extremely thin tubes made out of carbon atoms and called "buckytubes" (after architect and inventor Buckminster Fuller) are only a few atoms (10 nm) wide. Find the cross-sectional area of a buckytube, assuming it is circular.

39. $A = \pi(10 \text{ nm})^2/4 = 25\pi \approx 79 \text{ nm}^2.$

Section 1.5 Volume, Surface Area, and Geometric Models

What You Need to Know

- How to calculate areas of two-dimensional figures

- How to change units of length and area

What You Will Learn

- To compute volumes of some three-dimensional figures

- To use formulas to compute volumes

- To use formulas to compute surface areas of some three-dimensional figures

- To change units of volume

- To construct geometric models

- To distinguish among the quantities perimeter, area, volume, and surface area

Materials

- Rectangular card stock or cardboard

- Scissors

- Tape

- Ruler

According to one of the project managers for Thoughtforms Corp., one problem with excavation can be underground rock. If a buried rock ledge is found during excavation, blasting may be required. Since the cost of blasting may run into the tens of thousands of dollars, estimates of rock volumes are needed. The shapes of ledges are usually irregular, so their size is usually approximated by rectangular geometry. Measurements of a ledge can be made at different heights and a topological map drawn. Then the ledge is visualized as being made up of many small rectangular solids whose volumes can be computed and then added up.

One of the first tasks that must be accomplished in a house construction project is excavation of the building site. Trees and other vegetation may need to be cleared, and the ground may need to be leveled. Then a hole must be dug for the foundation. Earth that is removed is often carried away from the site in dump trucks. A typical foundation depth for a house with a basement is 10 feet below ground level. The manager of the construction project would have to use the depth and the other dimensions of the house to determine how much earth would need to be removed. From that information, the number of trucks needed could then be predicted.

The amount of three-dimensional space contained in such things as the bed of a truck and the foundation of a house is called **volume.**

In addition to the cubic inch, other common units of volume used in the United States are the *cubic foot* (ft³) and the *cubic yard* (yd³), which is sometimes referred to as simply a "yard" in the construction business. Liquid volumes are usually measured in *gallons, quarts, pints,* etc., with 1 cubic foot equal to 7.48 gallons.

Common metric units of volume are the *cubic meter* (m³) and *cubic centimeter* (cm³ or sometimes cc). For liquid volumes, the *liter* (l) is usually used. One liter is equal to 1000 cubic centimeters.

Calculating Volume

In order to measure area, we needed a unit based on a simple shape that could fill a plane surface. Similarly, volume must be measured in a unit that can fill a three-dimensional space. In this case there are not many candidates, as only a few regular figures can fill a volume without leaving gaps. The cube is a convenient shape.

Figure 1.83 pictures a rectangular box 2 inches x 4 inches x 3 inches that is filled with cubes that are 1 inch on each side. Each cube has a volume of 1 cubic inch. We can find the volume of the box by finding the number of 1-inch cubes that fit into it.

To find the number of cubes in the box, we find the number in one layer (2 x 4 = 8) and multiply the number of cubes in one layer by 3 to get 24 cubes. Hence, the volume of the box is 24 cubic inches, or 24 in³.

Three-dimensional objects, such as cubes, are often referred to as geometric solids. We refer to the flat surfaces of an object as **faces.** The lines formed when two faces meet are called **edges,** and the points where the edges meet are called **vertices.** (See **Figure 1.84.**)

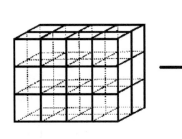
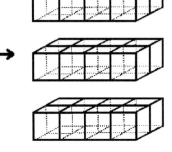

Figure 1.83

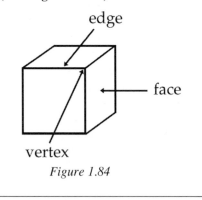

Figure 1.84

The rectangular box in Figure 1.83 is an example of a **right solid.** A right solid is a figure with two parallel faces, either of which can be referred to as a **base.** Its sides are perpendicular to its base. The method used to find the volume of the box can be used to find the volume of any right solid, regardless of the shape of the base.

The volume of a right solid is equal to the product of the area of one face (the base of the figure) and the length of the sides (the height of the figure):
$V =$ (area of base)(height).

Example 28

Figure 1.85 shows a right solid with a hexagonal base. Its height is 15 cm, and its hexagonal base has an area of 12 cm². Find the volume of the prism.

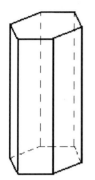

Figure 1.85

Solution:

V = (area of base)(height)

$\quad$ = (12 cm²)(15 cm)

$\quad$ = 180 cm³.

There are a few common three-dimensional shapes for which more specific volume formulas can be used.

- Volume of a rectangular solid with length l, width w, and height h: $V = lwh$.

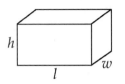

Figure 1.86

- Volume of a cube with edge e: $V = e^3$.

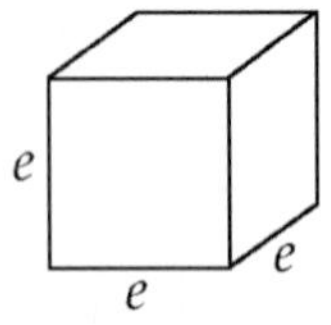

Figure 1.87

- Volume of a sphere with radius r: $V = \dfrac{4}{3}\pi r^3$.

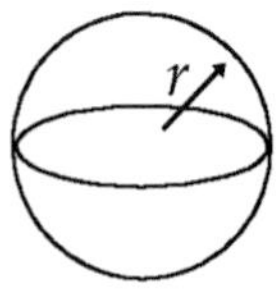

Figure 1.88

- Volume of a cylinder with radius r and height h: $V = \pi r^2 h$.

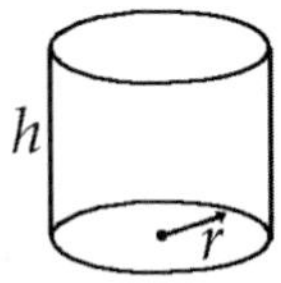

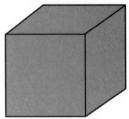

Figure 1.89

Example 29

Find the volume of the cube in **Figure 1.90.**

3.5 cm

Figure 1.90

Solution:

Each edge of the cube is 3.5 cm long.

$$V = e^3$$
$$= (3.5 \text{ cm})^3$$
$$= 42.875 \approx 43 \text{ cm}^3.$$

Example 30

Liquid natural gas is often stored in spherical tanks. This is done partly to minimize stresses on edges that might result in leaks. Find the capacity of the tank in **Figure 1.91** if its diameter is 41.6 m.

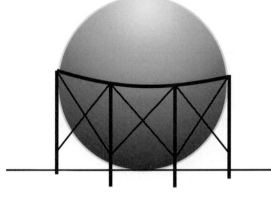

Figure 1.91

Solution:

First translate the word *capacity* into a measurable quantity, which in this case is volume. The formula for the volume of a sphere is $V = \dfrac{4}{3}\pi r^3$. The radius is half the diameter, or 20.8 m.

$$V = \frac{4}{3}\pi r^3$$
$$= \frac{4}{3}\pi (20.8 \text{ m})^3$$
$$= 37,694.554... \approx 37,700 \text{ m}^3.$$

Example 31

Find the volume of water that can be contained in a cylindrical 14-foot-long pipe that has an inside diameter of 0.75 inches. Give the volume in cubic inches and in gallons (1 gal = 231 in^3).

Solution:

The volume of a cylinder is given by $V = \pi r^2 h$. The radius is half the diameter, or 0.375 inches. The h in the formula is in this case equal to the length of the pipe. The length must be changed to inches in order to find the volume in cubic inches.

$$(14 \text{ ft})\left(\frac{12 \text{ in}}{1 \text{ ft}}\right) = 168 \text{ in.}$$

$$V = \pi r^2 h$$

$$= \pi(0.375 \text{ in})^2(168 \text{ in})$$

$$= 74.2201... \approx 74 \text{ in}^3.$$

$$(74 \text{ in}^3)\left(\frac{1 \text{ gal}}{231 \text{ in}^3}\right) = 0.3203... \approx 0.32 \text{ gallons.}$$

Volumes of objects with more complicated shapes can sometimes be found by breaking them up into simpler figures.

Example 32

Find the volume enclosed by a planetarium that has cylindrical walls 25 feet 6 inches high and 86 feet 0 inches in diameter, topped by a domed roof in the shape of a hemisphere with the same diameter as the walls. (See **Figure 1.92.**)

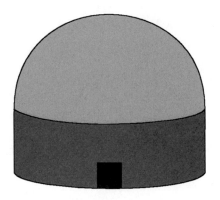

Figure 1.92

Solution:

This figure can be broken up into a cylinder and the top half of a sphere.

Total volume = (volume inside walls) + (volume inside roof)

$$= \pi r^2 h + \frac{1}{2}\left(\frac{4}{3}\pi r^3\right)$$

$$= \pi(43 \text{ ft})^2(25.5 \text{ ft}) + \frac{1}{2}\left(\frac{4}{3}\pi\right)(43 \text{ ft})^3$$

$$\approx 314{,}644 \approx 315{,}000 \text{ ft}^3.$$

Discovery 1.3 A Geometric Model for Container Design *(SE page 82)*

Materials: Rectangular card stock or cardboard, scissors, tape, rulers

1. Examine the rectangular card stock provided. Measure the dimensions, using the maximum precision of the available instruments. Calculate the area of the sheet, using the appropriate accuracy.

1. **Assuming $8\frac{1}{2}$ in x 11 in stock, area is $(8\frac{1}{2}$ in$)(11$ in$) = 93.5$ in^2.**

2. Now consider how you might fold the sheet in order to create an open-top, rectangular, box-shaped container. You may have to make some cuts, but try to keep the sheet in one piece and minimize waste material.

2. **A common method is to cut identical squares from each corner and fold up to create a box. The squares could also be left on as "flaps" to be folded over and taped, or the diagonals of squares could be cut with triangular flaps then folded across each other. On the other hand, a completely different design might be tried, such as folding a few times across the width of the sheet and forming a tall, thin box.**

3. When you have found a workable design, make a box and calculate its enclosed volume. Then experiment with new sheets of card stock. Using your design, vary the dimensions to see how the volume is affected. Discuss your findings, including an examination of what dimensions seem to produce a box with the largest volume.

3. **For an $8\frac{1}{2}$ in x 11 in sheet, using the design of item 2, the maximum volume of 66.15 in^3 results from cutting a 1.585 in (about $1\frac{9}{16}$ in) square from each corner.**

4. Discuss possible practical uses for the different shapes that are possible when the dimensions of the box are varied. Consider the following in your discussion:

   • For what uses would it be important to use a box of maximum volume?

   • When would other considerations be more important?

   • How would the choice of material for such a box affect the requirements?

4. **Of course, many boxes have to conform to the shapes of their contents, but boxes containing liquids (e.g., a milk carton) or particulate solids (e.g., cereal) could be optimized for volume. Aesthetics (a pleasing shape) may override optimal size for marketing purposes. Ease of handling may be a factor: a milk carton or cereal box should not be so big around that it can't be picked up with one hand, unless a handle is provided. The more expensive the material, the more important efficient use of the material becomes.**

5. How could your box be held together? The answer to this may vary, depending on how you transformed your two-dimensional sheet into a box. Discuss some of the possibilities, and consider the following questions:

- Could your box be held together without separate fasteners?

- What if the box was made of plywood?

- What if the box was made of metal? Would the type of metal used make a difference?

5. **If squares were cut out, sides would have to be taped, but if flaps were left on, some sort of tab-and-slit arrangement (like on a pizza box) might work. Wood could be nailed, screwed, or glued. Metal could be welded, braised, or soldered, depending on type and thickness.**

As you saw in Discovery 1.3, geometrical models can provide useful information. The physical models you explored made it possible to examine actual container designs, determine their volumes, and discuss advantages and disadvantages of the various models.

Surface Area

The total area of all the surfaces of a three-dimensional object is called the **surface area** of the object. In many cases, finding the surface area is just a matter of adding the areas of the separate faces. For a few common shapes, special formulas can be used.

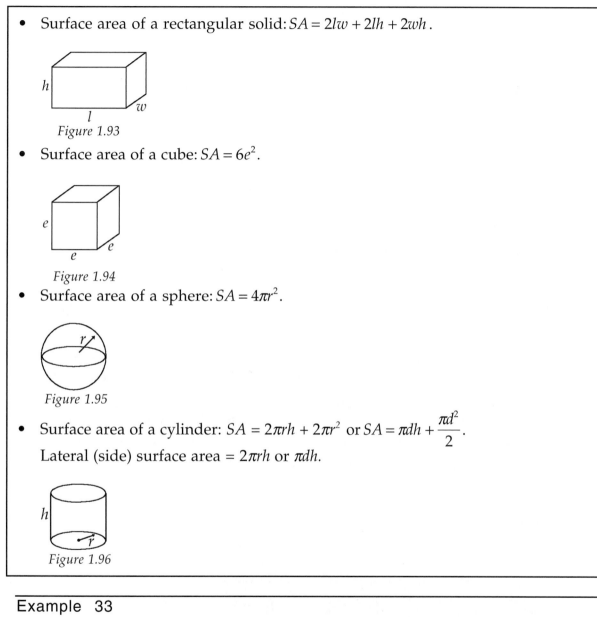

- Surface area of a rectangular solid: $SA = 2lw + 2lh + 2wh$.

  Figure 1.93

- Surface area of a cube: $SA = 6e^2$.

  Figure 1.94

- Surface area of a sphere: $SA = 4\pi r^2$.

  Figure 1.95

- Surface area of a cylinder: $SA = 2\pi rh + 2\pi r^2$ or $SA = \pi dh + \dfrac{\pi d^2}{2}$.

  Lateral (side) surface area $= 2\pi rh$ or πdh.

  Figure 1.96

Example 33

Find the surface area of a basketball that has a diameter of 10 inches.

Solution:

The radius of the basketball is 5 inches.

$SA = 4\pi r^2$

$\quad = 4\pi(5 \text{ in})^2$

$\quad = 100\pi \approx 314 \text{ in}^2$.

Exercises 1.5

I. Investigations *(SE pages 84–86)*

1. A tunnel-boring machine is used to dig tunnels for municipal water supplies and sewage disposal. The machine has a cylindrical cutting head that is 45 feet long and 16 feet in diameter.

   a) Try estimating the volume of the cutting head before doing any precise computations.

1. **a) It is relatively easy to estimate volumes of rectangular box shapes. While a 45 x 16 x 16 box might be hard to compute mentally, a 45 x 20 x 10 box should be similar in size, and the product of 45 x 20 x 10 = (45 x 2 x 1)(10 x 10) = 9000 ft³ is a good estimate.**

   b) A slice of the cutting head (its cross section) is circular. What is the cross-sectional area? (Give your answer in both ft² and m².)

   b) $A = \dfrac{\pi(16.0 \text{ ft})^2}{4} \approx 201 \text{ ft}^2; A = (201 \text{ ft}^2)\left(\dfrac{1 \text{ m}}{3.281 \text{ ft}}\right)^2 \approx 18.7 \text{ m}^2.$

   c) What is the volume of the cutting head (in ft³ and m³)?

   c) $V = Ah = (201 \text{ ft}^2)(45 \text{ ft}) = 9045 \approx 9050 \text{ ft}^3$, or 256 m³.

   d) Try to picture in your mind how big this cutting head is. Would it fit in someone's garage? How many could fit in your math classroom?

   d) It is probably too long for even a three-car garage. Two or three might fit side-by-side in a fairly large classroom; maybe a dozen in a lecture hall.

2. The Pentagon in Arlington, Virginia, was named for the pentagonal shape of its horizontal cross section (see **Figure 1.97**). Each side of the Pentagon is 921 feet long, and the points where each pair of sides meet are 783 feet from the center of the building. The Pentagon is 77 ft $3\frac{1}{2}$ in tall.

   a) To find the volume occupied by the Pentagon, begin by finding the area of its base.

Figure 1.97

2. **a)** The base consists of five congruent isosceles triangles. The altitude h of one of the triangles is $\sqrt{(783)^2 - \left(\dfrac{921}{2}\right)^2} = 633.268\ldots \approx 633$ ft.

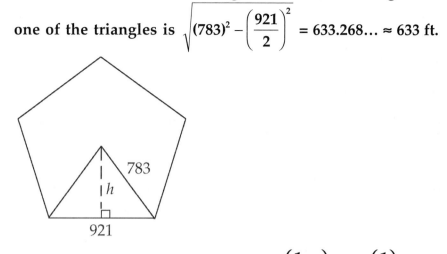

The entire Pentagon has an area of $5\left(\dfrac{1}{2}bh\right) = (5)\left(\dfrac{1}{2}\right)(921)(633) \approx$ 1,457,000 ft².

b) Use your answer to (a) to find the volume of the building.

b) V = (base area)(height) = (1,457,000 ft²)(77.29 ft) = 112,688,820 ≈ 113,000,000 ft³.

c) Your answer to (b) is the volume enclosed by the outer walls of the Pentagon. But it is not a solid building. It has an open court space in the center, which is also in the shape of a regular pentagon. At ground level, the court is 382 ft on a side with a "radius" to each vertex of 325 ft.

Find the volume of the inner court space, and then use it to find the actual volume of the Pentagon.

c) Area of court is $(5)\left(\dfrac{1}{2}\right)(382)\sqrt{(325)^2 - (382/2)^2} = 251{,}119$ ft². **Volume of the court is then (251,119 ft²)(77.29 ft) = 19,408,988 ft³, and the building volume is about (112,600,000 ft³ – 19,400,000 ft³) ≈ 93,000,000 ft³.**

3. A garbage dumpster is to be constructed out of 1/4-inch-thick steel. Its inner dimensions will be 7 feet 9 inches x 4 feet, with an inner height of 5 feet. There will be a cover that overlaps the sides by 2 inches at the top.

There are several ways of measuring the amount of steel required for the job. The word "amount" may mean length, thickness, area, volume, or weight, depending on the context. So the question of how much steel is needed has more than one answer.

a) If you work for the company that is fabricating the dumpster out of sheet steel, how would you answer the question of how much steel is needed? (Hint: Before answering the question, decide what type of quantity is meant by the word "amount" in this case.)

3. a) "How much" in this case would refer to area of the sheet steel. The surface area of the dumpster (without top, and assuming 1/16-inch accuracy) would be:

S = (area of bottom) + 2(area of a long side) + 2(area of a short side)

= (7.75 ft)(4.00 ft) + 2(7.75 ft)(5.00 ft) + 2(4.00 ft)(5.00 ft) = 148.5 ft².

Area of top must take into account the 2-inch overlap, so use dimensions 8 ft 1 in × 4 ft 4 in: S_{top} = (8.17 ft)(4.33 ft) ≈ 33.4 ft².

Total sheet metal area needed is (148.5 ft² + 33.4 ft²) ≈ 182 ft².

b) If you work for the steel manufacturer as the manager of the production process that creates steel sheets from molten steel, how would you answer the same question? (Again, decide how to interpret the word "amount.")

b) **Total volume of the steel is probably needed. 182 ft² of 1/4-inch steel would have a volume of $(1/4 \text{ in})\left(\dfrac{1 \text{ ft}}{12 \text{ in}}\right)(182 \text{ ft}^2) \approx 3.8 \text{ ft}^3$. The weight might also be desired, but the density of steel would be needed to find the weight.**

c) If you work for the distributor of the sheet steel and must decide how to transport the steel from the steel plant to the dumpster manufacturer, what kinds of measures of amount of steel would you need to know?

c) **In order to decide on truck size, the distributor would need to know three different measures of amount: total weight of steel (for load requirements), area of sheets (for cargo bed size), and volume of steel (for total cargo capacity).**

Note that it is important in situations like this to clearly define words like "amount" in terms of some specific mathematical quantity. Other words that are often encountered in problem situations and that can have vague meanings are *size, capacity, output,* to name a few. Always translate such words into the appropriate measurable quantity before attempting a solution.

4. One of the possible solutions to the container design problem (Discovery 1.3) is to cut a square of equal size out of each corner of the rectangular sheet and then fold up the sides to create the box (see **Figure 1.98**). (This might require taping the sides, or welding if the box is made of steel.)

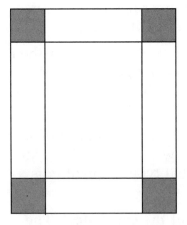

Figure 1.98

a) If the length of a side of the cutout square is $1\frac{1}{2}$ inches, what is the length of the box after the sides are folded up?

4. a) $11 - 2\left(1\frac{1}{2}\right) = 8$ **inches.**

b) What is the width of the box?

b) $8\frac{1}{2} - 2\left(1\frac{1}{2}\right) = 5\frac{1}{2}$ **inches.**

c) What is the height of the box?

c) $1\frac{1}{2}$ **inches**

d) What is the volume of the box that results when $1\frac{1}{2}$-inch squares are cut from the corners of the sheet? (Hint: For ease of computation, you may want to change the width and height to decimal numbers.)

d) **(8 in)(5.5 in)(1.5 in) = 66 in³.**

e) Now let the size of the cutout square be variable. Let x represent the length of a side of the square. Repeat (a)–(c) using x in place of $1\frac{1}{2}$ inches, and find the dimensions of the box in terms of x.

e) **Length = (11 − 2x); Width = $\left(8\frac{1}{2} - 2x\right)$; Height = x.**

f) Use the formula for the volume of a rectangular solid and your answers to (e) to write a formula for the volume of the box in terms of x only.

f) **$V = lwh$, so the box's volume is $V = (11 − 2x)(8.5 − 2x)(x)$.**

g) Your answer to (f) gives the volume V of the box as a function of x, the length of a side of the cutout square. Examine the formula carefully. What numbers can be substituted for x in the formula? (In other words, are there any restrictions on the values you can use for x in this formula?)

g) **Any number can be substituted for x.**

h) The function you found in (f) is more than just a mathematical formula, since in this case it models a real-world situation. Now consider the values for x that make sense in this problem. What values for x make sense?

h) **The side of the cutout square cannot have a negative length. It also can't be greater than half the width of the paper. So the values of x that make sense are $0 \leq x \leq 4.25$.**

i) Use a calculator table or spreadsheet to examine the volume values that would result from x-values that make sense in this problem. Find an approximate maximum value for the volume of the box.

i) **The volume can vary between 0 in³ and about 66.15 in³, so $V_{max} \approx 66.15$ in³.**

j) How big a square should be cut from each corner of the sheet to produce a box with maximum volume?

j) The maximum volume results for $x \approx 1.585$ in.

5. In Discovery 1.3, you measured the length and width of the sheet of card stock in order to do calculations for the container design problem. If you needed the *thickness* of a sheet of that kind of card stock, how could you have accurately determined it?

5. Students might suggest using a micrometer, or vernier calipers, if they are familiar with them. Otherwise, the thickness of, say 100 sheets, could be measured, then divided by 100.

II. Projects and Group Activities *(SE pages 86–87)*

6. Consider again the classroom renovation problem discussed earlier in this chapter. An engineer designing a heating or air conditioning system for the building might not need to know individual room dimensions or floor area. Instead, the volume of the room would be important in determining the total energy requirements. This is because the volume of the room is a direct measurement of the amount of air that would need to be heated or cooled.

a) You already have data on the length and width of your classroom. It may not be possible to easily measure the height of the room. Instead, try to *estimate* the height to the nearest tenth of a meter. Share your estimate with the class, and find a sample mean and range for the estimates.

6. a) Sample data: 3.8 m, 3.5 m, 4.0 m, 3.7 m, 3.0 m, 3.5 m, 4.0 m, 3.8 m, 4.2 m, 3.5 m. The sample mean is 3.7 m, and the range is (4.2 m – 3.0 m) = 1.2 m.

b) What is the maximum likely error in your height?

b) Sample answer: The minimum value of 3.0 m is the farthest from the mean of 3.7 m, so the maximum likely error is (3.7 m – 3.0 m) = 0.7 m.

c) Use your answer to (a) and the class data on length and width from Activity 1.1 to calculate the volume of the room to the nearest m³.

c) Sample answer: (11.33 m)(7.08 m)(3.7 m) = 297 m³.

d) Determine the maximum likely error in your volume result.

d) Sample answer: Using the smallest values in each data set, the minimum volume is (11.318 m)(7.060 m)(3.0 m) = 240 m³. Using the largest values in each data set, the maximum volume is (11.352 m)(7.095 m)(4.2 m) = 338 m³. The maximum likely error is (297 m³ – 240 m³) = 57 m³.

e) People doing HVAC (Heating, Ventilating, and Air Conditioning) work may use both metric and U.S. Customary units in their design calculations. You should therefore be able to change your metric volume result into an equivalent volume measured in cubic feet. And to get a sense of how volume units compare, express your volume in cm³ as well as m³.

e) $(297 \text{ m}^3) \left(\dfrac{3.281 \text{ ft}}{1 \text{ m}} \right)^3 = 10{,}489.99\ldots \approx 10{,}500 \text{ ft}^3;$

$(297 \text{ m}^3) \left(\dfrac{100 \text{ cm}}{1 \text{ m}} \right)^3 = 297{,}000{,}000 \text{ cm}^3.$

7. Try designing a *covered* box from a single sheet of card stock (or just use a sheet of paper if you are working on this at home). You will probably find that there are a greater number of possibilities for this design than there were for the open box. After experimenting, again see if you can write a formula for the box's volume in terms of the dimensions of the original rectangular sheet.

    As with the open box, investigate how shape affects volume and what strategies produce the largest volume while using a minimum of material. Also, decide how the intended contents of the package—e.g., soda or pizza—would affect your design.

7. **One possibility is a typical pizza box:**

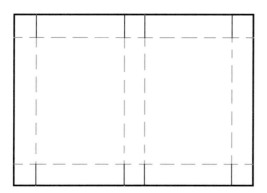

Sheet is folded on dashed lines, cut on solid ones, for no waste. Here, optimum volume would be less important than accommodating the size of the pizza with minimum height. This particular box would not be good for a circular pizza, but some companies make rectangular pizzas.

8. Many of the products we buy come in cylindrical containers. Experiment with creating cylinders out of card stock. As you try different designs, keep the following guidelines in mind:

    • See if you can find a way of making cylinders out of flat sheets without a significant amount of waste; this may be harder to do than in the case of the rectangular box problems.

    • Try to maximize the volume that can be contained in the cylinder. One way of gauging the success of this would be to calculate the ratio of volume to surface area for the cylinder and to find what shape makes this ratio as large as possible. (Or make the ratio of surface area to volume as small as possible, which accomplishes the same thing.)

    • Cans come in many shapes. Some, such as drink cans, are relatively tall compared to their diameter. Cans of tuna, on the other hand, are comparatively flat. Others, such as coffee cans, have proportions somewhere in between. Are there reasons, other than those of material cost, why some cans are given certain shapes?

8. The volume-to-surface-area ratio should be largest when the radius and height of the can are of similar size. A tuna can has this kind of shape. However, vegetable cans and soup cans have a greater height-to-radius ratio, probably as much for aesthetic reasons as anything else. One-pound coffee cans, on the other hand, would be difficult to hold in one hand if they were the shape of a tuna can.

III. Additional Practice *(SE pages 87–93)*

For 9–11, find (a) the volume and (b) the surface area of the given figure.

9. A cube with each edge 5.63 mm long.

9. a) $V = (5.63 \text{ mm})^3 = 178.453... \approx 178 \text{ mm}^3$.

    b) $SA = 6(5.63 \text{ mm})^2 = 190.1814 \approx 190 \text{ mm}^2$.

10. The rectangular solid in **Figure 1.99**.

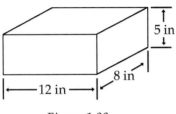

Figure 1.99

10. a) $V = (12 \text{ in})(8 \text{ in})(5 \text{ in}) = 480 \text{ in}^3$.

    b) $SA = 2(12 \text{ in})(8 \text{ in}) + 2(12 \text{ in})(5 \text{ in}) + 2(8 \text{ in})(5 \text{ in}) = 392 \text{ in}^2$.

11. A sphere with radius 0.78 m.

11. a) $V = \dfrac{4}{3}\pi(0.78 \text{ m})^3 = 1.9877... \approx 2.0 \text{ m}^3$.

    b) $SA = 4\pi(0.78 \text{ m})^2 = 7.645... \approx 7.6 \text{ m}^2$.

12. Consider the cylinder in **Figure 1.100.**

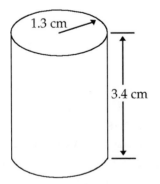

Figure 1.100

a) Find its volume.

12. a) $V = \pi(1.3 \text{ cm})^2(3.4 \text{ cm}) = 18.051... \approx 18 \text{ cm}^3$.

b) Find its lateral surface area.

b) $2\pi(1.3 \text{ cm})(3.4 \text{ cm}) = 27.771... \approx 28 \text{ cm}^2$.

c) Find its total surface area.

c) $SA = 2\pi(1.3 \text{ cm})(3.4 \text{ cm}) + 2\pi(1.3 \text{ cm})^2 = 38.390... \approx 38 \text{ cm}^2$.

For 13–19, express each of the volumes as indicated.

13. 21.0 ft^3 as in^3

13. $21.0 \text{ ft}^3 \left(\dfrac{12 \text{ in}}{1 \text{ ft}} \right)^3 \approx 36{,}000 \text{ in}^3$.

14. 3284 in^3 as ft^3

14. $3284 \text{ in}^3 \left(\dfrac{1 \text{ ft}}{12 \text{ in}} \right)^3 \approx 1.900 \text{ ft}^3$.

15. 13.2 ft^3 as gallons ($1 \text{ ft}^3 = 7.48$ gallons)

15. $13.2 \text{ ft}^3 \left(\dfrac{7.48 \text{ gal}}{1 \text{ ft}^3} \right) \approx 98.7 \text{ gal}$.

16. 18 ft^3 as yd^3

16. $18 \text{ ft}^3 \left(\dfrac{1 \text{ yd}}{3 \text{ ft}} \right)^3 \approx 0.67 \text{ yd}^3$.

17. 3.4 m^3 as cm^3

17. $3.4 \text{ m}^3 \left(\dfrac{100 \text{ cm}}{1 \text{ m}} \right)^3 = 3{,}400{,}000 \text{ cm}^3$.

18. 1400 mm^3 as cm^3

18. $1400 \text{ mm}^3 \left(\dfrac{1 \text{ cm}}{10 \text{ mm}} \right)^3 = 1.4 \text{ cm}^3$.

19. 49.12 ft^3 as m^3 ($1 \text{ m} = 3.281 \text{ ft}$)

19. $49.12 \text{ ft}^3 \left(\dfrac{1 \text{ m}}{3.281 \text{ ft}} \right)^3 \approx 1.391 \text{ m}^3$.

20. As part of the "Big Dig" harbor reconstruction project in Boston, a *casting basin* had to be created to allow construction of new underwater tunnel connections. The average dimensions of the concrete canyon were 50 ft deep, 250 ft wide, and 1000 ft long.

a) If we model this basin as a rectangular solid, what is the name of the quantity you would compute in order to determine how much ground space was taken up by the casting basin? Find its value using the given units and also in metric units.

20. a) Area = 250,000 ft²; $A = 250{,}000 \text{ ft}^2 \left(\dfrac{1 \text{ m}}{3.281 \text{ ft}} \right)^2 \approx 23{,}000 \text{ m}^2.$

b) Again, assuming that the basin was a rectangular solid, what is the name of the quantity you would compute in order to determine how much earth had to be removed during the excavation of the casting basin? Find its value using the given units and also in metric units.

b) Volume = 12,500,000 ft³; $V = 12{,}500{,}000 \text{ ft}^3 \left(\dfrac{1 \text{ m}}{3.281 \text{ ft}} \right)^3 \approx 354{,}000 \text{ m}^3.$

21. The smallest useful box ever produced is made of atoms of rhodium and cobalt. The box is in the shape of a cube. It is a billionth of a meter across, just big enough to hold a single atom.

a) Find the volume of the box in cubic millimeters.

21. a) $(0.000001 \text{ mm})^3 = 0.000000000000000001 \text{ mm}^3.$

b) What might be a more convenient unit for expressing this volume?

b) Cubic nanometers, or nm³. Since one side of the box is 1 nanometer long, its volume is 1 nm³.

22. A typical Douglas fir forest in Texas is covered by a litter layer that contains needles, cones, twigs, and small branches. This litter layer has an average depth of about 3 cm. How many cubic meters of such litter are contained in an acre of forest?

22. $(3 \text{ cm}) \left(\dfrac{1 \text{ m}}{100 \text{ cm}} \right) (1 \text{ acre}) \left(\dfrac{43{,}560 \text{ ft}^2}{1 \text{ acre}} \right) \left(\dfrac{1 \text{ m}}{3.28 \text{ ft}} \right)^2 = 121.39\ldots \approx 121 \text{ m}^3.$

23. There has been significant loss of land area in Louisiana in recent years due to a combination of factors including erosion and human-made changes in the path of the Mississippi River. Assume that a Louisiana developer has purchased 6 acres of low-lying land at a good price with the intention of creating a housing development. In order to protect the investment, the developer proposes raising the flood plain by 8 feet by trucking in landfill.

   a) How much dirt is needed?

23. a) Volume of dirt required = (6 acres)(8 ft) $\left(\dfrac{43,560 \text{ ft}^2}{1 \text{ acre}}\right)\left(\dfrac{1 \text{ yd}}{3 \text{ ft}}\right)^3 = 77,440 \text{ yd}^3.$

   b) If the type of dump truck used can hold 16.5 cubic yards of dirt, how many truckloads will be required?

b) Number of truckloads required = $\left(\dfrac{17,440 \text{ yd}^3}{16.5 \text{ yd}^3}\right) = 4693.333... \approx$
4700 truckloads.

   c) If ten trucks are available for 8 hours per day and each truck can make two round-trip hauls of dirt in 1 hour, how many days will it take to complete the job of raising the land level?

c) Number of truckloads delivered in a day is (10)(8)(2) = 160. Therefore, it will take $\left(\dfrac{4700 \text{ truckloads}}{160 \text{ truckloads / day}}\right) = 29.375 \text{ days, meaning the job will be}$
finished on the 30th day.

24. A *cord* of firewood is defined as the amount of firewood that will fit in a space with dimensions 4 ft x 4 ft x 8 ft.

   a) What is the volume of the rectangular space taken up by a cord of firewood?

24. a) (4 ft)(4 ft)(8 ft) = 128 ft³.

   b) From your answer to (a), what can you say about the actual solid volume of the wood in a cord of wood?

b) The actual wood volume is less than 128 ft³ due to the air spaces between logs.

25. A new gymnasium in Houston has 48-foot-high ceilings and contains 3,370,000 cubic feet of space. What is the floor area? (Hint: Divide the volume by the height.)

25. $\left(\dfrac{3{,}370{,}000 \text{ ft}^3}{48 \text{ ft}}\right) = 70208.333\ldots \approx 70{,}000 \text{ ft}^2.$

26. The Quabbin reservoir in central Massachusetts supplies much of the eastern part of the state with water. It covers an area of 25,000 acres. (Several towns were eliminated to create the reservoir.) Its capacity is 412 billion gallons.

   a) What geometrical property does the word *capacity* refer to in this context?

26. a) Volume

   b) What is the average depth of the reservoir? (Hint: Assume the reservoir is a right solid with a constant depth. The depth is then equal to the reservoir's volume divided by its area.)

b) $\left(\dfrac{412{,}000{,}000{,}000 \text{ gal}}{25{,}000 \text{ acres}}\right)\left(\dfrac{1 \text{ ft}^3}{7.48 \text{ gal}}\right)\left(\dfrac{1 \text{ acre}}{43{,}560 \text{ ft}^2}\right) = 50.578\ldots \approx 51 \text{ ft.}$

   c) On an average day, 300 million gallons of the reservoir's water are used. How many days' supply is contained in the reservoir when it is full?

c) $\left(\dfrac{412{,}000{,}000{,}000 \text{ gal}}{300{,}000{,}000 \text{ gal / day}}\right) = 1373.33\ldots \approx 1370 \text{ days.}$

27. An iceberg called B10A broke off from Antarctica in 1995, began drifting northward, and reached the vicinity of Tierra del Fuego in 1999. At that time it was approximately rectangular in shape and about 48 miles long, 24 miles wide, and 1/3 mile high (including the part under the water). What was the approximate volume of the iceberg in 1999?

27. Assuming a rectangular shape, the volume would be (48 mi)(24 mi)(1/3 mi) = 384 mi^3 $\approx$ 400 mi^3.

28. A two-passenger AX7 hot-air balloon has a radius of 8.1 meters. If it is spherical in shape, what volume of air does it contain?

28. $(4/3)\pi(8.1 \text{ m})^3 = 2226.89\ldots \approx 2200 \text{ m}^3.$

29. The recently discovered substance buckminsterfullerene (named after the noted architect and inventor) was first isolated in 1985 as a circular ball of 60 carbon atoms, arranged in the geodesic sphere form used by Fuller in his designs. Varieties of this substance may eventually find use in such diverse applications as drug design, superconductivity, and reinforcing materials. The interior cavity of a "buckyball" has an extremely small diameter of 0.36 nanometers. What is the cavity's volume? Give your answer both in cubic nanometers and in cubic meters.

29. $\dfrac{4}{3}\pi(0.18 \text{ nm})^3 \approx 0.024 \text{ nm}^3$.

$(0.024 \text{ nm}^3)\left(\dfrac{1 \text{ m}}{1,000,000,000 \text{ nm}}\right)^3 = 0.000000000000000000000000000024 \text{ m}^3$.

30. What is the volume of a sphere that has a diameter of 8.9 cm?

30. $V = \dfrac{4}{3}\pi r^3 = \dfrac{4}{3}\pi\left(\dfrac{8.9}{2}\right)^3 \approx 369 \text{ cm}^3$.

31. The first communications satellite was launched by NASA in 1965. Named Echo I, it was a hollow 100-foot-diameter sphere with a thin metallic surface.

    a) What volume of gas was needed to keep Echo I inflated?

31. a) $V = \dfrac{4}{3}\pi r^2 = \dfrac{4}{3}\pi(50)^3 \approx 523,599 \approx 520,000 \text{ ft}^3$.

    b) What was the surface area of Echo I?

    b) $SA = 4\pi r^2 = 4\pi(50)^2 \approx 31,416 \approx 31,000 \text{ ft}^2$.

32. A 24-foot-diameter sewage tunnel has been extended 9.5 miles into the ocean to dispose of part of a city's waste. What is the capacity of the tunnel in gallons?

32. $(9.5 \text{ mi})\left(\dfrac{5280 \text{ ft}}{1 \text{ mi}}\right)(\pi)\left(\dfrac{(24 \text{ ft})^2}{4}\right)\left(\dfrac{7.48 \text{ gal}}{1 \text{ ft}^3}\right) \approx 169,735,033 \approx 170,000,000 \text{ gal}.$

33. The Subaru telescope in Japan has one of the largest mirrors in the world. With it, a baseball could be seen clearly from a distance of 180 miles. It is essentially a cylinder 8.3 meters in diameter with a thickness of 7.0 inches (which is actually fairly thin for such a large mirror). What is the volume of glass in the mirror?

33. Volume of a cylinder $= \pi r^2 h = \pi(4.15 \text{ m})^2 (7 \text{ in}) \left(\dfrac{1 \text{ m}}{39.37 \text{ in}} \right) = 9.620... \approx 9.6 \text{ m}^3$.

34. A 50-foot-high cylindrical grain storage silo has a diameter of 30 feet.

a) What volume of grain would fill the silo?

34. a) $V = \pi(15 \text{ ft})^2 (50 \text{ ft}) \approx 35,342 \approx 35,000 \text{ ft}^3$.

b) How many bushels of grain is this? (A bushel = 4 pecks, and a peck = 537.5 in^3.)

b) $(35,342 \text{ ft}^3) \left(\dfrac{12 \text{ in}}{1 \text{ ft}} \right)^3 \left(\dfrac{1 \text{ peck}}{537.5 \text{ in}^3} \right) \left(\dfrac{1 \text{ bushel}}{4 \text{ pecks}} \right) = 28,405.8 \approx 28,000 \text{ bushels.}$

35. A 12-ounce soda can has a diameter of 6.6 cm.

a) If the can were a perfect cylinder, what would be the height of the soda in the can? (Hint: Divide the volume by the cross-sectional area.)

35. a) If $V = \pi r^2 h$, then $h = \dfrac{V}{\pi r^2} = \left(\dfrac{12 \text{ oz}}{\pi(3.3 \text{ cm})^2} \right) \left(\dfrac{1 \text{ gal}}{128 \text{ oz}} \right) \left(\dfrac{231 \text{ in}^3}{\text{gal}} \right) \left(\dfrac{2.54 \text{ cm}}{1 \text{ in}} \right)^3 =$

$10.373... \approx 10 \text{ cm.}$

b) The actual height of a soda can is usually 12.2 cm. How can you account for the discrepancy between this value and your answer to (a)?

b) The bottom of the can is indented, and the soda does not completely fill the can.

36. Hazardous waste is often stored in 55-gallon cylindrical drums. What are possible dimensions for the drums?

36. $(55 \text{ gallons}) \left(\dfrac{1 \text{ ft}^3}{7.48 \text{ gal}} \right) \approx 7.3529 \text{ ft}^3$. **One possibility: Let the diameter be 2 ft**

so that the circular cross section has an area of $\pi \left(\dfrac{(2 \text{ ft})^2}{4} \right) = \pi \text{ ft}^2$**; then the**

length is $\left(\dfrac{7.3529 \text{ ft}^3}{\pi \text{ ft}^2} \right) \approx 2.3 \text{ ft.}$

37. Find the volume of concrete used to make the 30-inch-thick T section in **Figure 1.101.** (All dimensions are accurate to the nearest inch.) Concrete volume is usually measured by the cubic yard (yd³), commonly referred to as just a "yard of concrete."

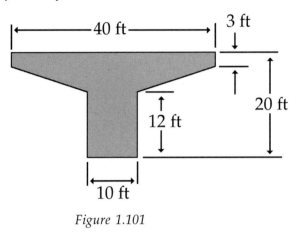

Figure 1.101

37. **The cross section can be treated as two rectangles and a trapezoid with area**

$$(40 \text{ ft})(3 \text{ ft}) + \left(\frac{1}{2}\right)(40 \text{ ft} + 10 \text{ ft})(5 \text{ ft}) + (12 \text{ ft})(10 \text{ ft}) = 365 \text{ ft}^2. \text{ The total}$$

volume is then $(365 \text{ ft}^2)(2.5 \text{ ft}) = 912.5 \text{ ft}^3 \left(\frac{1 \text{ yd}}{3 \text{ ft}}\right)^3 \approx 34 \text{ yd}^3,$ **or 34 "yards" of**

concrete.

38. The rain gauge in **Figure 1.102** is in the shape of an inverted cone 21 cm deep and 4.5 cm in diameter at the top. What is the maximum amount of water it can hold? (The volume of a cone with radius r and height h is given by $V = \frac{1}{3}\pi r^2 h$.)

Figure 1.102

38. $\left(\frac{1}{3}\right)\pi r^2 h = \left(\frac{1}{3}\right)\pi(2.25 \text{ cm})^2(21 \text{ cm}) \approx 111 \approx 110 \text{ cm}^3.$

39. **Figure 1.103** shows a cross section of a 35-foot-long concrete retaining wall. How much concrete is needed to make the wall?

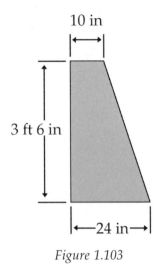

10 in

3 ft 6 in

24 in

Figure 1.103

39. **The area of the trapezoidal cross section is $\left(\dfrac{1}{2}\right)(b_1 + b_2)h = \left(\dfrac{1}{2}\right)(10\ \text{in} +$**

$24\ \text{in})(42\ \text{in}) = 714\ \text{in}^2$. The volume is $714\ \text{in}^2\left(\dfrac{1\ \text{ft}}{12\ \text{in}}\right)^2(35\ \text{ft})\left(\dfrac{1\ \text{yd}}{3\ \text{ft}}\right)^3 \approx 6.4\ \text{yd}^3$,

or 6.4 "yards."

40. The label on a gallon of paint states that a gallon will cover 400–450 ft² of surface. How many gallons should be bought in order to paint a gymnasium (walls and ceiling only) that is 180 ft long, 150 ft wide, and 80 ft high?

40. **First find the total area of the four walls and ceiling: 2(180 ft)(80 ft) + 2(150 ft)(80 ft) + (180 ft)(150 ft) = 79,500 ft². Using the higher estimate, it**

would take $\left(\dfrac{79{,}800\ \text{ft}^2}{450\ \text{ft}^2\ /\ \text{gal}}\right) \approx 177.3$ gallons, while with the lower estimate, it

would take $\left(\dfrac{79{,}800\ \text{ft}^2}{400\ \text{ft}^2\ /\ \text{gal}}\right) \approx 199.5$ gallons. So it should take somewhere

between 177 and 200 gallons to cover the walls and ceiling.

41. If the log in Exercise 29 of Section 1.4 is 3 feet 3 inches long, what is the outer surface area of bark on the log?

41. **The log's (cylindrical) surface area equals its circumference multiplied by**

its length, or $\pi dh = \pi(8.6\ \text{in})(39\ \text{in}) = 1054\ \text{in}^2\left(\dfrac{1\ \text{ft}}{12\ \text{in}}\right)^2 \approx 7.3\ \text{ft}^2$.

42. How much cardboard is needed to make the packaging for the 12-pack of cans in Exercise 37 of Section 1.4? (Assume that each can is 12.2 cm high.)

42. The measure of the amount of cardboard needed is *area*. Dimensions of bottom (and top) of the package are 26.4 cm and 19.8 cm, so total surface area is the sum of the areas of the six sides (three pairs of sides) = 2(26.4 cm)(19.8 cm) + 2(26.4 cm)(12.2 cm) + 2(19.8 cm)(12.2 cm) = 2172.72 ≈ 2170 cm².

43. The Climatron display greenhouse at the Missouri Botanical Garden in St. Louis (**Figure 1.104**) is a geodesic dome structure that has a capacity of 1.3 million cubic feet.

Roger H. Clark, Professor of Architecture, North Carolina State University

Figure 1.104

a) What geometrical property does the word *capacity* refer to here?

43. a) Volume

b) The Climatron is a portion of a sphere that, if completed, would have a radius of 103 feet. What is the ratio of the capacity of the Climatron to the capacity of the sphere of which it is a part?

b) A sphere with radius 103 ft has a volume of $\left(\dfrac{4}{3}\right)\pi(103 \text{ ft})^3 \approx 4{,}577{,}000 \text{ ft}^3$.

The ratio of the volumes is $\left(\dfrac{1{,}300{,}000 \text{ ft}^3}{4{,}577{,}000 \text{ ft}^3}\right) \approx 0.28$, or 28%.

44. What is the capacity of the gutter shown in the cross section in **Figure 1.105**?

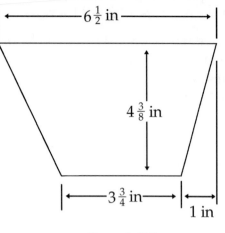

Figure 1.105

44. **Capacity of the gutter is measured by cross-sectional area. Since the gutter is a trapezoid, the area is** $\left(\dfrac{1}{2}\right)$(6.5 in + 3.75 in)(4.375 in) = 22.421... ≈ 22 in².

Section 1.6 Other Kinds of Measurement

What You Need to Know

- How to use a protractor to measure angles

What You Will Learn

- To identify rates as indicating relationships between variables

- To convert the units of any type of quantity into other units

- To write numbers using scientific notation

- To identify vector quantities

- To distinguish between exact and approximate values

Materials

- Graph paper

- Protractor

- Ruler

In addition to the many geometrical measurements that we have examined in this chapter, there are a number of other types of quantities that are frequently measured. Consider again the case of a construction company. It is often important to know the moisture content of lumber, since changes in humidity can cause wood to swell or shrink after installation. HVAC work requires knowledge of such things as radiant energy levels, R-values of insulation, and heat output of furnaces. The power requirements of all the appliances and other electrical devices in a house determine the level of electrical current service needed, measured in amperes. The chief engineer of a construction company must be able to estimate these and other quantities.

The metric system was introduced more than 200 years ago. It provided conversions to larger or smaller units using multiples of 10, since our number system is based on 10. But units for times longer than a second are not measured in multiples of 10. Although short time durations may be measured in milliseconds, nanoseconds, etc., units of kiloseconds or megaseconds are not used.

Time Measurement

We all deal with the measurement of time in our daily lives. Some of us even use precision time measurements as part of our work. Although the standard unit of time is the second, it is often more convenient to use minutes, hours, or longer units, depending on the situation.

Angle Measurement

Angle measurement is important in many types of work. The angle through which the arm of a manufacturing robot turns is usually measured in *degrees*. Sometimes a unit called a *radian* is used, and in Europe a metric angle unit called a *grad* may be used for surveying.

SI Units

As we have seen throughout this chapter, a variety of units have been used for measurements. The second (for time), metric units such as the meter (for length), the liter (for volume), and the kilogram (for mass), and other related units are now part of the **International System** of units (abbreviated **SI** from the French *Systeme Internationale*). Traditional units such as feet and inches, miles, gallons, and pounds are now referred to as **U.S. Customary** units (formerly English units or British Engineering units). Few countries outside the United States still use them.

Rates

Some measured quantities have units that are combinations of other units. This is because they are compound quantities that involve two or more simpler quantities in their definition. For example, an environmental scientist studying wastewater discharge might use a flowmeter to measure the *flow rate* of a volume of liquid passing through a channel during a certain time interval. The standard units for such a flow rate are cubic meters per second (m^3/s).

Example   34

If 3000 cubic meters of wastewater pass through a point in a channel in one minute, what is the flow rate in m^3/s?

Solution:

$$\frac{3000 \text{ m}^3}{60 \text{ s}} = 50 \text{ m}^3/\text{s}.$$

Note that the use of the word *rate* implies that changes in two quantities are involved. In fact, a rate is a *ratio* involving the quantities. In Example 34, as time changes, so does the amount of water going through the channel. The flow rate can be described as the rate of change of liquid volume with respect to time. This notion of **rate of change** occurs in a wide range of applications and is a primary concern of the branch of mathematics called **calculus.**

Example 35

During the 20th century, the total worldwide area covered by rain forests decreased from 1.5 billion hectares to 700 million hectares. What was the average rate of change of rain forest area per year?

Solution:

$$\frac{1{,}500{,}000{,}000 \text{ hectares} - 700{,}000{,}000 \text{ hectares}}{100 \text{ yr}} = 8{,}000{,}000 \text{ hectares/yr.}$$

Sometimes compound units get complicated because of the combinations involved. Hence, they are then given simpler names, frequently in honor of some historical person. In terms of fundamental units, energy is measured in kilogram meters squared per second per second (kg-m^2/s^2). This compound unit has been replaced with the name *joule* (abbreviated J), after a scientist named James Joule.

Some quantities are written without units because they are actually ratios of similar quantities. Engineers measure the *strain* of a stretched material as a fractional increase in length. If a piece of plastic that is initially 5.0 cm long is stretched to 5.2 cm, the strain is equal to (0.2 cm)/(5.0 cm) = 0.04.

The previous examples describe things that might be called natural quantities because they occur naturally in the universe. People also measure other things that are related to the way we live and work. The Gross Domestic Product (GDP) of a nation measures the total value of goods and services produced and has units of currency. The production rate of a factory might be measured in parts per hour. A common kind of home price index measures the ratio of the price of an average house at a given time to a base price from an earlier reference time. An index of 1.08 means that the current average price is 1.08 times the base price, for an increase of 8%.

Careful attention to units, especially in conversions between unit systems, is extremely important in technical work. In September 1999, a $125 million space probe went off course and crashed onto the surface of Mars instead of going into a proper orbit. The manufacturer forgot to change force units of pounds into the SI equivalent of newtons, which are exclusively used in space navigation. Partly to avoid such mix-ups, most engineers never leave "naked" numbers in calculations and formulas. Instead, they always attach the appropriate units.

Scientific Notation

When a measurement is made of either a very large or a very small quantity, it may be awkward, and sometimes even misleading, to write out the entire number. When someone says, "Earth is 93 million miles from the sun," we intuitively understand that the distance in the statement is only accurate to the nearest million miles.

This figure of 93,000,000 miles has limited accuracy for two reasons. There is an inherent inaccuracy in the measuring technique, and the distance from Earth to the sun varies throughout the year. Earth is closer to the sun when it is winter in the northern hemisphere and farther from the sun during the northern summer.

A brief list of common metric prefixes was included in Section 1.1. Here is a list of prefixes used for large units that includes the corresponding powers of 10:

Prefix	Meaning	Powers of 10
tera-	trillions	10^{12}
giga-	billions	10^{9}
mega-	millions	10^{6}
kilo-	thousands	10^{3}
hecto-	hundreds	10^{2}
deca-	tens	10^{1}

Table 1.27

But it is possible to misinterpret the written figure 93,000,000 miles as implying greater precision than intended. Writing the distance as 93×10^6 miles (since $10^6 = 1,000,000$) eliminates any ambiguity.

Standard **scientific notation** involves writing numbers as the product of a number between 1 and 10 multiplied by an appropriate power of 10. So in standard scientific notation, the distance to the sun would be written as 9.3×10^7 miles. Notice that scientific notation clearly shows that only the 9 and the 3 are measured digits.

Example 36

It has been estimated that the world market for photocopying is 3,000,000,000,000 pages per year. Express this number in standard scientific notation.

Solution:

$3,000,000,000,000 = 3 \times 1,000,000,000,000$.

Since $1,000,000,000,000 = 10^{12}$, the number can be written 3×10^{12}.

Example 37

A Canadian government study in 1994 calculated that each year harp seals eat 1.4×10^5 tons of cod. Express this amount in standard numerical form.

Solution:

$10^5 = 100,000$.

$1.4 \times 100,000 = 140,000$ tons.

It is important to notice that most calculators and computer programs are not programmed to display scientific notation in the usual form. Instead of displaying 10^7, for example, a calculator set in a scientific notation mode would convert the Earth-sun distance as shown in **Figure 1.106.**

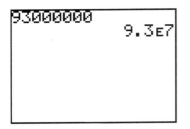

Figure 1.106

Some calculators also have an option to display results of calculations in **engineering notation** mode. It is similar to scientific notation, but the powers of 10 must be in multiples of three: 10^3, 10^6, 10^9, etc. In engineering notation, the Earth-sun distance would be 93×10^6 miles.

The calculator uses the symbol E7 to stand for 10^7. But written work should always use standard scientific notation, and not calculator symbolism.

Example 38

A calculator displays the result of a particular calculation as 2.57E14. Write this number in standard scientific notation.

Solution:

The notation E14 stands for a multiplication by 10^{14}, so the number is 2.57×10^{14}.

Example 39

How would the number 6.2×10^{11} be displayed by a typical calculator?

Solution:

Most calculators do not display the base of the power of 10, only the exponent. A typical display is 6.2E11.

Vectors

The values of most things such as length, time, and temperature can be given by a single number. However, there are some quantities that require two or more numbers to specify them, usually because the direction of the quantity is an essential part of its definition. For example, an airplane's approach to an airport is measured by a velocity **vector,** which includes both the plane's speed and its direction. When a meteorologist reports a "twenty-mile-an-hour wind from the southeast," we need both parts of the vector definition of velocity in order to understand the wind conditions. Vectors are also used to model quantities in fields as diverse as biology and economics, to name just two.

The two parts of most vectors are called **magnitude** and **direction. Figure 1.107** shows a basketball player exerting a force **F** with a magnitude of 100 newtons in a direction of 35° above the horizontal. If either the magnitude or direction were changed, the force would be different.

Figure 1.107

The newton of force is named after Isaac Newton, the English mathematician and physicist who first described the relationship between force and motion, as well as discovering the Law of Gravity. As with most units named for people, the name of the unit is not capitalized, but the abbreviation (N) is.

The symbol **F** for the force vector includes both the magnitude and direction of the force. In order to denote the magnitude only, the same vertical line symbol as used for the absolute value of a number is often employed: $|\mathbf{F}| = 100$ newtons.

Exact and Approximate Numbers

To increase the precision of a measurement, we can use more and more sensitive instruments. But the word "exact" has no meaning in some contexts. We can talk about "exactly four" doors on a car because doors are counted in integer amounts. However, any measured quantity that varies over a continuous range, such as length or time, cannot have its value determined exactly.

For a different example, the value of the number π exactly equals the ratio of a circle's circumference and its diameter. But this sort of theoretical exactness can't be described (other than

Other numbers that have no exact decimal equivalents include most roots, such as $\sqrt{2}$, which is approximately 1.4142. However, the decimal expansion of $\sqrt{2}$ is never-ending and also does not have regularly repeating sequences. On the other hand, decimal equivalents of fractions are either exact (e.g., $\frac{1}{2} = 0.5$, $\frac{1}{16} = 0.0625$, etc.) or have repeating digits or groups of digits (e.g., $\frac{1}{3} = 0.333...$ or $\frac{2}{7} = 0.28571428571428...$). Numbers such as these that equal ratios of integers are called **rational numbers**, whereas numbers like π and $\sqrt{2}$ are called **irrational numbers.**

approximately) by any decimal number, no matter how many decimal places are used. In some engineering and scientific work, a number may be described as being "exactly half of π" even though it has no exact decimal equivalent.

Example 40

How would you correctly state the capacity of a cylindrical sewage discharge pipe that is 347 meters long with a diameter of 2.8 meters?

Solution:

The "capacity" of the pipe here refers to the *volume* of the pipe. The volume of a circular cylinder can be found from the formula $V = \pi r^2 h$. (The h in this case actually stands for the *length* of the pipe.)

The least accurate measured value in the calculation is the cylinder's 1.4-meter radius (half of the diameter). Since the radius is known to only two significant figures, the calculated volume cannot really be known with more than two-figure accuracy.

What about the number π? We could actually use any decimal representation for π that has at least two digits, but it would be safer to use at least three (as in 3.14). However, almost all modern calculators have a button for π that will automatically use the maximum number of digits the calculator can produce. Therefore, it is best (and quickest) to use the π button for such calculations.

The volume calculation is

$V = \pi r^2 h$

$\quad = \pi (1.4 \text{ m})^2 (347 \text{ m})$

$\quad = 2136.659...$

$\quad \approx 2100 \text{ m}^3.$

Because of the two-figure accuracy of the radius, the best way to report the volume is 2100 m^3.

Exercises 1.6

I. Investigations *(SE pages 101–103)*

1. Vectors are important in navigation. In fact, airline routes into and out of airports are referred to as *vector routes*. **Figure 1.108** is a portion of a Visual Flight Rules (VFR) chart that shows some of these routes initiating at airports in the cities of Keene, New Hampshire, and Gardner, Massachusetts. Distances on such charts are measured in nautical miles (nm). (A nautical mile is equal to 1.15 standard miles.) Each airport is at the center of a *compass rose*, which is a circle calibrated with an angular scale measured in degrees.

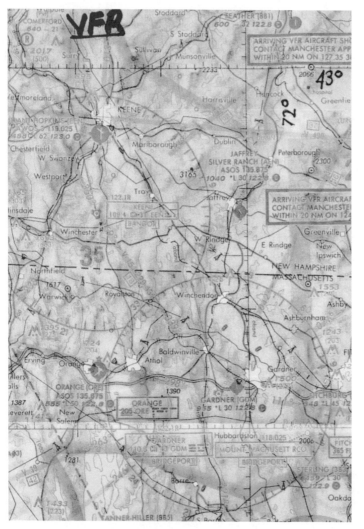

Figure 1.108

The angles of flight route vectors are always measured clockwise from the direction of the north magnetic pole, which would be the 0° direction (and which is actually a few degrees away from due north). The opposite direction from magnetic north would be 180°.

a) The vector flight path from Keene to Gardner has a length of 18 nautical miles and is in the 159° direction. This flight path is an example of a **displacement vector,** which consists of both a distance and a direction. How would you describe the displacement vector that represents the flight path *from* Gardner *to* Keene?

1. **a) 18 nm at 339°**

b) Besides displacement, there is another kind of vector associated with the plane's motion along each route into or out of an airport. It has the same direction as displacement. What is the name of this vector?

b) Velocity, consisting of speed and direction

c) Name some other kinds of quantities that are vector quantities. That is, what kinds of things can only be specified completely by giving a direction as well as a magnitude?

c) Sample answers: force, acceleration, momentum, torque, fields (electric, magnetic, gravitational)

2. The volume of the pipe in Example 40 was rounded to 2100 m^3. In practice, most people would still write 2137 m^3 for a case like this one, rounding to the nearest whole meter. But a more complete way to report the result is to state a range.

a) Show that the maximum likely error is 80 m^3.

2. **a) Given the measurement accuracy implied in the problem, the smallest the radius could actually be is 1.375 m (half of 2.75 m) and the smallest possible length is 346.5 m. Thus, the smallest possible volume is $\pi(1.375 \text{ m})^2(346.5 \text{ m}) = 2058.062...$ m^3. Similarly, the largest possible volume is $\pi(1.425 \text{ m})^2(347.5 \text{ m}) = 2216.8403...$ m^3. 2217 m^3 – 2137 m^3 = 80 m^3, the maximum likely error.**

b) Express the volume of the pipe using an appropriate indication of accuracy.

b) 2137 m^3 ± 80 m^3

3. The notion of a rate of change was mentioned at the beginning of this section in discussing the measurement of flow rate. We usually think of a rate of change as involving time, but some quantities change with respect to other things besides time. If a classroom wall 20 cm thick is made of solid concrete and the temperatures on the inner and outer surfaces in the winter are 25°C and –5°C, then the temperature changes by a total of 30°C over a distance of 20 cm. The average rate of temperature change with respect to distance is then equal to (30°C/20 cm) = 1.5°C/cm. (If this rate is the same at all points in the wall, it is called a *temperature gradient.*)

a) The temperature of Earth is cooler beneath its surface, and near the surface it changes by 1°F for each 200 feet of depth. What is the numerical value of the temperature gradient near the surface of Earth? (Include units with your answer.)

3. a) $\left(\dfrac{1°F}{200 \text{ ft}}\right) = 0.005°F/ft.$

b) The voltage of a particular discharging capacitor decreases from 3.4 volts to 0.8 volts in 0.002 seconds. What is the average rate of change of voltage with respect to time?

b) $\left(\dfrac{0.8 \text{ volts} - 3.4 \text{ volts}}{0.002 \text{ s}}\right) = \left(\dfrac{-2.6 \text{ volts}}{0.002 \text{ s}}\right) = -1300 \text{ volts/s.}$

c) The length of a steel girder in a bridge increases from 18.50 m to 18.51 m as the temperature goes from 0°C to 40°C. What is the average rate of change of length of the girder with respect to temperature?

c) $\left(\dfrac{18.51 \text{ m} - 18.50 \text{ m}}{40°C - 0°C}\right) = \left(\dfrac{0.01 \text{ m}}{40°C}\right) = 0.00025 \text{ m/°C} .$

d) The elevation of a highway increases from 500 feet to 780 feet over a horizontal distance of half a mile. What is the average rate of change of elevation with respect to horizontal travel?

d) $\left(\dfrac{780 \text{ ft} - 500 \text{ ft}}{0.5 \text{ mi}}\right) = \left(\dfrac{280 \text{ ft}}{0.5 \text{ mi}}\right) = 560 \text{ ft /mi;}$ also $(560 \text{ ft/mi})\left(\dfrac{1 \text{ mi}}{5280 \text{ ft}}\right) \approx$
0.106 ft/ft, for a "unitless" rate of change (*slope*) of 0.106.

4. There is a difference between *unit* and *dimension*. The flow rate in Example 34 can be said to have a dimension of (volume)/(time), or (length)^3/(time). Thus, the dimension indicates the type of quantity being measured, although the units themselves may vary and often depend on the measuring instrument used. The dimension of (volume)/(time) can be measured in units such as (ft^3/s), (cm^3/s), or even (gallons/min), in addition to (m^3/s). Note that this use of the word *dimension* is a different usage than the common notion of physical dimensions (length, width, height, diameter, etc.) of an object.

a) Speeds on U.S. highways are usually measured in units of miles per hour, whereas in Canada (and most other countries) they are measured in kilometers per hour. However, the dimension of speed is the same in all countries. What is the dimension of speed?

4. a) $\dfrac{\text{length}}{\text{time}}$ or $\dfrac{\text{distance}}{\text{time}}$

b) Pressure is measured in SI units of newtons per square meter and also in U.S. Customary units of pounds per square inch. What is the dimension of pressure?

b) $\dfrac{\text{force}}{(\text{length})^2}$ or $\dfrac{\text{weight}}{(\text{length})^2}$

c) Mechanical work can be measured in SI units of newton-meters or in U.S. Customary units of foot-pounds. What is the dimension of work?

c) (force)(length) or (length)(force)

II. Projects and Group Activities (SE pages 103–105)

5. Materials: Graph paper, protractor, ruler

Surveyors must locate boundaries of plots of land with great precision. Their work becomes a legal basis for identifying lots for real estate transactions. The use of displacement vectors is essential to this process.

A displacement vector consists of a straight-line distance measurement along with the direction angle of the measurement. The direction angle must be measured with respect to some reference direction. This direction is usually taken to be magnetic north. Angles are considered to be positive when measured in a clockwise direction. This is identical to the way angles are measured in navigation, as in Exercise 1.

Figure 1.109 shows an example of a displacement vector. It represents a displacement of 65 feet at an angle of 160° from magnetic north. The direction of this vector could also be described as 20° "east of south."

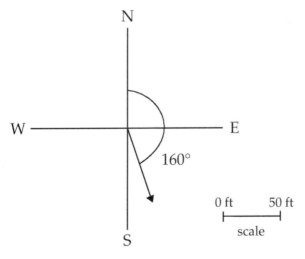

Figure 1.109

A survey of a nonrectangular plot of land with four straight-sided boundaries is carried out with the following results for the first three sides:

- A displacement of 78 feet at an angle of 102° (this is a direction just south of east)

- A displacement of 122 feet at an angle of 193° (this is a little west of south)

- A displacement of 105 feet at an angle of 270° (west)

a) On a sheet of graph paper, label a starting point and the directions N, E, W, and S. Then choose an appropriate scale and carefully draw in the displacement vector representing the first side of the plot. The vector should look like an arrow, with the arrowhead pointing in the direction of the vector.

5. a) **Sample answer:**

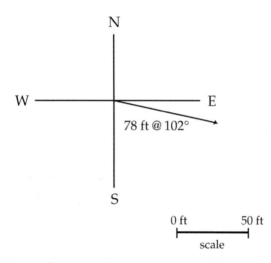

b) Now draw in the second and third displacement vectors. The tail of each succeeding vector should be placed at the head of the previous one.

b) Sample answer:

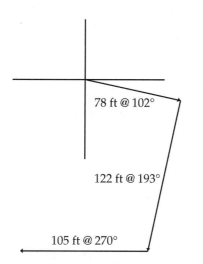

c) What *total distance* would you have traveled in order to walk the boundaries of the first three sides?

c) 305 feet

d) What would be your net *displacement* from the starting point after walking to the end of the third side. That is, what is the straight-line distance from the starting point? Measure the length of the displacement vector on your map.

d) Sample answer: 146 feet

e) In what direction would you have to walk to return to the starting point?

e) Sample answer: between 22° and 23° (east of north)

f) Draw the displacement vector that corresponds to the fourth boundary of the plot.

f) Sample answer:

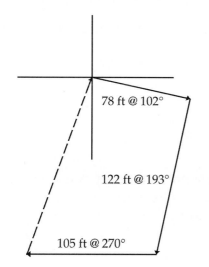

g) State the magnitude and direction of the vector you drew in (f).

g) 146 feet at 22.6°

6. Scientific notation provides a convenient way of describing the sizes of very large and very small things. When *estimating* such sizes, we often drop the first part of the number and round off to the nearest power of 10 to guess at an **order of magnitude** of the quantity being estimated. (Sometimes the exponent itself is referred to as the order of magnitude.) Thus, the distance from Earth to the sun is said to have an order of magnitude of 10^8 miles, because $10^8 = 100,000,000$ miles is the nearest power of 10 to the actual distance of $93,000,000$ miles.

Try to estimate an order of magnitude for the quantities in (a)–(k) (but don't be surprised if you miss by one or two orders of magnitude on some of them). Use the following benchmarks to help with your estimate:

- The height of a house in meters has an order of magnitude of 10^1.

- The height of a typical high-rise apartment building in meters has an order of magnitude of 10^2.

- The number of seconds in an hour has an order of magnitude of 10^3.

a) The height of Mount Everest in meters

6. a) 10^4

b) The height of the tallest human-made structure in feet

b) 10^3

c) The number of names in the New York City residential phone book

c) 10^7

d) The number of names in the residential phone book for your city or town

d) Variable, but could be as little as 10^2 for an extremely small town to as much as 10^6 for large U.S. cities

e) The internal temperature of the sun in °C

e) 10^7

f) The population of the world

f) 10^{10}

g) The number of instructions that a fast personal computer can carry out in 1 second (The speed of a computer is usually stated in megahertz, which are units of a million instructions per second.)

g) 10^9

h) The age of the universe in minutes

h) 10^{16}

i) The number of centimeters in a mile

i) 10^5

j) Number of times a human heart beats in a lifetime

j) 10^9

k) The number of basketballs that would stretch from Portland, Oregon, to Washington, D.C.

k) 10^7

7. Consider one last time the classroom renovation scenario that began this chapter. You have already thought about a few types of measurement and computed results that would be necessary for the renovations to proceed. These include things like the perimeter to enable the installation of floor molding, floor area for tiling or carpeting, room volume for heating and air conditioning requirements, etc.

   Now see how many other quantities you can identify that might need to be measured or computed in order to finish improvements to the room. Be creative and think about all the possible changes that might have to be made. Include possible installation of multimedia equipment, laboratory facilities, new lighting, etc. To be specific, list the following for each item you identify:

   - The nature of the change or improvement to be made

   - Who would do the work (i.e., what is the job of the person or persons who would do it)

   - What properties of the existing room would need to be communicated to them (what would be measured, with what instrument, with what kind of accuracy, and in what units)

   You may have to do a little research to determine some of these last things, such as what instruments would be used. Prepare a report or oral presentation to outline the requirements for the renovation, just as if you were charged with planning the project.

III. Additional Practice *(SE pages 106–107)*

For 8–11, write each number in scientific notation.

8. 500,000

8. 5×10^5

9. 4200

9. 4.2×10^3

10. 6,370,000,000

10. 6.37×10^9

11. 70

11. 7×10^1

For 12–15, write each number in standard numerical form.

12. 10^7

12. 10,000,000

13. 1.2×10^4

13. 12,000

14. 3×10^2

14. 300

15. 8.635×10^{10}

15. 86,350,000,000

For 16–18, rewrite each calculator display of a large number using (a) correct scientific notation and (b) standard numerical form.

16. 4.37E8

16. a) 4.37×10^8

   b) 437,000,000

17. 8.1663E5

17. a) 8.1663×10^5

   b) 816,630

18. 5E11

18. a) 5×10^{11}

   b) 500,000,000,000

For 19–21, write each number the way a calculator might display it in scientific mode.

19. 1.26×10^6

19. 1.26E6

20. 2,400,000,000

20. 2.4E9

21. 70,000,420

21. 7.000042E7

22. The two main tunnels providing New York City's water supply have a combined flow rate of 1.5 billion gallons a day. Express this amount in gallons per minute.

22. $\left(\dfrac{1,500,000,000 \text{ gal}}{1 \text{ day}}\right)\left(\dfrac{1 \text{ day}}{24 \text{ hr}}\right)\left(\dfrac{1 \text{ hr}}{60 \text{ min}}\right) = \mathbf{1{,}041{,}667 \approx 1.0 \text{ million gal/min.}}$

23. The world's population reached 6 billion in October 1999 and was then growing at the rate of 78 million per year.

a) Express each of these numbers in scientific notation.

23. a) 6 billion = 6.0×10^9 people (although at some point in October 1999 the population was exactly 6.000000000×10^9); 78 million = 7.8×10^6 people/yr.

b) If the rate of world population growth stayed the same, what would be the population of the world in October 2010?

b) 6,000,000,000 + (11)(7,800,000) = 6,085,800,000 people.

24. A watt is a unit of power that measures energy production per unit time. One watt equals a joule of energy per second. If a city of 1 million people typically uses energy at the rate of 2000 megawatts, how many joules of energy are used per day?

24. A megawatt is 1 million watts. (2,000,000,000 joules/s)$\left(\dfrac{3600 \text{ s}}{1 \text{ hr}}\right)\left(\dfrac{24 \text{ hr}}{1 \text{ day}}\right) =$ 1.728×10^{14} joules/day, or about 200 trillion joules per day.

25. In order to create a computer model of a nuclear bomb test, the U.S. Department of Energy uses a supercomputer named Pacific Blue, which can execute 3.9 teraflops per second. (*Flop* is a word that refers to an individual computational operation.)

a) How many operations can this computer perform in a second?

25. a) 3.9 trillion operations

b) How many times faster is Pacific Blue than a Pentium III home computer capable of 1.7 gigaflops?

b) $\left(\dfrac{3,900,000,000,000}{1,700,000,000}\right)$ **= 2294, or about 2300 times faster.**

26. The Cape Hatteras Lighthouse in North Carolina had to be moved back from the ocean because of shore erosion. At 4800 tons, it is one of the heaviest structures to have been moved on land.

   a) What is the weight of the lighthouse in newtons? (Assume that the given weight is accurate to the nearest 100 tons.)

26. a) (4800 tons) $\left(\dfrac{2000\ \text{lb}}{1\ \text{ton}}\right)\left(\dfrac{4.448\ \text{N}}{1\ \text{lb}}\right)$ **= 42,700,800 ≈ 43,000,000 N.**

   b) Express the answer to (a) using scientific notation.

b) 4.3 x 10^7 N

27. The Human Genome Project was completed in 2001. It found that the human genome contains 3.2 x 10^9 "letters," which are actually DNA base pairs. Express the number of letters in the human genome in standard numerical form.

27. 3,200,000,000

28. Each tower of the Akashi Kaikyo Bridge (see Exercise 20 of Section 1.2) weighs 25,000 metric tons (or *tonnes*). Express the number of pounds that one of these towers weighs using scientific notation.

28. (25,000 metric tons) $\left(\dfrac{1000\ \text{kg}}{1\ \text{metric ton}}\right)\left(\dfrac{2.205\ \text{lb}}{1\ \text{kg}}\right)$ **= 55,125,000 ≈ 55,000,000 lb**

or 5.5 x 10^7 lb.

29. The X-43A is expected to become the world's fastest airplane when it flies at a speed of 7200 miles per hour. Express this speed in feet per second.

29. $\left(\dfrac{7200\ \text{mi}}{1\ \text{hr}}\right)\left(\dfrac{5280\ \text{ft}}{1\ \text{mi}}\right)\left(\dfrac{1\ \text{hr}}{3600\ \text{s}}\right)$ **= 10,560 ≈ 11,000 ft/s.**

30. If a number used in a calculation is supposed to be exactly $\dfrac{1}{3}$ but you round it off to 0.33, what is the percent error that will result in the calculation? What if you round off to 0.3? (See item 17 of Extend the Activity in Section 1.1 for information on percent error.)

30. $\left(\dfrac{1/3 - 0.33}{1/3}\right)$**(100) = 1%;** $\left(\dfrac{1/3 - 0.3}{1/3}\right)$**(100) = 10%.**

31. The calculation for the surface area of a sphere of measured radius 3.2 cm is $(4)(\pi)(3.2)^2$. Which of the quantities in the calculation are exact?

31. The 4 and the π are exact.

32. The calculation for the perimeter of a rectangle with measured width 3.7 meters and length 5.4 meters is $(2)(5.4) + (2)(3.7)$. Which of the quantities in the calculation are exact?

32. Only the 2s are exact.

Chapter 1 Summary

Estimation of physical quantities

Precision and accuracy in measurement

Unit systems

Unit conversions

Perimeter

Pythagorean theorem

Numerical statistics: mean, median, mode, range

Graphs of data: dot plots, histograms

Inequality symbols

Calculator/computer lists and histograms

Area

Volume

Surface area

Rates of change

Scientific notation

Definition of a vector

Chapter 1 Review *(SE pages 109–113)*

1. Write a summary of the important mathematical ideas found in Chapter 1.

1. **Answers will vary. Following are some of the important ideas that should be listed:**

   Numbers that result from measurements are never exact.

   Care must be taken in reporting measurement results.

   Mathematical models can be represented in many ways: verbal models, algebraic models, statistical models, geometric models.

   Statistical models can be used to show how data are distributed.

   Geometric models can be used to explore properties of objects.

   Data can be summarized and described numerically by finding the mean, median, mode, and/or range of the data set.

   Data can be described graphically through the use of dot plots and histograms.

   The Pythagorean theorem can be used to find a missing side of a right triangle if two sides are given.

   Formulas can be used to calculate properties of geometric figures, such as perimeter, area, and volume.

   Inequality can be expressed symbolically with the symbols $<$, $>$, $\leq$, $\geq$, and $\neq$.

   Inequality can be shown graphically on a number line.

   Calculators and computers can be used to create histograms.

   Units of physical quantities can be changed using fractional equivalents.

   Statistical models can be used to show how data are distributed.

   Geometric models can be used to explore properties of objects.

2. **Figure 1.110** shows a portion of a carpenter's square, with the numbers representing inches. What is the precision of the square?

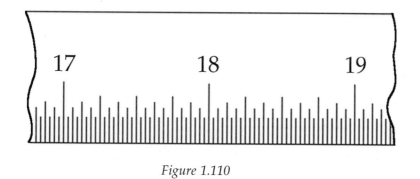

Figure 1.110

2. $\dfrac{1}{32}$ in (smallest division on the scale)

3. Consider the measurement 216.34 m. What is the precision of the measurement? Write the measurement with an appropriate indication of accuracy.

3. 0.01 m; 216.34 m ± 0.005 m

4. A rectangle has dimensions of 78.4 cm and 46.5 cm.

   a) Find the perimeter of the rectangle.

4. a) $P = 2l + 2w = 2(78.4 \text{ cm}) + 2(46.5 \text{ cm}) = 249.8$ cm.

   b) Find the length of a diagonal of the rectangle.

b) $d = \sqrt{(78.4 \text{ cm})^2 + (46.5 \text{ cm})^2} = 91.1526... \approx 91.2$ cm.

5. Find the perimeter of the polygon in **Figure 1.111.**

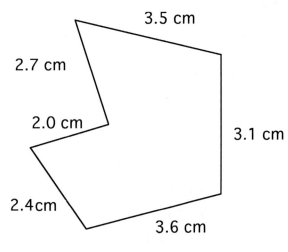

Figure 1.111

5. $P = 3.5 + 3.1 + 3.6 + 2.4 + 2.0 + 2.7 = 17.3$ cm.

6. Find the circumference of a nickel that is 2.1 cm in diameter.

6. $C = \pi d = \pi(2.1) = 6.5973... \approx 6.6$ cm.

7. For (a)–(d), express the following lengths as indicated.

   a) 2.53 feet as yards

7. a) $2.53 \text{ ft}\left(\dfrac{1 \text{ yd}}{3 \text{ ft}}\right) = 0.8433... \approx 0.843$ yd.

   b) 1.06 miles as feet

b) $1.06 \text{ mi}\left(\dfrac{5280 \text{ ft}}{1 \text{ mi}}\right) = 5596.8 \approx 5600$ ft.

   c) 45.8 kilometers as meters

c) $45.8 \text{ km}\left(\dfrac{1000 \text{ m}}{1 \text{ km}}\right) = 45{,}800$ m.

d) 723.8 centimeters as meters

d) $723.8 \text{ cm} \left(\dfrac{1 \text{ m}}{100 \text{ cm}} \right) = 7.238 \text{ m.}$

8. Find the perimeter of the rectangle in **Figure 1.112.**

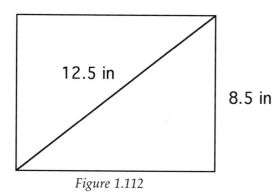

12.5 in

8.5 in

Figure 1.112

8. **Find the missing side of the rectangle:** $\sqrt{(12.5)^2 - (8.5)^2} = 9.1651... \approx 9.2$ **in.**
   $P = 8.5 + 9.2 + 8.5 + 9.2 = 35.4$ **in.**

9. The following data are masses (in kg) of logs from a log decomposition study of black locust trees:

   | 1.3724 | 1.3910 | 1.3046 | 1.2938 | 1.3059 | 1.3307 |

   a) What would be the best value to report for the sample mean for the data?

9. **a) Computation yields 1.3330666... kg, but since significant variation occurs in the hundredths place, round to that place: 1.33 kg.**

   b) What is the range of the data?

   b) (largest value – smallest value) = (1.3910 – 1.2938) = 0.0972 kg.

10. Find the mean, median, and mode of the following set of measurements of the pH of a lake:

    | 6.7 | 7.0 | 7.1 | 6.7 | 6.8 | 6.9 | 7.2 | 6.8 | 7.4 | 6.9 | 6.7 | 6.6 | 6.8 |

10. **The mean is** $\left(\dfrac{\Sigma x_i}{n} \right) = \left(\dfrac{89.6}{13} \right) = 6.8923 \approx 6.9$**. The median is the middle value of the data set when sorted in numerical order, or 6.8. There are two modes, 6.7 and 6.8, since both values appear three times, more than any other.**

11. The blood serum cholesterol levels (in mg/dl) of 50 patients in a hospital study are summarized in **Table 1.28.** Construct a well-labeled frequency histogram of these data.

Cholesterol Level (mg/dl)	Number of Patients
80–under 85	2
85–under 90	1
90–under 95	4
95–under 100	6
100–under 105	7
105–under 110	9
110–under 115	8
115–under 120	6
120–under 125	4
125–under 130	3

Table 1.28

11. Sample graph:

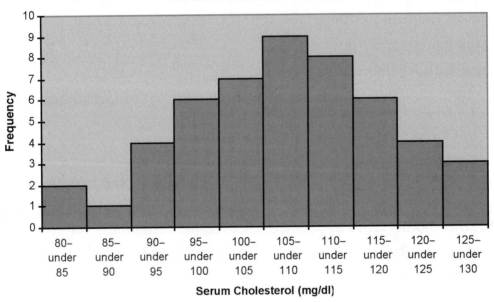

12. Use inequality notation to express the following relationships:

a) In a fiber optic cable, the core light-carrying medium is surrounded by a second material called the *cladding*. The index of refraction of the core (n_{core}) must be greater than the index of refraction of the cladding ($n_{cladding}$).

12. a) $n_{core} > n_{cladding}$.

b) Environmental regulations pertaining to trichloroethylene (TCE), a common industrial solvent, require that its concentration C in the soil be no more than 450 parts per billion.

b) $C \leq 450$ **ppb.**

13. Represent the inequality $-2 \leq x < 5$ on a number line.

13.

14. Find the perimeter and area of the trapezoid in **Figure 1.113.**

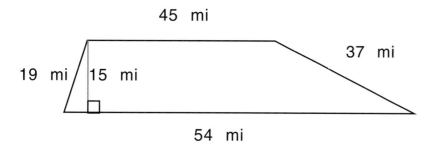

Figure 1.113

14. $P = 45 + 37 + 54 + 19 = 155$ **mi;** $A = \dfrac{1}{2}(45 + 54)(15) = 742.5 \approx 740$ **mi²**.

15. Find the area of the template in **Figure 1.114,** which is formed by removing a quarter circle from an isosceles triangle.

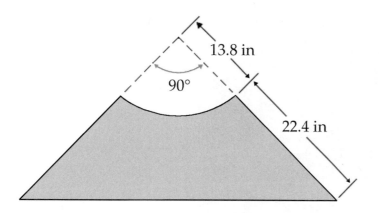

Figure 1.114

15. (Area of triangle) − (Area of quarter circle) = $(1/2)bh - (1/4)\pi r^2 =$ **(1/2)(36.2 in)(36.2 in) − (1/4)(π)(13.8 in)² = 505.648... ≈ 506 in².**

16. Find the area of the nickel in Exercise 6.

16. $A = \dfrac{\pi d^2}{4} = \dfrac{\pi(2.1)^2}{4} = 3.4636... \approx 3.5 \text{ cm}^2.$

17. For identical carpeting, which is the best buy: $21.00 per square yard or $6.00 per square foot? Explain your answer.

17. **The best buy is $21 per square yard. Since there are 9 square feet in 1 square yard, the $6 per square foot carpeting would cost $54 per square yard.**

18. Change 72 in² to ft².

18. $72 \text{ in}^2\left(\dfrac{1 \text{ ft}}{12 \text{ in}}\right)^2 = 0.5 \text{ ft}^2.$

19. Eastern Oregon is home to the world's largest living organism. This fungus known as the honey mushroom covers 2200 acres of forest and has been growing for an estimated 2400 years. How many square feet of forest does the organism cover?

19. $2200 \text{ acres}\left(\dfrac{43,560 \text{ ft}^2}{1 \text{ acre}}\right) = 95,832,000 \approx 96,000,000 \text{ ft}^2.$

20. The Vehicle Assembly Building at Kennedy Space Center in Florida (**Figure 1.115**) is one of the largest buildings in the world. The High Bay area of the building is used for the assembly of the Space Shuttle vehicle. It is approximately 160 meters long, 110 meters wide, and 160 meters high.

a) Find the volume of the High Bay area.

Photo courtesy NASA

Figure 1.115

20. a) $V = lwh = (160 \text{ m})(110 \text{ m})(160 \text{ m}) = 2,816,000 \approx 2,800,000 \text{ m}^3.$

b) Find the surface area of the building.

b) $SA = 2(110)(160) + 2(110)(160) + 2(160)(160) = 121,600 \approx 120,000 \text{ m}^2.$

21. The average official baseball is 2.9 inches in diameter.

a) How much material does it take to cover the ball?

21. a) $SA = 4\pi(1.45)^2 = 26.4207... \approx 26$ in^2.

b) How much material does it take to fill the ball?

b) $V = \dfrac{4}{3}\pi(1.5)^3 = 12.7700... \approx 13$ in^3.

22. 14.0 ft^3 is how many in^3?

22. $14.0 \text{ ft}^3\left(\dfrac{12 \text{ in}}{1 \text{ ft}}\right)^3 = 24{,}192 \approx 24{,}200$ in^3.

23. Find the volume of the metal casting in **Figure 1.116**.

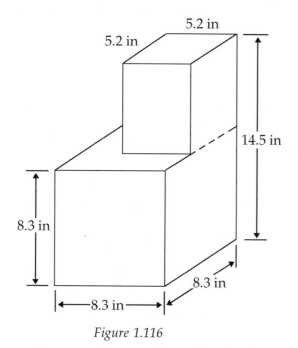

Figure 1.116

23. The figure can be broken up into a cube with edges = 8.3 inches and a rectangular solid with length and width of 5.2 inches and height of 6.2 inches. The total volume = volume of cube + volume of rectangular solid.

$V = e^3 + lwh$
  $= (8.3)^3 + (5.2)(5.2)(6.2)$
  $= 571.8 + 167.6$
  $= 739.4 \approx 740$ in^3.

24. The Ted Williams Tunnel under Boston Harbor consists of two steel tubes encased in concrete. Each tube is 3850 feet long, with an outside diameter of 37.5 feet, and the inside walls are lined with 14 inches of concrete.

a) Find the lateral surface area of the inside of one of the tubes.

24. a) Diameter of inner surface is (37 ft 6 in − 28 in) = 35 ft 2 in ≈ 35.17 ft. Lateral surface area = πdh = $\pi(35.17)(3850) \approx 425{,}000$ ft^2.

b) If 60% of the inner surface of each tunnel tube is tiled with 5-inch-square ceramic tiles, how many tiles are needed for the two tunnels?

b) Total tiled surface area is
S = (number of tubes)(inside lateral area)(% covered) =
(2)(425,000)(0.60) ≈ 510,000 ft². Area of a 5-in tile is 25 in² = 0.1736 ft².

Number of tiles needed is $\left(\dfrac{510{,}000 \text{ ft}^2}{0.1736 \text{ ft}^2}\right)$ **≈ 2,900,000 tiles.**

c) What assumptions did you make to arrive at your answer?

c) The difference between the curved side of the tunnel and the 5-in length of a tile is negligible. The grout space between tiles is ignored.

25. As we have seen, words like *size, amount,* and *capacity* can refer to different types of quantities, depending on the context, and correctly interpreting them may be essential in finding an appropriate solution to a problem. In the following examples, flow rates are referred to. Identify the quantities that are measured by the stated rates.

a) In whitewater rapids, water may flow at a rate of as much as 3000 ft³/min.

25. a) A ft³ is a measure of volume, so this is a flow rate of volume with respect to time.

b) The same whitewater flow may be described as 90 tons/s.

b) A ton is a weight measure, so this is a weight with respect to time rate.

26. Compact disks in computer CD-ROM drives can spin as fast as 12,000 revolutions per minute (rpm). At such speeds, vibrations of the outer edge can prevent the drive from functioning at its theoretical maximum data acquisition rate. At 12,000 rpm, how fast is a point on the edge of a $4\frac{5}{8}$-inch-diameter disk moving (measured in inches per second)?

26. The circumference of the disk is πd = π(4.625 in) ≈ 14.5 in, which is the distance through which a point on the edge of the disk moves in one
revolution. The speed is $\left(\dfrac{12{,}000 \text{ rev}}{1 \text{ min}}\right)\left(\dfrac{14.5 \text{ in}}{1 \text{ rev}}\right)\left(\dfrac{1 \text{ min}}{60 \text{ s}}\right)$ **≈ 2900 in/s.**

27. The sun travels through its galaxy, the Milky Way, in a curved path at a speed of 486,000 miles per hour. What distance does the sun travel through in a year?

27. $\left(\dfrac{486{,}000 \text{ mi}}{1 \text{ hr}}\right)\left(\dfrac{24 \text{ hr}}{1 \text{ day}}\right)\left(\dfrac{365 \text{ days}}{1 \text{ yr}}\right)$ **= 4,257,360,000 ≈ 4.26 billion mi in one year.**

28. Your answer to Exercise 27 is an actual distance of travel. A related quantity is the displacement of the sun from the beginning to the end of the year.

a) Since displacement is a vector quantity, what other information besides distance would have to be known in order to state the displacement of the sun?

28. a) The direction from initial position to final position of the sun.

b) The displacement vector would include a distance value as part of its description, but the distance would be *less* than the one calculated in Exercise 27. Why?

b) The distance in Exercise 26 is traveled along a curve. The distance between starting and ending positions would be a straight-line distance.

29. One formula for computing the side (or lateral) surface area of a cylinder is $S = 2\pi rh$, where r is the radius and h the height of the cylinder. If the surface area of an actual cylinder is computed, which of the numerical values in the formula would be exact, and which would be approximate?

29. The r and h values would be measured and therefore could only be known approximately. The 2 and the π are exact numbers and would not contribute to any inaccuracy in the result.

Chapter 2—Linear Models

Goals of the Chapter

- To model linear relationships using expressions, equations, graphs, and tables
- To recognize linear behavior and represent it mathematically
- To evaluate mathematical expressions
- To solve linear equations

Preparation Reading

In Chapter 1 we examined several mathematical methods for treating measured data and for describing characteristics of physical quantities. We created several types of mathematical models to describe real situations. Our models took on a variety of forms such as equations, graphs, tables, arrow diagrams, and verbal and geometric models. They allowed us to find out information about real objects or situations without complicated or costly real-life testing. This is one of the main reasons for modeling.

There are many kinds of situations for which it is impossible or inconvenient to measure some quantity directly. For example, many people want to monitor their body fat percentage for health and fitness reasons. But this percentage cannot be measured directly very easily. Fortunately, body fat content affects the skin's ability to conduct electricity. Inexpensive testers that take advantage of this fact are available. They measure the electrical resistance of the skin and use the mathematical relationship between resistance and body fat percentage to display the desired result.

Consider another situation in which the number of sheets of paper in a very large stack is needed. It might be very time-consuming to count each page. If we knew the relationship between the weight of a stack and the number of sheets it contains, we could calculate the number of sheets in the stack by weighing it.

In this chapter we will begin to explore in detail the construction of mathematical models that connect two or more quantities by observing patterns in their values. One of the most common types is called a *linear model* because of the shape of its graph. Later chapters will introduce other types of models, most of which are referred to as *nonlinear models*.

Reflect and Discuss

Identify some situations in which mathematical models might be useful. In other words, what are some pairs (or larger groups) of measurable quantities that are somehow related to each other in a sense that if you knew the value of one quantity, it might help you determine the value of another?

There are many possibilities, including geometrical relationships (e.g., finding area of a circle from diameter), physical relationships (e.g., finding electrical power from voltage), monetary relationships (e.g., calculating cost based on time and resources used), and forecasting (e.g., predicting future demand for a product from past trends).

Section 2.1 Measuring Indirectly

What You Need to Know

- How to use a pan balance

What You Will learn

- To evaluate simple expressions

Materials

- 10 tenpenny nails
- Pan balance with 0.1-gram precision
- Small box

People who work in pharmaceuticals and biotechnology often use very small samples of liquid solutions in their research. Sometimes the liquid must be poured into tiny wells with volumes of only a few drops. The liquid, which may contain a solution of an enzyme or DNA or some other substance, can then undergo chemical testing.

The Zymark Corporation in Hopkinton, Massachusetts, is a world leader in the design, development, and manufacture of laboratory automation equipment for the life sciences industry.

Zymark's SciClone Advanced Liquid Handling Workstation (**Figure 2.1**) allows hundreds of tiny plates to be filled with liquid solutions automatically. It is used for nucleic acid preparations for genome research and drug discovery applications.

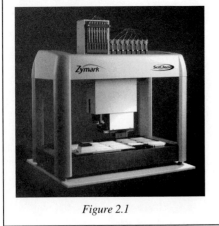

Figure 2.1

It is difficult to design a machine that can measure such small volumes accurately. But there are robotic systems that can measure the weights of small liquid samples instead of their volumes. Then the weights are converted automatically to volume values. In designing such a system, it is necessary to know how the volume and weight of a liquid sample are related. We will examine such relationships throughout this chapter and return to this particular one in Section 2.5.

There are many workplace situations for which the value of some quantity must be determined, but it is easier to measure a second related quantity. We can begin exploring such relationships with a simpler example.

A carpenter or a roofer might have to carry a box of nails from a parts trailer to the work site. Instead of counting individual nails, the nails could be weighed in the box to determine their number. In the following activity, you will find a mathematical relationship between the weight of a box and the number of nails it contains.

Activity 2.1 Predicting Weight *(SE pages 117–118)*

How heavy is a box of nails?

Finding an answer to this question requires that you carefully examine exactly what is being asked. Different interpretations of the question might result in widely differing answers.

1. List some things that you would need to know before you can find the weight of a box of nails.

1. **Sample answers: What kind of nails are in the box? How many nails are in the box? How heavy is the box itself? How is heaviness measured? (Note that both mass and weight are measures of heaviness and that the measuring device used determines which is being measured.)**

2. Use a balance to determine the weight of one tenpenny (10d) nail. Measure as accurately as possible.

2. **Sample answer: 7.3 grams**

3. Place two 10d nails on the balance, and determine their total weight.

3. **Sample answer: 14.5 grams**

4. In a similar manner, determine the total weights of 3, 4, 5, 6, up to 10 identical nails, and list all of the weights in a table such as **Table 2.1.**

Number of Nails	Total Weight of Nails (g)
1	
2	
3, etc.	

Table 2.1

> **Weight and Mass**
>
> The weight of an object is equal to the force that the Earth's gravity exerts on the object. Mass refers to the quantity of matter contained in the object. Therefore, whereas an object's mass is constant everywhere, its weight can vary depending on its location. An object weighs slightly less in Mexico City than it does in Los Angeles because Mexico City is farther from the center of the Earth. On the moon, it would weigh only a fraction of its Earth weight, but its mass would be unchanged.
>
> When measurements are made at the surface of the Earth, either mass or weight can be used for comparing heaviness. When using U.S. Customary units, weight in pounds or ounces is typically used for such comparisons. When metric units are used, mass comparisons in kilograms or grams are more common. The distinction between the two is important for some science and engineering applications. But here we will use the common practice of referring to an object's weight in grams, even though the quantity being measured is more properly called *mass*.

4. **Sample answer:**

Number of Nails	Total Weight of Nails (g)
1	7.3
2	14.5
3	21.9
4	28.2
5	36.6
6	43.8
7	51.1
8	58.3
9	65.6
10	72.8

5. Describe any patterns that you see in the second column of your table.

5. **Sample answers: Each weight is almost an exact multiple of the weight of one nail; the differences between any two adjacent weights are constant.**

6. Based on the table, what do you expect would be the approximate weight of 14 tenpenny nails, of 27 tenpenny nails, of 135 tenpenny nails, and of n tenpenny nails?

6. **Sample answer: 14 nails would weigh 14(7.3 g) = 102.2 g; 27 nails would weigh 27(7.3 g) = 197.1 g; 135 nails would weigh 135(7.3 g) = 985.5 g; n nails would weigh n(7.3 g) = 7.3n grams.**

In item 6 you used the variable n to represent the number of nails being weighed. Your answer for the weight of n tenpenny nails is called an **algebraic expression**. An algebraic expression can contain one or more variables, numbers, operation symbols, and grouping symbols. For example, $3t + 6$, $4x - 3y$, and $6(2L + 2W)$ are algebraic expressions.

If you replace the variables in an expression with their numerical values, we say that you are **evaluating the expression.** For instance, the expression $4s$ can be used to represent the perimeter of a square if s represents the length of one side. To evaluate $4s$ when $s = 5$, substitute 5 for s in the expression $4s$ and then simplify. The value of the expression in this case is $4(5) = 20$. The perimeter of the square is 20 inches.

Your expression for the weight of n tenpenny nails can be used as an algebraic model for the weight of the nails. This means that it can be used to predict the weight of any number of nails, even if you haven't weighed them.

7. Evaluate your expression from item 6 to find the weight of 20, 25, 30, 50, and 100 nails. List the number of nails and predicted weights in a two-column table.

7. **Sample answer:**

Number of Nails	Predicted Weight of Nails (g)
20	7.3(20) = 146
25	7.3(25) = 182.5
30	7.3(30) = 219
50	7.3(50) = 365
100	7.3(100) = 730

8. Up to this point you have weighed only the nails on the balance. Now place the box that contained the nails on the balance and weigh it by itself. Add a third column to your table from item 7. Label it "Predicted Weight of Box Plus Nails (g)." Complete the table by adding the weight of the box to each predicted weight of nails in the second column.

8. **Sample answer: The box weighs 132 grams.**

Number of Nails	Predicted Weight of Nails (g)	Predicted Weight of Box Plus Nails (g)
20	146	278
25	182.5	314.5
30	219	351
50	365	497
100	730	862

9. Write an expression that models the total weight of the box when it contains n nails.

9. **Sample answer: 7.3n + 132**

10. Evaluate your expression from item 9 to find the weight of the box when it contains 150, 200, and 300 nails.

10. Sample answer: When $n = 150$, weight of box and nails is 7.3(150) + 132 = 1227 g.

When $n = 200$, weight of box and nails is 7.3(200) + 132 = 1592 g.

When $n = 300$, weight of box and nails is 7.3(300) + 132 = 2322 g.

Extend the Activity (SE page 119)

11. When a carpenter frames a wall, he or she usually uses more than one size nail. Measure the weights of different quantities of another size nail than the ones you used in the activity and list them in a table. Then write an expression for the total weight of a box containing any number m of these nails.

11. Sample answer: For 8d nails:

Number of Nails	Actual Total Weight of Nails
1	4.9
2	9.9
3	14.8
4	19.7
5	24.8
6	29.7
7	34.6
8	39.4
9	44.3
10	49.2

Each 8d nail weighs about 4.9 g. Using the same box as before, the total weight of box and any number m of 8d nails is 4.9m + 132.

12. Consider the same box with a mixture of the two types of nails in it. Write an expression that models the total weight of the box if the numbers of the two types of nails in the box are represented by m and n.

12. Sample answer: 4.9m + 7.3n + 132

13. Measure the weights of a penny, nickel, dime, and quarter. Then write an expression that models the total weight (in grams) of a sack that weighs 300 grams and that contains p pennies, n nickels, d dimes, and q quarters.

13. Sample answer: Weight of one penny = 2.5 g, weight of one nickel = 3.7 g, weight of one dime = 1.8 g, weight of one quarter = 8.5 g. Total weight of sack and coins is $300 + 2.5p + 3.7n + 1.8d + 8.5q$.

14. The algebraic expressions you have written are mathematical models for the weights of various quantities of nails. What simplifying assumptions have been made in order to develop these models?

14. All nails or coins of a certain type have been assumed to have the same weight.

Section 2.2 Exploring Algebraic Expressions

What You Need to Know

- How to find the area of a rectangle
- How to evaluate simple expressions

What You Will Learn

- To use the distributive property
- To use the order of operations rules when evaluating expressions
- To use a calculator and/or spreadsheet to evaluate expressions
- To model real-world situations with algebraic expressions

Materials

- None

Constructing and Evaluating Expressions

In Section 2.1 we were able to determine the weight of a box of nails indirectly by counting the nails. To do this, we used a variable to represent the number of nails. Then using the chosen variable, we created an algebraic expression to represent the weight of the nails. Situations such as this one are encountered frequently in the workplace where the worker must call upon his or her mathematical knowledge to solve real-world problems.

Discovery 2.1 Using Expressions to Determine Length
(SE pages 120–122)

A fiber-optic cable company is laying cable in an area where new housing construction is about to begin. **Figure 2.2** shows partial plans for the housing development. The company itself is responsible for the cable along the street and for an as-yet-to-be-determined amount of cable extended into each lot. The owner of the lot is responsible for the remaining portion of the cable needed to "hook up" the house. Assume that each lot is rectangular in shape and has a street frontage of 80 feet.

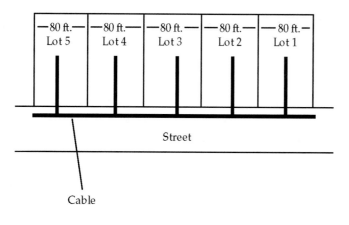

Figure 2.2

1. For the five lots shown in Figure 2.2, how much cable will be needed if the company plans to extend the cable 12 feet into each lot? How much is needed if the cable extends 15 feet, 18 feet, and 25 feet?

1. 5(80) + 5(12) = 460 feet; 5(80) + 5(15) = 475 feet; 5(80) + 5(18) = 490 feet; 5(80) + 5(25) = 525 feet.

2. Write an expression for the total length of cable used to wire the five lots if the cable extends *l* feet into each lot.

2. 400 + 5*l*

3. Assume that the company decides to extend the cable 12 feet into each lot. What is the cost of wiring the five lots if the cost of laying cable is $10 per foot? What is the cost of wiring if the cost is $8 per foot, $15 per foot, and $20 per foot?

3. 460(10) = $4600; 460(8) = $3680; 460(15) = $6900; 460(20) = $9200.

4. Write an expression for the cost of extending the cable 12 feet into each lot if the cost per foot is *c* dollars.

4. 460*c* dollars

5. Suppose the plans in Figure 2.2 are expanded so that several additional lots of the same size are added. How much cable is needed for six lots if the cable extends 10 feet into each lot? Show two different ways to determine the total amount of cable.

5. 6(80 + 10) = 6(90) = 540 feet, or 6(80) + 6(10) = 480 + 60 = 540 feet. Add the 80 + 10 to find the amount of cable in each lot, then multiply by 6 to find the total for the six lots. Or determine the total amount in the street first, 6(80), find the amount in the six lots, 6(10), and then add the two products.

6. To show the total amount of cable for six lots if the cable extends *l* feet into each lot, two different expressions can be used: $6(80) + 6l$ and $6(80 + l)$. Both expressions express the correct total amount of cable. Explain the thinking behind each of these expressions.

6. **For $6(80) + 6l$: The total amount of cable in the street, $6(80)$, is indicated, then the total amount extending into each lot, $6l$, is added. For $6(80 + l)$: The amount of cable for each lot $(80 + l)$ is indicated and then multiplied by 6 to find the total for the six lots.**

7. Write two different expressions that give the total amount of cable needed for *n* lots if the cable extends *l* feet into each lot.

7. **$80n + nl$ or $n(80 + l)$**

8. Use either of your expressions from item 7 to complete **Table 2.2.**

Number of Lots	Length of Cable Extending into Each Lot (ft)	Total Amount of Cable (ft)
5	10	
5	12	
6	10	
6	12	
20	10	
20	12	

Table 2.2

8.

Number of Lots	Length of Cable Extending into Each Lot (ft)	Total Amount of Cable (ft)
5	10	450
5	12	460
6	10	540
6	12	552
20	10	1800
20	12	1840

The Distributive Property (Algebraic Representation)

In item 6 of Discovery 2.1, we found that the total amount of cable for six lots could be written either as $6(80 + l)$ or as $6(80) + 6l$ and that both algebraic expressions could be justified in the context of the discovery exercise. This indicates that these two expressions must be equivalent; that is, $6(80 + l) = 6(80) + 6l$.

The property that confirms that these two expressions are equivalent is known as the **distributive property of multiplication over addition** or, simply, the **distributive property.** This property is one of the most important, most used properties in algebra.

The Distributive Property

For all numbers a, b, and c, $a(b + c) = ab + ac$.

The distributive property can be extended so that factors can be distributed over subtraction. For example, $a(b - c) = ab - ac$.

Example 1
Use the distributive property to write each expression without parentheses.

a) $3(a + 10)$

b) $4(x - 7)$

c) $-5(8 - 4t)$

d) $2(4y - 7) + 18$

e) $(2m - 1)3$

Solution:

a) $3(a + 10) = 3a + 30$

b) $4(x - 7) = 4x - 28$

c) $-5(8 - 4t) = -5(8) - (-5)(4t)$ Note: Care must be taken when the factor is negative. Both terms must be multiplied by the -5.

$= -40 + 20t$

d) $2(4y - 7) + 18 = 8y - 14 + 18$

$= 8y + 4$

e) $(2m - 1)3 = 6m - 3$

The Distributive Property (Geometric Representation)

The distributive property can be represented in more than one way. Algebraically, we know that $a(b + c) = ab + ac$. To visualize this property geometrically, look carefully at the **area models** in **Figures 2.3a** and **2.3b.**

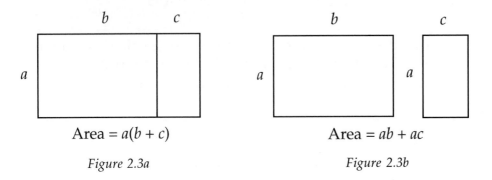

$$\text{Area} = a(b + c)$$

Figure 2.3a

$$\text{Area} = ab + ac$$

Figure 2.3b

Since both representations produce the same total area, we can once again conclude that $a(b + c) = ab + ac$.

Expressions and Order of Operations

In Chapter 1, when an arithmetic expression contained several operations, we made decisions about which operation to perform first by following the order of operations guidelines. These same guidelines must be followed when we evaluate algebraic expressions.

Example 2

Evaluate the expression $2n + 30 + n^2 - 1$ when $n = 5$.

Solution:

$2n + 30 + n^2 - 1 = 2(5) + 30 + (5)^2 - 1$	Substitute 5 for n.
$= 2(5) + 30 + 25 - 1$	Raise numbers to powers.
$= 10 + 30 + 25 - 1$	Multiply.
$= 64$	Add and subtract from left to right.

Example 3

Evaluate the expression $(t + 31) - (t)^2 + (4 - t)$ when $t = 2$.

Solution:

$(t + 31) - t^2 + (4 - t) = (2 + 31) - 2^2 + (4 - 2)$	Substitute 2 for t.
$= (33) - 2^2 + 2$	Perform operations within the ( ) first.
$= 33 - 4 + 2$	Raise numbers to powers.
$= 31$	Add and subtract from left to right.

Using Technology to Evaluate Algebraic Expressions

Most graphing calculators have multiple ways of evaluating expressions. In this section we will explore two specific methods. For example, suppose we want to evaluate the expression $3x^2 + 4(x - 15)$ when $x = 2$.

One way to use the calculator to do this evaluation is to use the variable x and the store key. Store 2 in x and then type in the expression $3x^2 + 4(x - 15)$. The calculator will return the value of the expression when $x = 2$. (See **Figure 2.4**.)

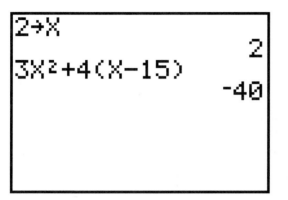

Figure 2.4

Another method that can be used to evaluate an expression for several different values is to set up and display a table. **Figure 2.5** shows how the expression is entered into the function editor, and **Figure 2.6** shows how the table is set up. **Figure 2.7** displays the resulting table.

Figure 2.5   *Figure 2.6*   *Figure 2.7*

Note that when the table is set up, the user must specify the initial value for x and the increment (or change) in x. From the table in Figure 2.7 we can find the value of $3x^2 + 4(x - 15)$ when $x = 2$, as well as the value of the expression when $x = 0, 1, 3, 4, 5,$ and 6. For example, when $x = 5$, the value of $3x^2 + 4(x - 15)$ is 35. By scrolling up or down, additional values can be determined.

Figures 2.8–2.10 show the same expression but a different table setup.

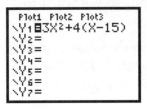

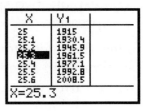

Figure 2.8   *Figure 2.9*   *Figure 2.10*

The table in Figure 2.10 indicates that the value of $3x^2 + 4(x - 15)$ when $x = 25.3$ is 1961.5.

Spreadsheets can also be used to evaluate expressions. **Figure 2.11** shows a sample spreadsheet with the value of the variable (5.1) in the cell A2 and the value of the expression (30.98) in cell B2. Notice the expression in the formula bar at the top of the spreadsheet.

| B2 | ▼ | = | =3.8*A2+4*(8-A2) |

Workbook

	A	B	C	D
1	Value of the variable	Value of the expression		
2	5.1	30.98		
3				
4				

Figure 2.11

Individual cells of spreadsheets are named by the column label (a letter) followed by the row number. For example, in Figure 2.11, cell B1 is in column B, row 1 and contains the words "Value of the expression."

Cells in spreadsheets, such as cell A2, can contain values. They can also contain algebraic formulas. Note that the cell B2 is highlighted. The formula bar at the top of the spreadsheet shows that cell B2 contains the formula 3.8*A2+4*(8 – A2), which is spreadsheet notation for the expression $3.8x + 4(8 - x)$. The A2 in the formula acts as a variable. To evaluate the expression 3.8*A2+4*(8 – A2), the spreadsheet looks up the value in cell A2 and makes the proper calculations. The value of the expression (30.98) appears in the cell.

Changing the value in cell A2 does not change the formula in cell B2, but it will change the value of the expression that appears in cell B2.

Exercises 2.2 *(SE pages 126–129)*

I. Investigations

1. According to the American Dietetic Association (ADA), the public should consume adequate amounts of dietary fiber as part of a healthy, balanced diet. Recommendations for adults generally fall in the range of 20–35 grams of fiber per day. Suppose a diet advertises that it is high in fiber and recommends four slices of bread, one bowl of cereal, and three servings of fruit daily.

   a) How many grams of fiber does this diet recommend per day if one slice of bread contains 2 g of fiber, each bowl of cereal contains 5 g of fiber, and each serving of fruit contains 3.5 g of fiber? Does this diet meet the fiber recommendations for adults?

1. **a)** $4(2) + 1(5) + 3(3.5) = 23.5$ **grams of fiber; yes, it falls within the recommendations.**

   b) Write an expression for the total daily amount of fiber in this diet if b represents the number of grams of fiber in a slice of bread, c represents the number of grams of fiber in a bowl of cereal, and f represents the number of grams of fiber in a serving of fruit.

   b) $4b + c + 3f$

   c) Write two different expressions for a week's total amount of fiber. Write one with parentheses and one without parentheses.

   c) $7(4b + c + 3f)$ **and** $28b + 7c + 21f$

   d) Suppose that in addition to the fiber in the bread, cereal, and fruit, a person following the diet consumes 3.7 g of fiber each day from a fiber supplement. Write an expression for a week's consumption. Use the distributive property to rewrite your expression without parentheses.

   d) $7(4b + c + 3f + 3.7) = 28b + 7c + 21f + 25.9$.

2. In order to furnish an existing office, the office manager has been given a budget of $2500. The office needs three bookcases, two file cabinets, one desk, and three chairs. It also has 20 square yards of floor space that need to be carpeted. And in addition to these major items, $500 needs to be spent on office supplies.

   a) Suppose a bookcase costs $100, file cabinets cost $200 each, an adequate desk is $600, chairs are $120 each, and carpeting costs $30 per square yard. Including the $500 for supplies, how much will it cost to furnish the office? Is this within the budget?

2. **a)** $3(100) + 2(200) + 1(600) + 3(120) + 20(30) + 500 = \$2760$. **This is not within the budget.**

b) Write an expression for the cost of furnishing the office if b is the cost of a bookcase, f is the cost of a file cabinet, d is the cost of a desk, c is the cost of a chair, and y is the cost per square yard for carpeting.

b) $3b + 2f + d + 3c + 20y + 500$

c) Write two different expressions for the total cost of furnishing six offices with the same furnishings. Evaluate both expressions using $b = 100$, $f = 150$, $d = 300$, $c = 150$, and $y = 25$. Are the results the same in both cases? Why or why not?

c) $6(3b + 2f + d + 3c + 20y + 500)$ and $18b + 12f + 6d + 18c + 120y + 3000$. Total cost is \$14,100 using either expression, since the expressions are equivalent.

3. Assume brewed tea has 45 mg of caffeine per 8-oz cup, caffeinated soft drinks have 55 mg per 12-oz can, and chocolate contains 10 mg of caffeine per bar.

a) Calculate the amount of caffeine consumed by a person having one 8-oz cup of tea, two 12-oz cans of soft drinks, and three bars of chocolate.

3. a) $1(45) + 2(55) + 3(10)$ mg of caffeine

b) Suppose a person consumes s 12-oz cans of sodas, b bars of chocolate, and t 8-oz cups of tea. Write an expression for the amount of caffeine consumed.

b) $55s + 10b + 45t$

c) Find a combination of tea, soda, and chocolate that results in 175 mg of caffeine.

c) One combination is 2 cups of tea, 1 soda, and 3 chocolate bars.

4. Walking at a moderate pace of about 3 miles per hour, an average person burns about 3.7 calories per minute.

a) About how many calories would a person burn when walking at a pace of about 3 miles per hour for 20 minutes, for 30 minutes, and for 90 minutes?

4. a) 74, 111, and 333 calories

b) Write an expression for the number of calories this person burns during the walk if w represents the number of minutes a person walks in one day.

b) $3.7w$

c) Use the expression from (b) to complete **Table 2.3.**

Time Walking (minutes)	Energy Expended (calories)
10	
20	
30	
40	

Table 2.3

c)

Time Walking (minutes)	Energy Expended (calories)
10	37
20	74
30	111
40	148

d) An average person burns about 2500 calories per day doing normal activities. Write an expression for the total number of calories burned per day if a person walks w minutes at a 3-miles-per-hour pace and completes all of his or her normal activities.

d) **3.7w + 2500 calories**

e) Write an expression for the number of calories this person burns in one week. Use the distributive property to rewrite the expression without parentheses.

e) **7(3.7w + 2500) or 25.9w + 17,500**

f) Suppose a person walks only three days per week. Write two different expressions for the total number of calories burned in a week if normal activities are performed on a daily basis.

f) **Sample answers: 3(3.7x + 2500) + 4(2500) or 3(3.7x) + 7(2500)**

5. Land developers often purchase large parcels of land, then subdivide the property into smaller plots for home builders. Suppose a developer buys a tract of land, divides it into eight smaller rectangular lots 100 feet wide, and constructs a road 30 feet wide between the houses. (See **Figure 2.12.**)

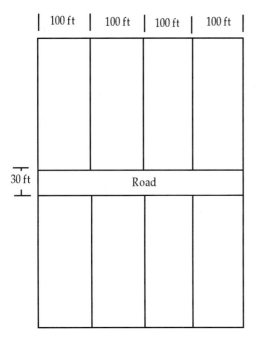

Figure 2.12

a) What is the area of the housing development including the road when the length of each lot is 150 feet?

5. **a) 8(100)(150) + 30(400) = 132,000 ft².**

b) What is the area including the road when the lots are 200 feet long?

b) 8(100)(200) + 30(400) = 172,000 ft².

c) Write an expression for the total area of the eight lots plus the area of the road if the length of each lot is l feet.

c) The expression is 8(100l) + 30(400) if adding lots and then road. It is 400(2l + 30) if considered as a large rectangle. Both expressions are equivalent to 800l + 12,000 when parentheses are removed.

d) Find the length of a lot that results in an area of 128,000 ft².

d) An area of 128,000 ft² occurs when the length of a lot is 145 ft.

6. Suppose the developer in Exercise 5 subdivides a new parcel of land into seven rectangular lots, each with a length of 120 feet. A 30-foot-wide road is constructed, as shown in **Figure 2.13.**

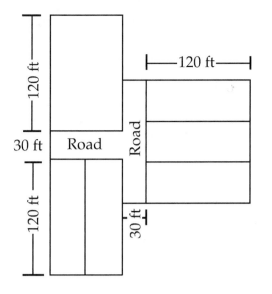

Figure 2.13

a) What is the total area of the development if the lots are 90 feet wide?

6. **a)** **7(90)(120) + 30(3)(90) + (30)(2)(90) = 89,100 ft².**

b) Write an expression that gives the total area of the housing development including the road if w represents the width of each lot.

b) **7(120)w + 30(5)w = 990w or 270(2w)+150(3w) if considered as two rectangles.**

II. Projects and Group Activities *(SE page 129)*

7. List a number of different physical activities you do during a week, such as walking, jogging, or climbing stairs. Use the Internet to find estimates for the number of calories you burn per minute for each of these activities. Develop an expression for the estimated number of calories you burn doing each of these activities in a week, using a variable for the number of minutes you do each activity. For example, you might use w for the estimated number of minutes you walk in a week and s for the number of minutes you spend climbing stairs. Use this expression to estimate how many more calories you would burn if you increased the time you do one of these activities by 30 minutes per week.

7. **The following Web sites may be helpful in finding information:**

   http://www.nutristrategy.com/activitylist.htm
   http://k2.kirtland.cc.mi.us/~balbachl/calorie.htm
   http://www.healthyideas.com/weight/bonfire

8. A computer or calculator is said to use *algebraic logic* if it evaluates expressions according to the order of operations rules.

   a) To test your calculator, enter the expression 5 + 3 · 8. What should be the value of the expression? What value did your calculator return? Does your calculator use algebraic logic?

8. a) A calculator with algebraic logic returns a value of 29. Without algebraic logic, the result is 64. Most scientific and graphing calculators use algebraic logic.

   b) Most calculators do use algebraic logic but not all of them. See if you can find a calculator that does not use it. Test the calculator in question by entering the expression from (a). If the calculator does the addition before the multiplication, it does not use algebraic logic. (Hint: Check inexpensive, 4-function calculators.)

III. Additional Practice (SE pages 129–132)

For 9–16, evaluate the algebraic expression.

9. $9a + 1$ when $a = -8$

9. –71

10. $3x - 4y$ when $x = 7$ and $y = 9$

10. –15

11. $15 - 4(2 + m)$ when $m = 1$

11. 3

12. $\dfrac{f}{3f - 2}$ when $f = 2$

12. $\dfrac{1}{2}$ or 0.5

13. $\dfrac{g}{4} + \dfrac{g}{8}$ when $g = 3$

13. $\dfrac{9}{8}$ or 1.125

14. $20 + (x - (3 + 2x))$ when $x = -5$

14. 22

15. $(2 + y) \div (y - 4)$ when $y = 1$

15. –1

16. $p + pr$ when $p = 7$ and $r = 3$

16. 28

17. A graphing calculator can be used to evaluate expressions that have more than one variable. For example, **Figure 2.14** shows the use of two variables a and b and the store key.

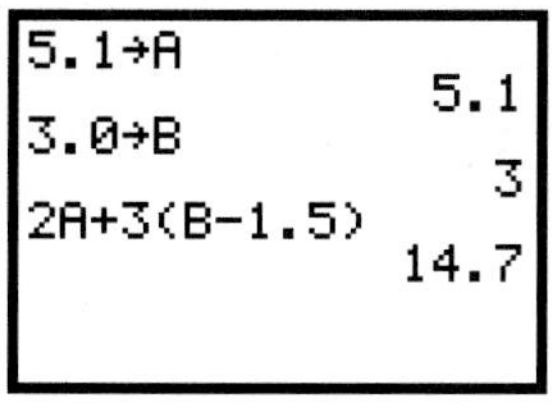

```
5.1→A
                5.1
3.0→B
                  3
2A+3(B-1.5)
             14.7
```

Figure 2.14

From the calculator screen, we see that when $a = 5.1$ and $b = 3.0$, the value of the expression $2a + 3(b - 1.5)$ is 14.7.

  a) Use a calculator or spreadsheet to evaluate $5a + 2ab - 4(a + b)$ when $a = 3.27$ and $b = 4.12$.

17. a) 13.7348

  b) Use a calculator or spreadsheet to evaluate $-3(m - n) + 4(3n - 4mn)$ when $m = -1.3$ and $n = 4.6$.

b) 168.58

18. The expression $0.866p$ can be used to determine the depth of a sharp V–thread bolt when the pitch p is known. Find the depth of the bolt when $p = 0.15$ inch.

18. $0.886(0.15) = 0.1329 \approx 0.13$ in.

19. The expression $\sqrt{30FS}$, where F is the coefficient of friction of the road and S is the skid length in feet, can be used to determine the speed of a car prior to an accident. Find the speed a car was traveling if it skidded 253 feet on a road with a coefficient of friction of 0.8.

19. $\sqrt{30(0.8)(253)} = 77.923... \approx 78$ mph.

20. The expression $P(1 + rt)$ represents the amount of money available on an investment after t years if P dollars were initially invested at a simple interest rate of r. If \$4300 is invested at a rate of 6%, find the amount of money available after three years.

20. $4300(1 + (.06)(3)) = \$5074.$

21. The size in horsepower of a motor required for a pumping system can be found using the following expression: $\dfrac{DH}{3960E}$, where D is the pump discharge rate in gallons per minute, H is the pressure head of the pump in feet, and E is the efficiency of the pump. Find the size motor required to pump 800 gallons per minute given a 150-foot head and a pump that is 60% efficient.

21. $\dfrac{(800)(150)}{(3960)(0.60)} = 50.5050... \approx 51$ **horsepower.**

For 22–27, write an algebraic expression for the given word phrase.

22. The sum of m and n

22. $m + n$

23. The product of 5, a, and b

23. $5ab$

24. 4 less than the product of x and y

24. $xy - 4$

25. 5 decreased by t

25. $5 - t$

26. The sum of twice a and twice b

26. $2a + 2b$

27. The quotient obtained when the sum of x and y is divided by 5

27. $\dfrac{x + y}{5}$ **or** $(x + y)/5$

28. A *rule of thumb* is a quick and easy tool for approximating a solution to a problem. For example, college students are often familiar with the rule of thumb that says two handwritten pages of text is equal to one typed page. For (a)–(d), consider the given rule of thumb statements.

a) People will eat one and a half times as many mashed potatoes as baked potatoes. If b represents the number of baked potatoes eaten by an individual, write an expression that represents the number of mashed potatoes that a person would eat.

28. a) $1.5b$ **mashed potatoes**

b) A hospital should have four and a half beds for every 1000 people in the community it serves. If p represents the number of people in the community, write an expression for the number of beds the hospital should have.

b) $4.5\left(\dfrac{p}{1000}\right)$ **or** $\dfrac{4.5p}{1000}$ **beds**

c) To estimate the outdoor temperature in degrees Fahrenheit, count the number of times a single cricket chirps in 15 seconds and add 37. Write an expression for the temperature if a cricket chirps c times in 15 seconds.

c) $c + 37°\text{F}$

d) You can tell how many miles you are from a lightning strike by counting the number of seconds between when you see the lightning and when you hear the thunder and dividing by five. If s is the number of seconds between the lightning and the thunder, write an expression for your distance from the strike.

d) $\dfrac{s}{5}$ miles

e) Freshly captured lobsters can be kept alive if they are fed one bushel of fish scraps per week per 1000 pounds of lobsters. If p is the number of pounds of lobsters captured, write an expression for the number of bushels of fish needed to feed 1000 pounds of lobsters each week.

e) $\dfrac{p}{1000}$ bushels

29. Insert parentheses in the following expression so that its value is 8:

$6 + 12 \div 2 + 4$

29. $6 + 12 \div (2 + 4)$

30. Insert parentheses in the following expression so that its value is 39:

$8 \cdot 3 + 2 - 1$

30. $8 \cdot (3 + 2) - 1$ or $8(3 + 2) - 1$

For 31–38, use the distributive property to rewrite the expressions without parentheses.

31. $2(4k - 6)$

31. $8k - 12$

32. $(-3 + 4g - h)5$

32. $-15 + 20g - 5h$

33. $-9(1 - n)$

33. $-9 + 9n$

34. $-3(r + 5)$

34. $-3r - 15$

35. $(4x - 3t + 1)(-2)$

35. $-8x + 6t - 2$

36. $-1(y - 6)$

36. $-y + 6$

37. $14(-1 - z)$

37. $-14 - 14z$

38. $(4 - m)(-1)$

38. $-4 + m$

39. The cost of one company's phone service in St. Louis is $15.87 per month plus $0.07 for each minute of long distance service used. Write an expression for the cost of one month's phone service if the consumer uses m minutes of long distance time.

39. $15.87 + 0.07m$ dollars

40. Write an expression for the perimeter of the trapezoid in **Figure 2.15.**

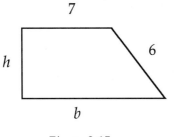

Figure 2.15

40. $b + h + 13$

41. Write an expression for the perimeter of the pentagon in **Figure 2.16.**

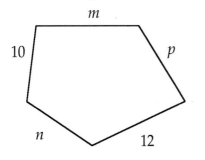

Figure 2.16

41. $m + n + p + 22$

Section 2.3 Solving Linear Equations

What You Need to Know

- How to use the order of operations guidelines
- How to use the distributive property
- How to construct expressions

What You Will Learn

- To translate statements into mathematical equations
- To identify terms, factors, and coefficients in an expression
- To use algebraic operations to solve an equation for the value of one unknown quantity
- To solve literal equations and formulas

Materials

- None

Writing Equations

When two expressions are set equal to each other, an **equation** is formed. The expressions may contain numbers and/or variables. They may also contain operation symbols. The following are all examples of equations:

$3x + 5 = 7 - 4$

$R = 1$

$d = 16t^2 + 25t - 100$

$3z = xy + 7$

Equations can be used to model real-world situations. For example, in a typical house the length of a stud used to frame a wall is 3 inches shorter than the height of the room's ceiling. An equation can be used to state this relationship in a more concise symbolic form that contains the essential elements found in the wording of the statement.

To help translate the statement into its mathematical equivalent, we can begin by eliminating words in the original statement that are not necessary for expressing the mathematical relationship and by replacing the word *is* with an = symbol.

Stud length = ceiling height minus 3 inches.

From this word equation, a symbolic equation can be formed. Since "stud length" is a single quantity, the left side of the equation can be represented by a single variable, such as L. Then using H to represent ceiling height, the phrase "ceiling height minus 3 inches" becomes the expression $H - 3$. The equation $L = H - 3$ is an algebraic model for the original statement relating stud length and ceiling height.

The relationship modeled by this equation can also be represented with an arrow diagram. (See **Figure 2.17.**)

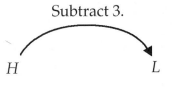

Subtract 3.

H L

Figure 2.17

Discovery 2.2 Equations in Staircase Design *(SE pages 134–135)*

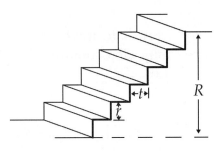

Figure 2.18

Figure 2.18 shows a drawing of a staircase with some typical dimensions labeled. Let t represent the depth of a tread and r the height of a riser. The rise R is the floor-to-floor height of the staircase.

1. The rise of the staircase is related to the height of a riser. Assume all of the risers are the same height. If there are 18 risers on the staircase, write an equation relating the rise R to the riser height r.

1. **Rise = (18)(Riser height), or $R = 18r$.**

2. Draw an arrow diagram that models your equation.

2.

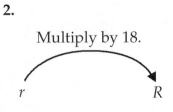

Multiply by 18.

r R

3. Use your equation from item 1 to find the rise for a staircase with 18 risers and a riser height of 8 inches.

3. $R = (18)(8 \text{ in}) = 144$ in.

4. If the rise is to be 153 inches, how can you calculate the riser height?

4. Divide 153 inches by 18 to get $r = 8.5$ in.

Division and multiplication are called **inverse operations,** meaning that either one will undo the result of the other. Addition and subtraction are also inverse operations. For example, subtraction of 5 will undo the result of adding 5. We can illustrate the use of division as the inverse operation of multiplication, as in item 4, with a reverse arrow diagram. (See **Figure 2.19.**)

Multiply by 18.

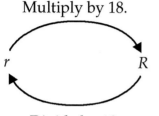

Divide by 18.

Figure 2.19

5. Use the arrow diagram in Figure 2.19 to find the riser height if the rise is 135 inches.

5. Divide 135 inches by 18, and $r = 7.5$ in.

6. Write an equation that models the reverse arrow drawn in Figure 2.19.

6. $r = R/18$.

In item 6, you **solved** your original equation for the riser height r. The inverse operation of division was used to undo the multiplication in the original equation for R. In a similar manner, inverse operations are used to solve a wide variety of equations.

7. Look again at Figure 2.18. Write a complete sentence that explains how the *number* of treads is related to the *number* of risers. (Note: The top and bottom landings of the staircase are not counted as treads.)

7. The number of treads is 1 less than the number of risers.

8. Write an equation and draw an arrow diagram that models your statement. Let M represent the number of treads and N the number of risers.

8. $M = N - 1$.

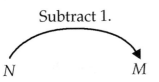

Subtract 1.

N M

9. Add the reverse arrow to your arrow diagram in item 8 and complete the equation $N = $_____.

9.

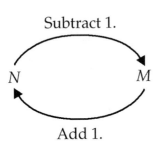

Subtract 1.

N M

Add 1.

$N = M + 1$.

10. For a staircase to be easy to walk on, twice the depth of a tread plus the height of a riser should be 24.5 inches. Write a word equation that expresses this relationship. Then use the variables r and t to write an algebraic equation for the relationship.

10. (Twice the tread depth) + (Riser height) = 24.5 in; $2t + r = 24.5$.

11. If riser height is 7 inches, rewrite your equation in item 10 to reflect this fact.

11. $2t + 7 = 24.5$.

12. Draw an arrow diagram that models your equation from item 11.

12.

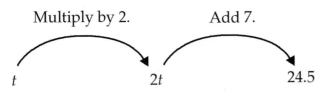

Multiply by 2.   Add 7.

t $2t$ 24.5

13. Add to your diagram arrows and inverse operations that show how to find the value of t, starting with 24.5.

13.

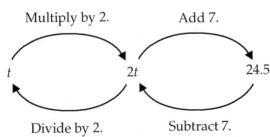

Multiply by 2.   Add 7.

t $2t$ 24.5

Divide by 2.   Subtract 7.

14. Use your answer to item 13 to find the value of t.

14. $t = (24.5 - 7)/2 = 8.75$ in.

Solving Equations Algebraically

Arrow diagrams like those used in Discovery 2.2 are helpful in visualizing the inverse operations that are needed to solve equations. Even though many equations can be solved easily this way, it is important to develop a systematic, algebraic method of finding the solution to an equation.

Consider again the equation $2t + 7 = 24.5$. We say that this equation is solved when it is rewritten in a form that isolates t on one side of the equation. To isolate t on one side of this equation, we use inverse operations to undo the addition of 7 and multiplication by 2.

Examine the arrow diagram in **Figure 2.20.** We see that to solve for t, we first need to undo the addition by subtracting 7. Then to undo the multiplication we divide by 2.

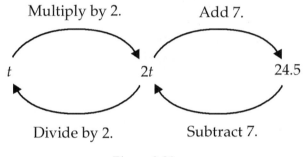

Figure 2.20

Algebraically, the solution proceeds in the following way:

$2t + 7 = 24.5$	Original equation.
$2t + 7 - 7 = 24.5 - 7$	Subtract 7 from both sides of the equation.
$2t = 17.5$	Simplify.
$\dfrac{2t}{2} = \dfrac{17.5}{2}$	Divide both sides by 2.
$t = 8.75$	Simplify.

By performing the same operation on both sides of the equation in each step, we create a series of equations: $2t + 7 = 24.5$, $2t = 17.5$, and $t = 8.75$. These equations are said to be **equivalent** because they are all true for the same value of t. The last of these equations, $t = 8.75$, shows the **solution.** A solution of an equation is any value of the variable that makes the original equation true.

Procedures similar to this can be used to solve many types of equations. They make use of the **properties of equality.** The properties of equality state that an equation can be changed into an equivalent equation by

- Adding or subtracting the same number on both sides of the equation; or

- Multiplying or dividing both sides of the equation by the same nonzero number.

Hints for Solving Equations

The operations of addition, subtraction, multiplication, and division can be performed on both sides of an equation to produce a new equation with the same solution.

- The choice of operation is made by examining the expression containing the variable of interest.

- Inverse operations are used to undo the operations in the expression.

- If there are no parentheses or other grouping symbols, the reverse of the usual order of operations is followed: first, additions and subtractions; next, multiplications and divisions; last, powers.

- If grouping symbols are present, the order may have to be altered. In particular, it may be helpful to use the distributive property to remove parentheses if they contain the variable.

Even when an equation is solved algebraically, an arrow diagram like the one in item 13 of Discovery 2.2 can be helpful in making decisions about which operations to undo first.

It is important to check a solution in order to verify that it actually satisfies the equation. This can be done by substituting the solution into the original equation. Then see if it makes the equation a true statement.

Example 4

Solve $5p - 9 = 21$ for p.

Solution:

Reverse the usual order of operations. Undo the subtraction first by adding 9 to both sides of the equation. Then divide both sides of the equation by 5.

$5p - 9 = 21$	Original equation.
$5p - 9 + 9 = 21 + 9$	Add 9 to both sides of the equation.
$5p = 30$	Simplify.
$\dfrac{5p}{5} = \dfrac{30}{5}$	Divide both sides by 5.
$p = 6$	Simplify.

Check:

$$5(6) - 9 \overset{?}{=} 21$$

$$30 - 9 \overset{?}{=} 21$$

$$21 = 21 \checkmark$$

Example 5

Solve $16 - 3(2 - x) = 12$ for x.

Solution:

$16 - 3(2 - x) = 12$	Original equation.
$16 - 3(2) - 3(-x) = 12$	Distributive property.
$16 - 6 + 3x = 12$	Simplify.
$10 + 3x = 12$	Simplify.
$10 + 3x - 10 = 12 - 10$	Subtract 10 from both sides.
$3x = 2$	Simplify.
$\dfrac{3x}{3} = \dfrac{2}{3}$	Divide both sides by 3.
$x = \dfrac{2}{3}$	Simplify.

Check:

$$16 - 3\left(2 - \frac{2}{3}\right) \overset{?}{=} 12$$

$$16 - 3\left(\frac{4}{3}\right) \overset{?}{=} 12$$

$$16 - 4 \overset{?}{=} 12$$

$$12 = 12 \checkmark$$

Notice that if we approximate $\dfrac{2}{3}$ with 0.667, the left side of the equation does not equal 12. Only $\dfrac{2}{3}$ is an *exact* solution to the equation.

Example 6

Solve $\dfrac{4t}{3} + 8 = 13$ for t.

Solution:

$$\dfrac{4t}{3} + 8 = 13 \qquad\qquad \text{Original equation.}$$

$$\dfrac{4t}{3} + 8 - 8 = 13 - 8 \qquad\qquad \text{Subtract 8 from both sides.}$$

$$\dfrac{4t}{3} = 5 \qquad\qquad \text{Simplify.}$$

$$3\left(\dfrac{4t}{3}\right) = 3(5) \qquad\qquad \text{Multiply both sides by 3.}$$

$$4t = 15 \qquad\qquad \text{Simplify.}$$

$$\dfrac{4t}{4} = \dfrac{15}{4} \qquad\qquad \text{Divide both sides by 4.}$$

$$t = \dfrac{15}{4} \qquad\qquad \text{Simplify.}$$

Check:

$$\dfrac{4\left(\dfrac{15}{4}\right)}{3} + 8 \overset{?}{=} 13$$

$$\dfrac{15}{3} + 8 \overset{?}{=} 13$$

$$5 + 8 \overset{?}{=} 13$$

$$13 = 13 \ \checkmark$$

Notice that in this case, if 3.75 is substituted for t in the equation, the left side does equal 12. The reason for this is that $\dfrac{15}{4}$ is exactly equal to 3.75.

Combining Like Terms

When solving equations, it will be helpful to be able to recognize various components of expressions. In an algebraic expression that denotes a sum, the parts that are added are called **terms.** For example, the expression $4x + 3y$ contains two terms. The first term is $4x$ and the second term is $3y$. The expression $7a - 2b$ can be thought of as $7a + (-2b)$. Here the first term is $7a$ and the second term is $-2b$.

In an expression that denotes a product, the parts that are multiplied are called **factors.** For example, in the expression $5R$, both the 5 and the R are called factors.

In a term that is the product of a number and a variable, the number is called the **coefficient.** For example, in the term $15h$, the number 15 is the coefficient of h.

Example 7

Consider the expression $4w - 12x + 7y + z - 138$.

a) How many terms does the expression contain?

b) What are the factors in the third term?

c) What is the coefficient of w in the first term?

d) What is the coefficient of x in the second term?

e) What is the coefficient of z in the fourth term?

Solution:

a) five

b) 7 and y

c) 4

d) –12

e) 1 (Notice that when the coefficient of a term is 1, it is not usually written.)

If the variable parts of two terms are the same, the terms are called **like terms.** For example, in the expression $5y - 2y + 3y$, the terms $5y$, $-2y$, and $3y$ are like terms. In the expression $4s + 7r - 2s$, only $4s$ and $-2s$ are like terms. In the expression $2t^2 + 18t - 20$, there are no like terms: t^2 and t are not the same.

Consider the expression $8m + 2m$, which contains two like terms. The distributive property allows us to combine like terms by simply adding the coefficients.

$8m + 2m = (8 + 2)m$ \qquad Distributive property.

$$= 10m$$

Example 8

Identify, collect, and combine like terms in the expression
$6p + 8 - q - 9p + 14q + 2p + 11$.

Solution:

$6p$, $-9p$, and $2p$ are like terms. So are $-q$ and $14q$, as well as 8 and 11.

$6p + 8 - q - 9p + 14q + 2p + 11 = 6p - 9p + 2p - q + 14q + 8 + 11$

$$= -p + 13q + 19$$

Example 9

Solve $5B - 7 = 3B + 1$ for B.

Solution:

$5B - 7 = 3B + 1$	Original equation.
$5B - 7 - 3B = 3B + 1 - 3B$	Subtract $3B$ from both sides.
$2B - 7 = 1$	Simplify.
$2B - 7 + 7 = 1 + 7$	Add 7 to both sides.
$2B = 8$	Simplify.
$\dfrac{2B}{2} = \dfrac{8}{2}$	Divide both sides by 2.
$B = 4$	Simplify.

Check:

$$5(4) - 7 \overset{?}{=} 3(4) + 1$$

$$20 - 7 \overset{?}{=} 12 + 1$$

$$13 = 13 \checkmark$$

Example 10

Solve $13x + 4(3 - 2x) = 17 - 5(4x - 9)$ for x.

Solution:

$13x + 4(3 - 2x) = 17 - 5(4x - 9)$	Original equation.
$13x + 4(3) + 4(-2x) = 17 - 5(4x) - 5(-9)$	Distributive property.
$13x + 12 - 8x = 17 - 20x + 45$	Simplify.
$5x + 12 = 62 - 20x$	Combine like terms.
$5x + 12 + 20x = 62 - 20x + 20x$	Add $20x$ to both sides.
$25x + 12 = 62$	Simplify.
$25x + 12 - 12 = 62 - 12$	Subtract 12 from both sides.
$25x = 50$	Simplify.
$\dfrac{25x}{25} = \dfrac{50}{25}$	Divide both sides by 25.
$x = 2$	Simplify.

Check:

$$13(2) + 4(3 - 2(2)) \overset{?}{=} 17 - 5(4(2) - 9)$$

$$26 + 4(-1) \overset{?}{=} 17 - 5(-1)$$

$$26 - 4 \overset{?}{=} 17 + 5$$

$$22 = 22 \checkmark$$

When an equation contains fractions, it is often helpful to eliminate the fractions by multiplying both sides of the equation by a common denominator.

Example 11

Solve $\dfrac{y+3}{2} = \dfrac{2y-1}{5} + 7$ for y.

Solution:

$\dfrac{y+3}{2} = \dfrac{2y-1}{5} + 7$	Original equation.
$10\left(\dfrac{y+3}{2}\right) = 10\left(\dfrac{2y-1}{5} + 7\right)$	Multiply both sides by 10.
$10\left(\dfrac{y+3}{2}\right) = 10\left(\dfrac{2y-1}{5}\right) + 10(7)$	Distributive property.
$5(y+3) = 2(2y-1) + 70$	Simplify.
$5y + 15 = 4y - 2 + 70$	Distributive property.
$5y + 15 = 4y + 68$	Simplify.
$5y - 4y + 15 - 15 = 4y + 68 - 4y - 15$	Subtract $4y$ and 15 from both sides.
$y = 53$	Simplify.

Check:

$$\dfrac{53+3}{2} \overset{?}{=} \dfrac{2(53)-1}{5} + 7$$

$$\dfrac{56}{2} \overset{?}{=} \dfrac{105}{5} + 7$$

$$28 \overset{?}{=} 21 + 7$$

$$28 = 28 \ \checkmark$$

Equations that result from real problem situations frequently contain decimal and/or fractional numbers. In such cases, a calculator may be helpful in carrying out some of the numerical computations that are needed to solve the equation. Since the numerical values may result from measurement, care should be taken in rounding off intermediate results so that accuracy is not lost.

Example 12

A homeowner's gas heating bill consists of three parts. A fixed customer charge of $10.06 per month is billed, no matter how much gas is used. The other parts of the bill depend on the amount of heat energy H (measured in *therms*) used. The distribution charge is $0.33830 per therm, and the supplier charge is $1.06260 per therm. The total cost C (in dollars) can be calculated using the equation $C = 10.06 + 0.33830H + 1.06260H$.

If the total cost in a particular month is $208.99, how many therms of heat were used during the month?

Solution:

The number of therms used can be found by solving the equation $208.99 = 10.06 + 0.33830H + 1.06260H$.

$208.99 = 10.06 + 0.33830H + 1.06260H$	Original equation.
$208.99 = 10.06 + 1.40090H$	Combine like terms.
$208.99 - 10.06 = 10.06 + 1.40090H - 10.06$	Subtract 10.06 from both sides.
$198.93 = 1.40090H$	Simplify.
$\dfrac{198.93}{1.40090} = \dfrac{1.40090H}{1.40090}$	Divide both sides by 1.40090.
$H = 142.0015704 \approx 142$ therms	Simplify.

Check:

$$208.99 \overset{?}{=} 10.06 + 0.33830(142) + 1.06260(142)$$

$$208.99 \approx 208.9878 \checkmark$$

Notice that because 142 is an approximate solution for H, substitution of the solution into the original equation results in two quantities that are only approximately equal.

Example 13

Solve $4.8x + 2.1 = 5.6x$ for x.

Solution:

In this case, multiplying both sides of the equation by 10 will eliminate the decimal numbers.

$4.8x + 2.1 = 5.6x$	Original equation.
$10(4.8x + 2.1) = 10(5.6x)$	Multiply both sides by 10.
$10(4.8x) + 10(2.1) = 10(5.6x)$	Distributive law.
$48x + 21 = 56x$	Simplify.
$48x + 21 - 48x = 56x - 48x$	Subtract $48x$ from both sides.
$21 = 8x$	Simplify.
$\dfrac{21}{8} = \dfrac{8x}{8}$	Divide both sides by 8.
$x = \dfrac{21}{8}$ or 2.625	Simplify.

Check:

$$4.8(2.625) + 2.1 \overset{?}{=} 5.6(2.625)$$

$$14.7 = 14.7 \checkmark$$

Formulas and Literal Equations

In Example 12, the cost of a monthly gas bill was given by the equation $C = 10.06 + 0.33830H + 1.06260H$. Recall from Chapter 1 that an equation such as this, which involves more than one variable, is often referred to as a formula. This formula allows calculation of total cost C for any value of H.

But what if we want to be able to specify *any* cost and calculate how many therms H of heat usage would result in that cost? We can leave the variable C in the equation and solve for H by using the methods discussed in this section.

$C = 10.06 + 0.33830H + 1.06260H$	Original equation.
$C = 10.06 + 1.40090H$	Combine like terms.
$C - 10.06 = 1.40090H$	Subtract 10.06 from both sides.
$\dfrac{C - 10.06}{1.40090} = \dfrac{1.40090H}{1.40090}$	Divide both sides by 1.40090.
$\dfrac{C - 10.06}{1.40090} = H$	

Hence, we have $H = \dfrac{C - 10.06}{1.40090}$, which is a formula for H in terms of C rather than a numerical value.

Formulas often contain more than two variables. Such formulas are sometimes called **literal equations,** since they contain primarily letters instead of numbers. They can be solved for any of the variables by using the methods discussed in this section.

Example 14

An undersea research vessel such as the one used to investigate the Titanic had to withstand enormous pressures. The formula $P = P_s + \rho g d$ is an algebraic model for the pressure P at any depth d in any liquid. In the formula, P_s is the pressure at the surface, ρ is the density of the liquid, and g is a gravitational constant. The formula helps designers of such a vessel determine how strong the hull must be.

A design engineer might also want to use a formula that gives the maximum depth at which the vessel could be used given a particular maximum design pressure. This would require solving a literal equation.

Solve the formula $P = P_s + \rho g d$ for the depth d.

Solution:

$$P = P_s + \rho g d$$ Original equation.

$$P - P_s = P_s + \rho g d - P_s$$ Subtract P_s from each side.

$$P - P_s = \rho g d$$ Simplify.

$$\frac{P - P_s}{\rho g} = \frac{\rho g d}{\rho g}$$ Divide both sides by ρg.

$$\frac{P - P_s}{\rho g} = d$$ Simplify.

$$d = \frac{P - P_s}{\rho g}$$ Exchange the sides of the equation.

Exercises 2.3 *(SE pages 146–154)*

I. Investigations

1. As we have seen, solving equations involves the use of inverse operations. An inverse operation will undo, or reverse, another operation. Similarly, many actions can be reversed by performing a step (or sequence of steps) that is equivalent to inverse operations. For example, the reverse of filling a thermos with coffee and covering it is removing the cover and emptying the thermos.

   For (a)–(f), describe how each action can be reversed.

   a) Wrapping a package

1. **a) Unwrap the package.**

   b) Flying from Portland, Oregon, to Atlanta and then setting a watch ahead 3 hours

   b) Set the watch back 3 hours and fly from Atlanta to Portland.

   c) Putting on roller blades and clamping the buckles

   c) Unclamp the buckles and take off the roller blades.

   d) Getting into a car, putting the key into the ignition, and turning the ignition switch clockwise

   d) Turn the ignition switch counterclockwise, take the key out of the ignition, and get out of the car.

   e) Opening a suitcase, packing it with clothes, and then closing it

   e) Open the suitcase, unpack it, and then close it.

   f) Driving north for three blocks, turning right, driving east for two blocks, turning left, and driving north for one block

   f) Drive south for one block, turn right, drive west for two blocks, turn left, and drive south for three blocks.

   g) Below are the seven steps for flushing a pool filter.
   - Turn off the filter.
   - Plug the drain.
   - Remove the blue filter hose from the water.
   - Loosen the clamp on the green filter hose.
   - Detach the green filter hose.
   - Attach the blue hose to the yard hose.
   - Turn on the water to flush the filter.

   Describe how to reassemble the filter system.

g) Turn off the water.

Detach the blue hose from the yard hose.

Reattach the green filter hose.

Tighten the clamp on the green filter hose.

Place the blue filter hose in the water.

Unplug the drain.

Turn on the filter.

2. Secret codes have been used to protect sensitive information throughout history. The famous Zimmermann telegram, shown in **Figure 2.21,** revealed Germany's attempt to form an alliance with Mexico against the United States during World War I. It was decoded by the British and helped bring the United States into the war. In the current Information Age, coding (also called *encryption*) is used to protect monetary transactions over the Internet, as well as commercial and military information.

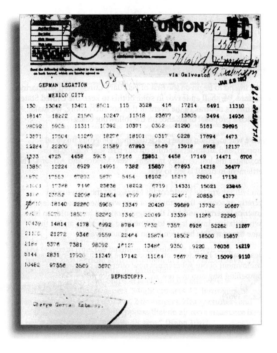

Figure 2.21

One way of coding a message begins with converting each letter of the message to a position number. The letter A can be represented by the position number 1, B by 2, etc., with 0 representing a space between words. **Table 2.4** shows the complete alphabet with its corresponding position numbers.

A	B	C	D	E	F	G	H	I	J	K	L	M
1	2	3	4	5	6	7	8	9	10	11	12	13
N	O	P	Q	R	S	T	U	V	W	X	Y	Z
14	15	16	17	18	19	20	21	22	23	24	25	26

Table 2.4

Using the position numbers in Table 2.4, the message "Send money" can be written as:

19 5 14 4 0 13 15 14 5 25

a) Use Table 2.4 to rewrite the message "To be or not to be" using the position numbers.

2. **a) 20 15 0 2 5 0 15 18 0 14 15 20 0 20 15 0 2 5**

b) To code a message, we choose a rule by which each position number in the message is converted into a new number. For example, one possible coding rule is to multiply each number by 4 and then add 20. Using this rule, the position number 2 (representing the letter B) is converted to 4(2) + 20 = 28. Therefore, 28 is the coded version of B. Similarly, the coded version of P is 4(16) + 20 = 84. Label the arrow diagram in **Figure 2.22** to show how to get from a letter's position number to its coded value.

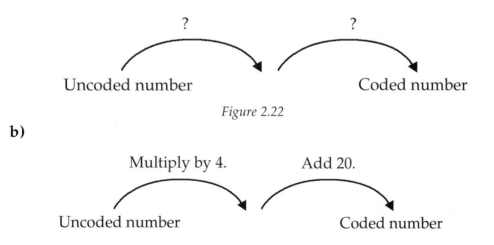

Figure 2.22

b)

Multiply by 4.   Add 20.

Uncoded number   Coded number

c) Let p represent any letter's position number in an uncoded message, and let c represent the coded value. Write an equation that represents the coding rule stated in (b).

c) $c = 4p + 20$.

d) Use the rule to code the message from (a).

d) 100 80 20 28 40 20 80 92 20 76 80 100 20 100 80 20 28 40

An effective coding process makes coding and decoding relatively easy for whoever is sending and receiving the messages. For example, to decode a message that adds 4 to the position number, we would reverse the process and subtract 4 from the coded value. The arrow diagram in **Figure 2.23** shows this decoding process.

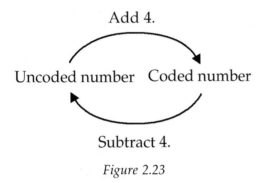

Figure 2.23

e) The message in (d) was coded using the rule "multiply by 4, then add 20." Complete the arrow diagram in **Figure 2.24** to show the decoding process.

Multiply by 4.   Add 20.

Uncoded number   Coded number

Figure 2.24

e)

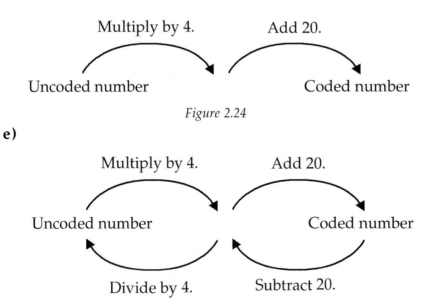

f) Write an equation that expresses the decoding process and gives p in terms of c.

f) $p = \dfrac{c - 20}{4}$.

g) Use your equation from (f) to decode the message
"32 80 36 40 20 32 92 24 32 64 40 92."

g) "Code cracker"

3. In this section we used arrow diagrams and algebra to solve the equation $2t + 7 = 24.5$. Tables can also be used to solve equations. **Table 2.5** shows the value of the left side of the equation for several values of t.

t	$2t + 7$
0	$2(0) + 7 = 7$
1	$2(1) + 7 = 9$
2	$2(2) + 7 = 11$
3	$2(3) + 7 = 13$
4	$2(4) + 7 = 15$
5	$2(5) + 7 = 17$
6	$2(6) + 7 = 19$
7	$2(7) + 7 = 21$
8	$2(8) + 7 = 23$
9	$2(9) + 7 = 25$
10	$2(10) + 7 = 27$
11	$2(11) + 7 = 29$
12	$2(12) + 7 = 31$

Table 2.5

From the pattern in the table, we can see that the left side of the equation will equal 24.5 for some value of t between 8 and 9.

A graphing calculator can be used to create tables that allow an efficient search for the solution to the equation. **Figure 2.25** shows part of a table similar to Table 2.5, where the expression $2x + 7$ has been entered as Y_1. (Remember that on many calculators only x can be used as an active variable. Here it represents t in the equation.)

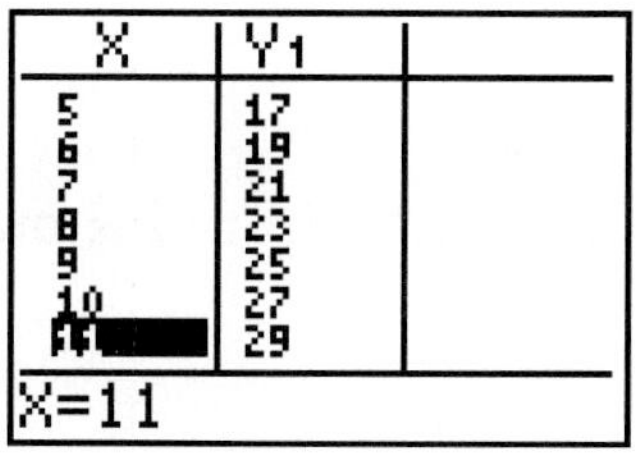

Figure 2.25

From the pattern in either of these tables, it can be seen that the value of the expression $2t + 7$ will equal 24.5 for some value of t between 8 and 9, and probably closer to 9 than to 8 (because 24.5 is closer to 25 than to 23). In order to investigate more closely, we can "zoom in" on the solution by using a smaller increment for the *t*-values. **Figure 2.26** shows the result of changing the increment from 1 to 0.1 and beginning the table with *t* = 8.4.

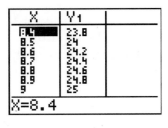

Figure 2.26

Now we see that 2*t* + 7 equals 24.5 for some value of *t* between 8.7 and 8.8, and in fact the table suggests a solution of about 8.75. To check whether 8.75 is indeed a solution, we can zoom in once more using an increment of 0.01 and beginning the table at a *t*-value of 8.7.

Figure 2.27 confirms that the value of the expression 2*t* + 7 is 24.5 when *t* = 8.75. Therefore, the solution to the equation 2*t* + 7 = 24.5 is *t* = 8.75. The process of zooming in with finer increments can be repeated as many times as necessary to achieve a desired degree of accuracy.

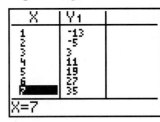

Figure 2.27

a) Solve 3 − 4(6 − 2*m*) = 12 to the nearest thousandth using calculator tables.

3. **a) 3 − 4(6 − 2*x*) is entered as Y₁ on a TI-83 calculator, and a table with increments of 1 is created. This suggests a solution between 4 and 5, so another table is created by zooming in with an increment of 0.1 and beginning at 4.**

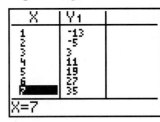 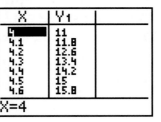

This narrows the solution to between 4.1 and 4.2. Zooming in twice more reveals the solution of *m* = 4.125.

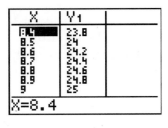

b) Use calculator tables to solve $\dfrac{2x}{7} - 3(1.9x + 0.36) = 6.3$ to the nearest hundredth.

b)

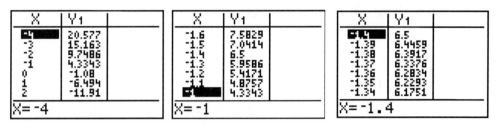

The expression $\dfrac{2x}{7} - 3(1.9x + 0.36)$ is entered as Y_1, and a table with increments of 1 is created. This suggests a solution between –2 and –1, so another table is created by zooming in with an increment of 0.1. The solution can be seen to be between –1.4 and –1.3, so another table with increments of 0.01 is created. Y_1 is closest to 6.3 when $x = -1.36$, so this is the (approximate) solution to the equation.

4. Equations can arise in a number of ways. Some are statements of established rules. The equation $2t + r = 24.5$ from Discovery 2.2, which relates tread depth to riser height for a staircase, is based on a 300-year-old guideline for staircase design. The equation $P = P_s + \rho g d$ in Example 14 is a well-known physics formula for liquid pressure. But problem-solving situations frequently require construction of unique mathematical models, such as the equation $L = 6(80 + l)$ used to model the cable wiring problem in Discovery 2.1.

Consider the design of an amusement park swing ride where the seat is suspended from four identical steel cables. (See **Figure 2.28.**) When the ride is in motion, the total force pulling on the cables is 1.4 times the weight of the seat and rider. As a safety factor, the cables should be able to withstand a force five times as great as the maximum pulling force without breaking. How is the strength of one cable related to the weight of the rider?

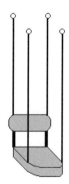

Figure 2.28

a) We can often begin modeling a problem like this by writing a simple statement expressing some total amount contained in the problem statement. Using the word *equals,* write a statement that compares the total strength of all the cables with the total force pulling on the cables while the ride is in motion.

4. **a) Total strength of all cables equals five times the total pulling force.**

   b) If one cable has a strength S, rewrite your equation in an algebraic form that contains the variable S but still contains the words *pulling force.*

   b) $4S = 5$(pulling force).

   c) If the weight of a rider is W, replace the pulling force with an expression containing W and the weight of a 35-pound seat.

   c) $4S = 5(1.4(W + 35))$ or $4S = 7(W + 35)$.

   d) For a cable strength of 500 pounds, how heavy a rider can be safely accommodated?

   d) Solve $2000 = 7(W + 35)$ to get $W = 250.714...$, or about 250 pounds.

For (e)–(h), begin your modeling process with a word equation.

   e) A gas company charges its residential customers a base rate of $32. In addition, for each therm of gas used, the company charges $0.64. Write an equation that relates the total monthly bill B (in dollars) to the amount of gas g (in therms). Then determine how much gas was used if the bill for one month totals $97.23.

   e) Total monthly bill equals base rate plus cost of gas:

   $B = 32 + 0.64g$.

   For $B = 97.23$, $g = 101.92... \approx 102$ therms.

   f) If your scores on the first three exams in a course are 70, 72, and 87 and there is one more exam to take, write an equation relating your score E on the final exam to your final grade average G in the course. (Assume all four exams have equal weight.) If you need an average of 80 to get a B, what is the minimum score on the fourth exam that will give you a B in the course?

   f) Average of four exams equals G.

   $$\frac{70 + 72 + 87 + E}{4} = G \text{ or } \frac{229 + E}{4} = G.$$

   If $G = 80$, $E = 91$.

g) **Figure 2.29** shows the configuration of 2 x 4 lumber for a window frame. Let h and w represent the height and width of the window, respectively. Then write an equation that relates h and w if the total length of framing lumber used for 20 windows in a house is 240 feet. (Note: Finished "2-inch" lumber is actually only $1\frac{1}{2}$ inches thick.) If the height of each window is 46 inches, what is the width?

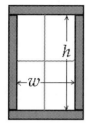

Figure 2.29

g) **Total length of lumber equals 240 feet.**

$20(2h + 2(w + 2(1.5))) = 12(240)$.

For $h = 46$ in, $w = 23$ in.

h) How many CDs can be bought from an Internet music retailer for $100 if each CD costs $14.99 and shipping and handling for the entire order is $8.50?

h) **Total cost equals cost of CDs plus S/H cost.**

$C = 14.99N + 8.50$.

For $C = 100$, $N = 6.104...$, so 6 CDs can be bought.

5. Exercise 18 of Section 1.3 stated that the U.S. Postal Service will accept a package for mailing only if its length L and girth (distance around) G satisfy the inequality $L + G \leq 108$, where L and G are measured in inches.

a) What can you say about the acceptable length for a package that has a girth of 76 inches?

5. a) **Its length must be less than or equal to 32 inches.**

b) For a package with a girth of 76 inches, the statement of the acceptable dimensions becomes $L + 76 \leq 108$. What algebraic operation can be performed on each side of this inequality to produce the answer you gave for (a)?

b) **Subtract 76 from each side.**

Just as with solving an equation, an inequality can be solved algebraically by performing appropriate operations on both sides. As you found in (b), subtraction (or addition) of the same number on both sides will result in an equivalent inequality. One way of demonstrating this is to use only numbers. For example, adding 6 to each side of the inequality $4 < 7$ results in $10 < 13$, which is certainly true.

c) Add –6 (or subtract 6) to each side of the inequality 4 < 7. Does it result in a true statement?

c) The result is –2 < 1, which is true.

d) To determine whether a similar property holds for multiplication, multiply both sides of the inequality 4 < 7, first by 6 and then by –6. What do you find?

d) Multiplying each side by 6 results in 24 < 42, which is true. Multiplying each side by –6 results in –24 < –42, which is false.

e) What do you find when you divide both sides of the inequality 4 < 7 by 2 and then by –2?

e) Dividing each side by 2 results in 2 < 3.5, which is true. Dividing by –2 results in –2 < –3.5, which is false.

f) How can the direction of the inequality symbols be changed in the results of (d) and (e) so that the results are true?

f) Reverse the direction of the inequality when it is multiplied or divided by a negative number.

The properties of inequalities that you have observed in this exercise can be summarized as follows:

Solving Inequalities

- Any number can be added to or subtracted from both sides of an inequality without changing the direction of the inequality.

- When an inequality is multiplied or divided by a positive number, the direction of the inequality is unchanged.

- When an inequality is multiplied or divided by a negative number, the direction of the inequality is reversed.

Using these guidelines for solving inequalities, notice how we can solve the inequality $5 - 3x > 2$:

$5 - 3x - 5 > 2 - 5$ Subtract 5 from both sides.

$-3x > -3$ Simplify.

$\dfrac{-3x}{-3} < \dfrac{-3}{-3}$ Divide both sides by –3 and reverse the direction of the inequality.

$x < 1$ Simplify.

One way to check if such a solution makes sense is to choose any number in the solution interval. Then substitute the number for the variable in the original inequality and see if it is satisfied. For example, 0 is less than 1:

$$5 - 3(0) \overset{?}{>} 2$$

$$5 - 0 \overset{?}{>} 2$$

$$5 > 2 \checkmark$$

g) Solve the following inequalities:

i. $3t + 12 \leq 27$

ii. $6(3 - a) > 72$

iii. $\dfrac{R}{-2} + 4 < -1$

g) i) $t \leq 5$; ii) $a < -9$; iii) $R > 10$

6. There is frequently more than one correct sequence of algebraic operations that can be used to solve an equation. Consider the equation $P = P_s + \rho g d$ from Example 14, which was solved for d. Instead of subtracting P_s from each side of the equation, an alternative first step might be to divide each side by ρg. The following solution for d would result:

$P = P_s + \rho g d$	Original equation.
$\dfrac{P}{\rho g} = \dfrac{P_s + \rho g d}{\rho g}$	Divide both sides by ρg.
$\dfrac{P}{\rho g} = \dfrac{P_s}{\rho g} + \dfrac{\rho g d}{\rho g}$	Distributive property.
$\dfrac{P}{\rho g} = \dfrac{P_s}{\rho g} + d$	Simplify.
$\dfrac{P}{\rho g} - \dfrac{P_s}{\rho g} = \dfrac{P_s}{\rho g} + d - \dfrac{P_s}{\rho g}$	Subtract $\dfrac{P_s}{\rho g}$ from both sides.
$\dfrac{P}{\rho g} - \dfrac{P_s}{\rho g} = d$	Simplify.

This solution does not have the same form as the solution from Example 14, which was $d = \dfrac{P - P_s}{\rho g}$, but using the distributive property, we can show that they are equivalent.

a) The equation $W = \dfrac{D}{25} + 0.035$ is a formula for the center web thickness W of a spade drill in terms of blade diameter D. Solve the equation for D by first subtracting 0.035 from each side.

6. **a)** $\qquad W - 0.035 = \dfrac{D}{25} + 0.035 - 0.035$

$\qquad\qquad W - 0.035 = \dfrac{D}{25}$

$\qquad 25(W - 0.035) = 25\left(\dfrac{D}{25}\right)$

$\qquad 25(W - 0.035) = D$

b) Now solve the equation again, but this time begin by multiplying both sides by 25.

b) $\qquad 25(W) = 25\left(\dfrac{D}{25} + 0.035\right)$

$\qquad\qquad 25W = 25\left(\dfrac{D}{25}\right) + 25(0.035)$

$\qquad\qquad 25W = D + 0.875$

$\qquad 25W - 0.875 = D + 0.875 - 0.875$

$\qquad 25W - 0.875 = D$

c) Show that your answers to (a) and (b) are equivalent.

c) $25(W - 0.035) = 25W - 25(0.035) = 25W - 0.875.$

d) The equation $l = a + (n - 1)d$ is a formula for the last term in a sequence of numbers. Solve the equation for the number of terms n in two different ways: (1) by first dividing both sides by d and (2) by first using the distributive property. Show that the two results are equivalent.

d) Method 1

$\dfrac{l}{d} = \dfrac{a}{d} + n - 1$

$\dfrac{l}{d} - \dfrac{a}{d} + 1 = n$

Method 2

$l = a + nd - d$

$l - a + d = nd$

$\dfrac{l - a + d}{d} = n$

If each term in the second solution is divided by d, the solutions are shown to be equal: $\dfrac{l - a + d}{d} = \dfrac{l}{d} - \dfrac{a}{d} + \dfrac{d}{d} = \dfrac{l}{d} - \dfrac{a}{d} + 1.$

II. Projects and Group Activities *(SE pages 154–156)*

7. Working with another student, you can help each other practice your equation-solving skills. Make up a simple expression, like $3x - 15$. Then pick a number without telling your partner what it is. Evaluate the expression by substituting your number into it. Then tell your partner your expression and the value you found. He or she must then solve an equation in order to be able to tell you what original number you picked.

   For example, if you pick the number 12, you will give your partner the number 21 and the expression $3x - 15$. Your partner will have to solve the equation $3x - 15 = 21$ in order to find your number.

   Once you have both mastered the solution of this kind of equation, you can move on to equations with more involved expressions.

8. In Exercise 2 we examined a simple coding process that assigned a position number to each letter of the alphabet (Table 2.4). Then each position number was coded using a two-step algebraic expression. By making up your own messages and coding expressions, you and other students can practice equation solving by decoding each other's messages.

   But code breakers know that certain letters and words are used more often than others. For example, the letter *e* occurs frequently in the English language, so a number that occurs frequently in a simply coded message has a greater chance of being a code for *e* than a number that occurs rarely. Even by adding more steps to the coding expressions, you cannot avoid giving frequency clues.

   One tool for hiding frequency clues is a keyword that can be used to code a *keyword matrix*. Suppose you want to code the message "going bananas." This can be written using position numbers as 7 15 9 14 7 0 2 1 14 1 14 1 19. If the keyword is *cat*, rearrange the numbers into a three-column **matrix,** one column for each letter in *cat*:

$$\begin{bmatrix} 7 & 15 & 9 \\ 14 & 7 & 0 \\ 2 & 1 & 14 \\ 1 & 14 & 1 \\ 19 & & \end{bmatrix}$$

Then add the position number 3 (for *c*) to each number in the first column, add 1 (for *a*) to each number in the second column, and 20 (for *t*) to each number in the third column. The resulting coded matrix is

$$\begin{bmatrix} 10 & 16 & 29 \\ 17 & 8 & 20 \\ 5 & 2 & 34 \\ 4 & 15 & 21 \\ 22 & & \end{bmatrix}$$

The message is sent as 10 16 29 17 8 20 5 2 34 4 15 21 22.

a) Explain why the message is hard to crack.

8. **a) The same letter can be coded by more than one number so there are no frequency clues. For example, the letter *g* is coded as both 10 and 8, and *a* is coded as 2, 4, and 21.**

b) Explain how the person receiving the message would use the word *cat* to decode the message.

b) **Since *cat* has three letters, the receiver of the message would arrange the message in a three-column matrix. Then by subtracting 3, 1, and 20 from each number in the first, second, and third columns, respectively, the original position numbers could be reconstructed. The message could then be decoded using Table 2.4.**

c) Decode the message 16 20 9 25 3 28 9 5 4 21 24 10 21 15 7 17 4 34 23 using the keyword *code*.

c) **The matrix is** $\begin{bmatrix} 16 & 20 & 9 & 25 \\ 3 & 28 & 9 & 5 \\ 4 & 21 & 24 & 10 \\ 21 & 15 & 7 & 17 \\ 4 & 34 & 23 & \end{bmatrix}$. **Subtracting 3 (for *c*), 15 (for *o*), 4 (for *d*),**

and 5 (for *e*) results in the uncoded matrix $\begin{bmatrix} 13 & 5 & 5 & 20 \\ 0 & 13 & 5 & 0 \\ 1 & 6 & 20 & 5 \\ 18 & 0 & 3 & 12 \\ 1 & 19 & 19 & \end{bmatrix}$.

The message is "Meet me after class."

Make up your own messages and coding schemes based on this kind of *keyword cryptography*, and exchange them with other students to practice cracking codes.

III. Additional Practice

9. Explain what happens when you add the same number to both sides of an equation.

9. The result is an equivalent equation. The new equation will have the same solution as the original equation.

10. The maximum allowable wind drift d for high-rise buildings in New York City is given by $d = 0.0015h$, where h is the height of a building and d and h are measured in identical units. How high must a building be in order for allowable wind drift to reach 18 inches?

10. $18 = 0.0015h$; $h = 12{,}000$ in, or 1000 ft.

11. The weight w (in grams) of a nestling great blue heron can be approximated by the equation $w = 55.6t - 47.4$, where t is the age of the nestling in days. Find the age of an 800-gram nestling.

11. $800 = 55.6t - 47.4$; $t = 15.24$, or about 15 days.

12. A Houston sporting goods store orders Astros baseball caps in quantities of 500. Store records show that the number N of caps in inventory decreases with time t (in weeks after delivery), according to the equation $N = 500 - 18t$.

   a) How many weeks does it take for all caps to be sold, that is, for inventory to be reduced to zero?

12. a) $0 = 500 - 18t$; $t = 27.8$ weeks.

   b) To avoid running out of caps, they will be reordered when inventory drops to 80 caps. How long after delivery will this reorder point occur?

   b) $80 = 500 - 18t$; $t = 23.3$ weeks.

13. The circumference c of a 6-foot-wide concrete apron surrounding a circular swimming pool can be written in terms of the pool's diameter d as $c = \pi(d + 12)$. For what diameter will the apron's circumference be 120 feet?

13. $120 = \pi(d + 12)$; $d \approx 26$ ft.

14. The equation $A = 400(2l + 30)$ provides a model for the land development problem in Exercise 5 of Section 2.2. Here l represents the length of a house lot and A the total area of the development. What is the total area of the development if each house lot has a length of 235 ft?

14. $A = 400(2(235) + 30)$; $A = 200{,}000$ ft^2.

15. The equation $A = P(1 + rt)$ is a model for the amount A of money available on an investment after t years if P dollars were initially invested at a simple interest rate r. (See Exercise 20 of Section 2.2.)

   a) What initial investment would result in an amount of \$10,000 after 5 years if the interest rate were to stay at 6%?

15. a) $10{,}000 = P(1 + (0.06)(5))$; $P = \$7692.31$.

b) What interest rate would be necessary for the same initial investment to grow to $11,000 after 5 years?

b) 11,000 = 7692.31(1 + 5r); r ≈ 0.086, or 8.6%.

16. **Figure 2.30** shows a schematic of an electrical circuit that contains three resistors and a battery. If the battery has a voltage of 1.5 volts and an internal resistance of 2 ohms, then the equation for the current I (in amperes) is $30I + 50I + 40I + 2I = 1.5$.

Solve for I.

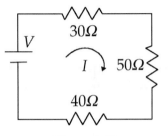

Figure 2.30

16. $122I = 1.5$; $I ≈ 0.012$ amperes.

17. A painting contractor uses the equation $C = N(t + 1.25)(16)$ to prepare cost estimates C for large painting jobs. N represents the number of painters used. Each painter makes $16 per hour. Seventy-five minutes (1.25 hours) of preparation and cleanup time is assumed. If eight painters are used on a particular job, how much actual painting time t (in hours) will be available for a cost of $900?

17. $900 = 8(t + 1.25)(16)$; $t ≈ 5.78$ hours.

For 18–37, solve algebraically for the variable.

18. $3b + 2 = 14$.

18. $b = 4$.

19. $5r − 7 = 15$.

19. $r = 22/5 = 4.4$.

20. $20 = 4 − 9t$.

20. $t = −16/9 ≈ −1.78$.

21. $8(2z + 6) − 1 = 39$.

21. $z = −1/2$.

22. $13 − 7(g + 4) = 20$.

22. $g = −5$.

23. $10 = 16 - (9 - 4d)$.

23. $d = 3/4$.

24. $\dfrac{x}{6} + 2 = 11$.

24. $x = 54$.

25. $(1/4)(20 - C) = 3$.

25. $C = 8$.

26. $23 = \dfrac{2y - 5}{3} + 7$.

26. $y = 53/2 = 26.5$.

27. $5 - 6b = 9b$.

27. $b = 1/3$.

28. $3k + 1 = 7k + 11$.

28. $k = -5/2$.

29. $\dfrac{2}{5}t + \dfrac{1}{5} = \dfrac{3}{5}t - 2$.

29. $t = 11$.

30. $\left(\dfrac{1}{2}\right)x - 11 = \left(\dfrac{1}{4}\right)x$.

30. $x = 44$.

31. $\dfrac{3p - 7}{4} = \dfrac{2p + 1}{3} + 1$.

31. $p = 37$.

32. $\dfrac{h}{6} + 2 = \dfrac{1}{5} - h$.

32. $h = 54/35$.

33. $y + 3 = 18 - 4y$.

33. $y = 3$.

34. $2(d + 1) + 3(2d + 3) = 3$.

34. $d = -1$.

35. $9 - (M - 3) = 2(4M - 1) - 6M$.

35. $M = 14/3$.

36. $16 - 4(q - 1) = 5q + 3(2q + 7)$.

36. $q = -1/15$.

37. $2.4d = 4d - 6.2$.

37. $d = 3.875$.

For 38–40, solve for the variable and round each answer to hundredths.

38. $5.78w = 4.6(3.9 - 2w)$.

38. $w = 1.1975... \approx 1.20$.

39. $1.26 - 4(6.73x + 2.7) = 5.94x$.

39. $x = -0.2903... \approx -0.29$.

40. $4.71(3 - 2.9A) = 12.4(A + 53.8)$.

40. $A = -25.0581... \approx -25.06$.

For 41–45, solve algebraically for the indicated variable.

41. $PV = nRT$ (pressure-volume-temperature relationship for an ideal gas) for temperature T.

41. $T = \dfrac{PV}{nR}$.

42. $P = 2l + 2w$ (perimeter of a rectangle) for width w.

42. $w = \dfrac{P - 2l}{2}$ or $w = \dfrac{P}{2} - l$.

43. $v_f = v_o + at$ (final velocity of an accelerated object) for acceleration a.

43. $a = \dfrac{v_f - v_o}{t}$ or $a = \dfrac{v_f}{t} - \dfrac{v_o}{t}$.

44. $D = W - \dfrac{WM}{100}$ (dry weight of a log) for percent moisture M.

44. $M = \dfrac{100}{W}(W - D)$ or $M = 100 - \dfrac{100D}{W}$.

45. $E = \dfrac{Q_i - Q_o}{Q_i}$ (thermal efficiency of a heater) for output heat quantity Q_o.

45. $Q_o = Q_i - EQ_i$ or $Q_o = Q_i(1 - E)$.

Section 2.4 Functions and Their Representations

What You Need to Know

- How to solve an equation
- How to read simple graphs and charts

What You Will Learn

- To identify the independent and dependent variables in a given situation
- To identify the range and domain of a function
- To recognize a function when given the equation or graph
- To recognize and use different representations of functions such as verbal descriptions, equations, arrow diagrams, tables, and graphs
- To determine if a point lies on the graph of a function when given its graph or equation

Materials

- None

In Activity 2.1 we used a table such as the one in **Table 2.6** to help identify the relationship between the number of nails being weighed and the total weight of the nails. This table is an example of an **input/output table,** where the **input** is the number of nails and the **output** is the total weight of the nails.

Number of 10d Nails	Total Weight (g)
1	7.3
2	14.6
3	21.9
4	29.2
5	36.5
6	43.8

Table 2.6

In the table we can see a pattern that indicates that as the number of nails increases by one, the total weight of the nails increases by 7.3 grams. If W represents the total weight and n represents the number of nails, we can use the equation $W = 7.3n$ to model the relationship between these two variables. Recall from Section 1.4 that since the weight depends on the number of nails, we call n the independent variable and W the dependent variable.

When two variables are related in such a way that for each input value there is exactly one output value, the relationship is called a **function.** Note that in this relationship, for each input value there is exactly one output value. Hence, we can say that the total weight of the nails is a function of the number of nails.

Not all tables represent functions. **Table 2.7** shows the relationship between time worked and wages earned at a local convenience store. At this particular store, some employees are paid overtime and others are not. Notice in the table that the input value of 50 hours has two output values, $280 and $385, associated with it. Hence, this table does not represent a function.

Time Worked (hours)	Wages (dollars)
20	140
30	210
40	280
50	280
50	385

Table 2.7

Domain and Range

The set of all possible input values for the independent variable is called the **domain** of the function. The mathematical domain contains all numbers that can be substituted in the function's equation to produce a real number output value. Corresponding to the domain, the set of all possible output values that a function generates from its domain is called the **range** of the function.

In real-world situations, the input values that make sense for the independent variable may be only a portion of the mathematical domain of the function. We call this restricted domain the **problem domain.** The problem domain includes only numbers that (1) can actually be physical values of the independent variable and that (2) will produce a physically possible value for the dependent variable.

In our weight function $W = 7.3n$, we can substitute mathematically any real number for n, but in our context, n can only be an integer greater than or equal to zero. So the mathematical domain of the function is all real numbers, but the problem domain is restricted to integers greater than or equal to zero.

Example 15

a) Determine the domain for the function defined by the equation $A = 6.28r^2$.

b) Determine the problem domain for the function in (a) if r represents the radius of a circular object and A represents the total area of two such objects.

c) Determine the domain for the function defined by the equation $y = \dfrac{1}{x}$.

Solution:

a) Any number can be substituted for r, so the mathematical domain is all real numbers, including 0 and negative numbers.

b) The problem domain in this situation consists of all numbers greater than zero. There is no largest reasonable value for the independent variable.

c) The domain of $y = \dfrac{1}{x}$ does not include 0, since division by 0 is impossible. In this case, $x \neq 0$ is a **restriction** on the domain.

Representations

Functions can be represented by verbal descriptions, symbolic rules, arrow diagrams, tables, and graphs. For simple functions, a **verbal description** may be all we need. For example, the doubling function doubles each input value, and the squaring function squares each input value.

Since functions involve mathematics operations, equations are frequently the most compact representation. We can write the doubling function as $y = 2x$ and the squaring function as $y = x^2$.

Arrow diagrams can be used to show a value for the independent variable being selected from the domain and then a rule being applied to it. The resulting value of the dependent variable, a value in the range, is shown at the end of the last arrow. **Figure 2.31** represents the function $h = 3t - 2$.

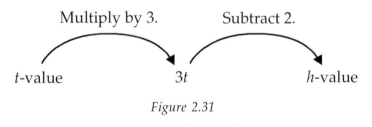

Multiply by 3. Subtract 2.

t-value $3t$ h-value

Figure 2.31

A table is another important function representation. In tables, the column headings represent the variables and the numbers in the columns are the values of the variables. Examine the spreadsheet table in **Figure 2.32** and the calculator lists in **Figure 2.33.** In Figure 2.32, the formula for the column of the spreadsheet is shown at the top of the figure. In Figure 2.33, the formula for the calculator list L2 is shown at the bottom of the first screen. In each case, for the input value 3, the value of the function is 7. Exactly two table columns are needed to define a function's input and output.

B5 = =3*A5-2

	A	B	C
1	Input	Output	
2	1	1	
3	4	10	
4	-2	-8	
5	3	7	
6	0	-2	
7	-4	-14	

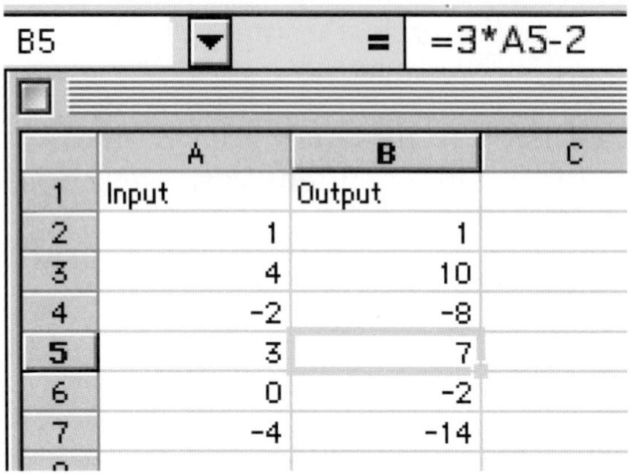

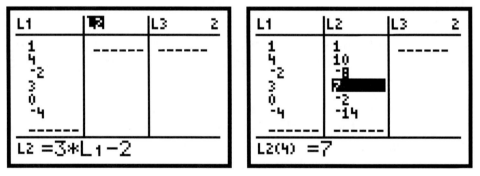

Figure 2.32

Figure 2.33

Perhaps the most familiar representation for a function is a **graph.** When graphing functions, it is customary to use the horizontal axis for the independent variable and the vertical axis for the dependent variable.

For example, it is well known to automobile drivers that braking distance is a function of the speed of the automobile. A graph representing this function is shown in **Figure 2.34.** Notice that the graph shows the independent variable speed (in miles per hour) on the horizontal axis. The dependent variable braking distance (in feet) is shown on the vertical axis. By looking at each speed on the horizontal axis of the graph and observing that there is only one distance corresponding to it, we can confirm that this relationship is a function.

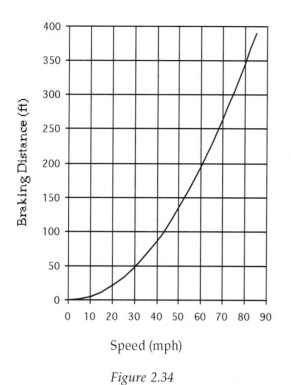

Speed (mph)

Figure 2.34

Example 16

a) In the graph shown in Figure 2.34, what is the braking distance when the speed of the automobile is 60 mph?

b) What is the value of the independent variable when the dependent variable is 50?

c) Which of these points are on the graph?

 i. (65, 225)   ii. (65, 35)   iii. (43, 100)   iv. (80, 300)

d) The function in the figure can also be represented by the equation $d = 0.054s^2$, where d represents the braking distance and s represents the speed of the vehicle. Use the equation to show that the point (100, 540) lies on the graph of the function.

Solution:

a) Find 60 on the horizontal axis, move up to the curve, then over to the vertical axis to read the braking distance of 200 feet.

b) Locate the value of the dependent variable (50) on the vertical axis, move over to the curve, then down to the horizontal axis to read the speed of 30.

c) Recall that a point is named by an **ordered pair** such as (65, 225). The first number in the pair is the **horizontal coordinate,** and the second number is called the **vertical coordinate.** So to check the point (65, 225), move 65 units to the right of the **origin,** which is the point (0, 0), on the horizontal axis and up vertically 225 units. This point lies on the graph. The point in (iii) is also on the graph.

The point in (ii) is not on the graph, as its coordinates are in the wrong order. That is, the point (35, 65) rather than the point (65, 35) lies on the graph.

The point in (iv) does not lie on the graph. When the car's speed is 80 mph, the braking distance is 350 ft. So the point (80, 350) rather than the point (80, 300) lies on the graph.

d) Substituting 100 in the equation for s and 540 for d, we get $540 = 0.054(100)^2$, which is a true statement. And since the ordered pair (100, 540) satisfies the equation, the point (100, 540) is on the graph of the function.

As we investigate different types of functions, we will be moving from one form of representation to another. For example, it is possible to move from a table to a verbal description to an equation, as we did when we weighed the nails in Activity 2.1. Or we can move from an equation to a table and then use the table to create the graph, as we will see in Section 2.5.

One advantage of graphs and tables over verbal descriptions, equations, and arrow diagrams is that both graphs and tables display many input-output pairs at the same time. This makes important properties of the function more visible.

Exercises 2.4 *(SE pages 165–168)*

I. Investigations

1. **Table 2.8** shows the relationship between the volume of a cylindrical container that is 6 inches tall and the radius of the container.

Radius (inches)	Volume (cubic inches)
0.5	4.7
1.0	18.9
1.5	42.4
2.0	75.4
2.5	118
3.0	170
3.5	231

Table 2.8

a) Does the table represent a function? Explain.

1. **a) Yes, the table represents a function, since there is exactly one volume for each radius length.**

b) Which variable is the independent variable, and which is the dependent variable?

b) The radius of the can is the independent variable, and the volume of the can is the dependent variable.

c) What is a reasonable problem domain for this relationship? Explain.

c) Sample answer: All numbers greater than zero are possible, although when the radius gets too large, the shape of the can is no longer reasonable. It makes no sense to talk about a negative or zero radius.

2. **Table 2.9** shows data for the temperature of a cup of coffee as it cools down.

Time (minutes)	0	1	2	3	4	5	6	7	8
Temperature (°F)	176	151	132	117	105	96	89	84	80

Table 2.9

a) Does Table 2.9 represent a function? Explain.

2. **a) Yes, each input value of the domain is paired with one and only one output value.**

b) What is the independent variable? What is the dependent variable?

b) Time is the independent variable; temperature is the dependent variable.

c) What is a reasonable problem domain for this relationship? Explain.

c) Sample answer: All numbers greater than or equal to zero. It makes no sense to talk about negative time.

3. If an electric company charges $12 per month plus 8 cents for each kilowatt hour of electricity used, then the function $c = \dfrac{12 + 0.08n}{n}$ represents the average cost in dollars per kilowatt hour c when n hours of electricity are used.

a) Is the point (100, 0.2) on the graph of the function?

3. a) Yes, $0.2 = \dfrac{12 + 0.08(100)}{100}$.

b) Determine the value of c when $n = 250$ hours.

b) $c = \dfrac{12 + 0.08(250)}{250} = 0.128$ dollars per kwh.

c) What is the mathematical domain of this function?

c) The domain of $c = \dfrac{12 + 0.08n}{n}$ does not include 0, since division by 0 is impossible. In this case, $n \neq 0$ is a restriction on the domain.

d) What is the problem domain of this function?

d) Only numbers greater than zero make sense. There would seem to be no upper limit to the function, since there is no limit on how much electricity is used.

4. The graph in **Figure 2.35** represents the relationship between the distance a car travels and the amount of gasoline it uses.

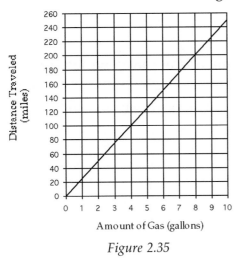

Figure 2.35

a) Use the graph in Figure 2.35 to complete **Table 2.10.**

Gas (gal)	0	1	2	3	4	5	6	7	8	9	10
Distance (mi)											

Table 2.10

a)

Gas (gal)	0	1	2	3	4	5	6	7	8	9	10
Distance (mi)	0	25	50	75	100	125	150	175	200	225	250

b) Is the relationship between the distance a car travels and the number of gallons of gas used a function? Explain. If so, what is the independent variable?

b) Yes, the relationship is a function. In this case, either variable could be considered the independent variable. One might argue that the distance traveled depends on the amount of gas used, or the amount of gas used depends on the distance traveled. The graph shows the amount of gas as the independent variable.

c) Examine the pattern in your table in (a) and write an equation that relates the distance *d* in miles traveled and the amount of gas *g* in gallons consumed.

c) $d = 25g$.

5. Consider the graphs in **Figures 2.36–2.39.** Determine whether each is the graph of a function. Explain your reasoning.

a)

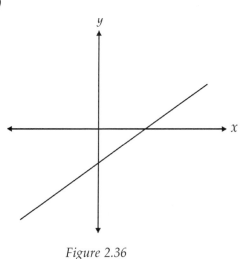

Figure 2.36

b)

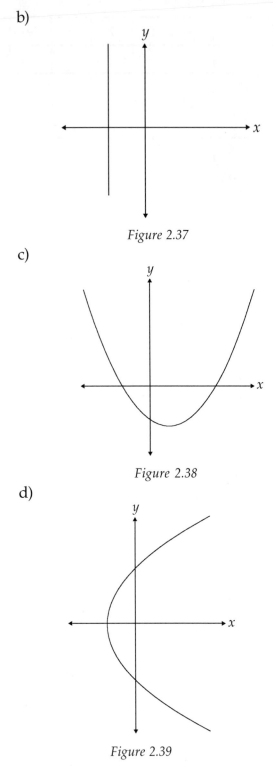

Figure 2.37

c)

Figure 2.38

d)

Figure 2.39

5. **Graphs (a) and (c) are graphs of functions. Graphs (b) and (d) are not, because in each case at least one input value of the domain has more than one output value.**

6. One test of whether a graph represents a function is the **vertical line test.** This simple test states that if you can find any vertical line that intersects the graph in more than one place, the graph is not a function. If no such line exists, then the graph is a function.

Consider the graphs shown in **Figure 2.40.**

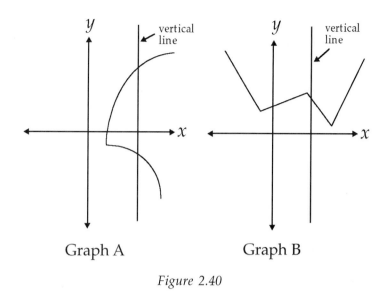

Graph A   Graph B

Figure 2.40

Since graph A intersects the vertical line in two places, it does not pass the vertical line test and therefore is not the graph of a function. But in graph B, no matter where you move the vertical line, it will never intersect the graph in more than one point, so this is the graph of a function.

a) Use the definition of *function* to explain why the vertical line test is a valid test.

6. **a) Our definition says that for relationship to be a function, each input value in its domain must have one and only one output value associated with it. When a vertical line is drawn, this represents all of the output values that can be associated with a specific input value. If the vertical line intersects the graph you are examining in more than one point, then the graph has more than one output value associated with a particular input value in the domain, so it is not a function. If this does not occur, then the graph is a function.**

b) Apply the vertical line test to the graphs in Exercise 5. Which graphs pass the test and are functions, and which do not?

b) (a) and (c) pass the vertical line test, (b) and (d) do not.

II. Projects and Group Activities *(SE pages 168–170)*

7. To demonstrate the important features of a relationship without worrying about exact scales, we can use a **qualitative graph.** The graphs in (a)–(d) are qualitative graphs.

For each of the following scenarios, a context and figure showing two graphs are given. After discussing the context with your group, answer the following questions for each situation.

i. In the figure, which graph best models the situation?

ii. Why did you choose that particular graph?

iii. For the given situation, what is the independent variable? What is the dependent variable?

a) The height of a ball above the ground as it is dropped from a balcony (see **Figure 2.41**)

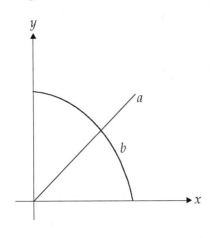

Figure 2.41

7. **a) i. Graph *b* seems to best model the situation.**

   ii. The graph shows the height of the ball greater than zero at time zero. The height decreases as time increases until the height is zero (ground level).

   iii. Independent: time; dependent: height of the ball

   b) The area of a square as the length of its side changes (see **Figure 2.42**)

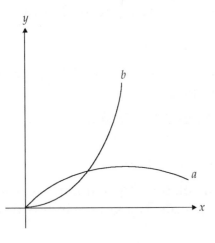

Figure 2.42

b) i. Graph *b* best models the situation.

   ii. As the length of the side of a square increases, so does the area.

   iii. Independent: length of the side; dependent: area of the square

c) The grade earned on an exam and the amount of time spent studying (see **Figure 2.43**)

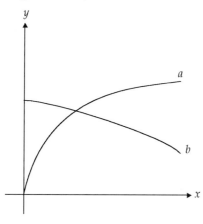

Figure 2.43

c) i. **Graph *a* best models the situation.**

ii. **The graph shows the initial grade of zero if no studying occurs. The graph increases then steadies off, just as a person's grade should increase more quickly at first then continue to increase until the exam is almost perfect.**

iii. **Independent: time; dependent: score on the exam**

d) The height of the Sears Tower in Chicago since its completion to the present time (see **Figure 2.44**)

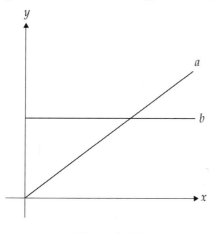

Figure 2.44

d) i. **Graph *b* best models the situation.**

ii. **The graph of the height stays constant (a horizontal line), since the skyscraper's height does not change over time.**

iii. **Independent: time; dependent: height**

8. For (a)–(d), sketch a qualitative graph for the situation.

   a) Height of a ball as it is thrown into the air

   b) The number of leaves on a maple tree during the year

   c) Depth of the water in a swimming pool as it fills with a steady stream of water

   d) The temperature of a hot drink as it sits at room temperature

8. **The graphs sketched will vary, but some of the important features that should appear on each graph are:**

   a) **This should be an increasing function to a point (the maximum height of the ball), and then the function should decrease, ending with height equal to zero (when the ball hits the ground).**

   b) **The graph should be close to zero during the winter months, increase about springtime, stay constant during the summer to fall, and then decrease to near zero again.**

   c) **This should be an increasing function up to some value of time, and then the function should be constant as the pool can hold no more water.**

   d) **This graph should show a decreasing function until it gets to some point (room temperature), and the function should then stay constant.**

III. Additional Practice

9. In each of **Tables 2.11–2.14,** x is the independent variable and y is the dependent variable. Which of the tables represent functions, and which do not? Explain.

   a)

x	-2	5	0	1
y	-5	-2	0	8

   Table 2.11

   b)

x	3	4	3	-4
y	2	4	6	8

   Table 2.12

   c)

x	3	3	3	3
y	-1	0	1	2

   Table 2.13

   d)

x	-1	0	1	2
y	4	4	4	4

   Table 2.14

9. Tables (a) and (d) are functions; (b) and (c) are not, because in both of them there is at least one input value in the domain for which there is more than one output value.

10. For each of the following situations, identify two quantities that vary. Which is the independent variable? Which is the dependent variable?

a) The daily average low temperature in North Dakota

10. a) Independent: day or month of the year; dependent: low temperature

b) The amount of time spent studying and the grade earned on the test

b) Independent: amount of time spent studying; dependent: grade on the test

c) Depth of the water in a swimming pool with a steady stream of water running in

c) Independent: time the water has run; dependent: depth of water

d) The height of a candle as it burns down

d) Independent: time; dependent: height of the candle

e) The number of car accidents in a certain city and the amount of alcohol consumed per person

e) Independent: amount of alcohol consumed; dependent: number of accidents

For 11–14, find two points that lie on the graph of the function.

11. $y = 4(2x + 1)$.

11. Sample answer: (0, 4) and (1, 12)

12. $y = -2x^3$.

12. Sample answer: (0, 0) and (1, –2)

13. $x + 4y = 6$.

13. Sample answer: (2, 1) and (–2, 2)

14. $2x = 5 - 3y$.

14. Sample answer: (0, 5/3) and (1, 1)

For each function described in 15–19, determine (a) the value of y when $x = 3$ and (b) the value(s) of x for which $y = 3$.

15. $y = 5x + 2$.

15. a) $y = 17$; b) $x = 1/5$.

16. $y = -2(x - 1)$.

16. a) $y = -4$; b) $x = -1/2$.

17. $y = x$.

17. a) $y = 3$; b) $x = 3$.

18. $y - 2x = 11$.

18. a) $y = 17$; **b)** $x = -4$.

19. See **Figure 2.45.**

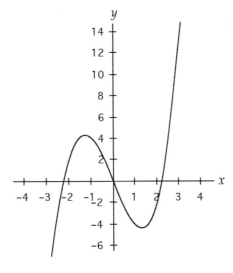

Figure 2.45

19. Sample: a) When $x = 3$, $y = 12$. **b)** When $y = 3$, $x = -1.8$, -0.7, and 2.5. **Student answers may vary slightly.**

20. Write the equation for the function that is represented by the arrow diagram in **Figure 2.46.**

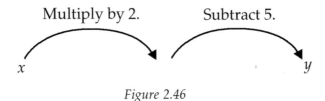

Figure 2.46

20. $y = 2x - 5$.

21. Write the equation for the function that is represented by the arrow diagram in **Figure 2.47.**

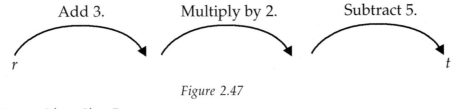

Figure 2.47

21. $t = 2(r + 3) - 5$.

For 22–25, find the domain of the function.

22. $y = \dfrac{9(x-4)}{x+3}$.

22. All real numbers except $x = -3$

23. $y = \dfrac{9x-5}{3}$.

23. All real numbers. There are no restrictions on the domain.

24. $\dfrac{n}{n-2} = m$.

24. All real numbers except $n = 2$

25. $r = \dfrac{4-s}{6-s}$.

25. All real numbers except $s = 6$

26. Consider the function $y = \dfrac{x+1}{x-5}$.

   a) Is the point $(6, 7)$ on the graph of the function?

26. a) Yes, $7 = \dfrac{6+1}{6-5}$.

   b) Determine the value of y when $x = 3$.

b) $y = \dfrac{3+1}{3-5} = \dfrac{4}{-2} = -2$

   c) What is the domain of this function?

c) The domain of $y = \dfrac{x+1}{x-5}$ does not include 5, since $5 - 5 = 0$ and division by 0 is impossible. In this case, $x \neq 5$ is a restriction on the domain.

For 27–32, use the graph in **Figure 2.48**.

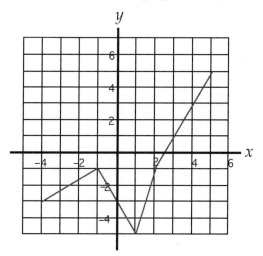

Figure 2.48

27. Explain how you know that the graph represents a function.

27. Each input value of the domain is paired with one and only one output value.

28. What is the domain of the function?

28. All numbers greater than or equal to –4 and less than or equal to 5

29. What is the range of the function?

29. All numbers greater than or equal to –5 and less than or equal to 5

30. When $x = 0$, what is the value of the function?

30. –3

31. When the value of the function is 3, what is the value of x?

31. 4

32. Is the point $(-3, -4)$ on the graph?

32. No, but (–4, –3) is.

33. Use the equation $4x + 2y = 5$ to complete **Table 2.15.**

x	–3	–2	–1	0	1	2	3
y							

Table 2.15

33.

x	–3	–2	–1	0	1	2	3
y	17/2	13/2	9/2	5/2	1/2	–3/2	–7/2

34. Use the equation $y = -0.5x^2$ to complete **Table 2.16.**

x	–3	–2	–1	0	1	2	3
y							

Table 2.16

34.

x	–3	–2	–1	0	1	2	3
y	–4.5	–2	–0.5	0	–0.5	–2	–4.5

Section 2.5 Linear Functions

What You Need to Know

- How to identify the independent and dependent variables for a given situation
- How to identify the range and domain of a function
- How to recognize a function when given a table or graph
- How to recognize and use different representations of functions such as verbal descriptions, equations, arrow diagrams, tables, and graphs

What You Will Learn

- To recognize a function as a linear function given an equation, a table, or a graph
- To construct a graph of a linear function from a table of values
- To find the intercepts of the graph of a linear function
- To find the slope of a line given two points on the line
- To use slope-intercept form to sketch the graph of a linear function
- To find an equation of a linear function given the slope and y-intercept of its graph

Materials

- None

In Section 2.4 we explored the concept of function. In this section we will focus on one particular type of function, the linear function. We will explore the characteristics of this function along with the important features of its graphs. In Section 2.6 and Chapter 3 we will continue to explore how a linear function can be used to model real-world situations.

Discovery 2.3 Relating Weight and Volume (SE pages 174–176)

The use of automatic measuring systems was discussed in Section 2.1. In these systems, a small amount of liquid is weighed and from the weight, the volume of the liquid is determined.

Imagine that you are in charge of calibrating the automatic measuring system. To do so, you must determine the relationship between the volumes and weights of small amounts of a liquid by carefully weighing amounts of liquids with known volumes.

1. Examine the data recorded in **Table 2.17.** Describe the patterns you see.

Liquid Volume (μl)	Weight (mg)
0	52
20	72
40	92
60	112
80	132
100	152

Table 2.17

1. **Sample answers: Volume and weight both increase by constant amounts. The numerical value of the weight is always 52 greater than that of the volume. As the volume of the liquid increases by 20 μl, the weight increases by 20 mg.**

2. Is the relationship shown in Table 2.17 a function? Explain.

2. **Yes, because there is exactly one weight value for each volume value.**

3. Because the weights measured by the machine depend on the volume of the solution, volume is the independent variable and weight is the dependent variable. Draw an arrow diagram that shows how to find weight W from volume V.

3.

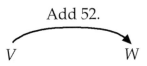
Add 52.

V W

4. Write an equation for the function that is represented by your arrow diagram in item 3.

4. **$W = V + 52$.**

5. Use your equation from item 4 to find the weight of 75 microliters of solution.

5. **$W = 75 + 52 = 127$ mg.**

6. What is the domain of the function? That is, mathematically, what numerical values can be substituted for V in your equation from item 4?

6. **All real numbers will work.**

7. What is a reasonable problem domain for the function? That is, what actual volume values make sense in the context of this application?

7. **Zero up to the largest liquid volume that will fit in the well**

We know from Section 2.4 that functions can be represented by graphs. To construct a graph of this function, we begin by creating a **coordinate plane** that contains a **horizontal axis** and a **vertical axis**. (See **Figure 2.50.**) The name of the independent variable is indicated on a horizontal axis (in this case, the V-axis), along with a scale of values for that variable. Similarly, the name and a scale of values for the dependent variable are indicated on a vertical axis (the W-axis).

For this situation, we can then think of each pair of corresponding volume and weight values as an ordered pair in the form (V, W). For example, from Table 2.17 we see that a volume of 40 μl results in a weight of 92 mg. The ordered pair (40, 92) can be plotted as a point having coordinates of 40 along the horizontal direction and 92 along the vertical direction. (See **Figure 2.50.**)

In general, we refer to the coordinate plane as the **xy-plane**, where the horizontal axis is called the **x-axis** and the vertical axis is called the **y-axis**. Points are identified by ordered pairs (x, y), where x is referred to as the **x-coordinate** of the point and y is called the **y-coordinate**.

The x- and y-axes divide the coordinate plane into four **quadrants**. (See **Figure 2.49.**)

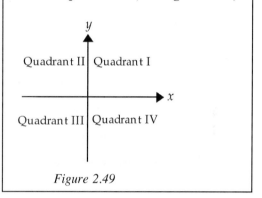

Figure 2.49

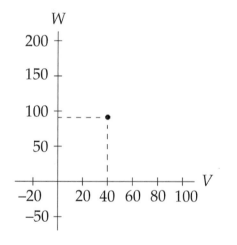

Figure 2.50

8. Draw a set of axes similar to those in Figure 2.50. Plot on your coordinate plane the six ordered pairs from Table 2.17.

8.

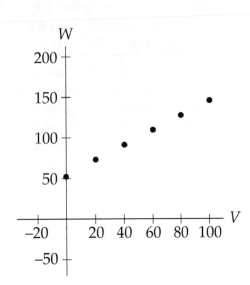

9. Use your equation from item 4 to find two more points that lie on the graph of the function. Plot those points.

9. **Sample answer: When volume is 30 μl, weight is 30 + 52 = 82 mg. When volume is 85 μl, weight is 85 + 52 = 137 mg. Hence, the points (30, 82) and (85, 137) belong to the graph of the function.**

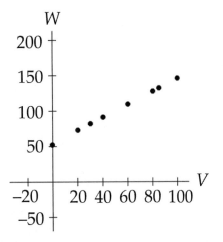

10. Explain the pattern you see in your graph.

10. **All the points lie on a straight line.**

11. Connect the points in your graph with a straight line. Keeping in mind that this line consists of an unlimited number of points, what does this line indicate?

11.

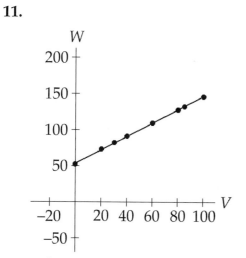

Volume values for each of the points on the line result in weights that fit the pattern of the graph.

12. For this situation, would it make sense to extend the graph to the left and right of the plotted points?

12. The graph should not extend to the left because negative volumes make no sense in this context. The graph could be extended to the right but only up to the maximum volume of the well.

13. Any point where a graph touches or crosses either of the coordinate axes is called an **intercept.** An intercept is usually given the name of the appropriate variable. In this case, it would be possible to have either a V-intercept, a W-intercept, or both. Give the coordinates and interpret the meaning of any intercepts on your graph.

13. The W-intercept is the point (0, 52). It means that when there is no liquid in the well, the machine records a weight of 52 mg (the weight of the empty well). There is no V-intercept, because that would require a negative volume.

14. If a different liquid were used in the measuring system, the resulting equation relating volume and weight might be $W = 1.2V + 52$. Construct a graph of this function. How does the graph of $W = 1.2V + 52$ compare with the graph of $W = V + 52$ in item 11?

14. The graphs have the same W-intercept of (0, 52), but the graph of $W = 1.2V + 52$ is steeper than the graph of $W = V + 52$.

Identifying Linear Functions

As we begin our study of various types of functions, it is important to notice the key features and characteristics of each function. For example, in Discovery 2.3 we examined the function $W = V + 52$ and observed that its graph is a straight line.

We also noticed in item 1 that as the volume of the liquid increased from 0 to 20 microliters, the weight of the liquid increased from 52 to 72 milligrams. This means that for each 1 microliter change in volume, there is 1 milligram change in weight. We say that the **average rate of change** of weight with respect to volume is 1 milligram per microliter of liquid.

If we examine any two additional pairs of data in the table, we find that the average rate of change remains the same. Therefore, we conclude that another characteristic of this function is that the rate of change of the function is constant.

Functions, such as the one in Discovery 2.3, whose equations can be written in the form $y = mx + b$, where m and b are real numbers, are known as **linear functions.**

Linear functions are characterized by the following:

- Equations of the form $y = mx + b$, where m and b are real numbers

- Graphs that are nonvertical straight lines

- Rates of change that are constant

Example 17

According to the 1999 Internal Revenue Tax Code, a computer used for business purposes can be depreciated over a period of 5 years. The function $v = -720t + 3600$ can be used to model the value v in dollars of a computer that was purchased for $3600, where t represents the age in years of the computer.

a) Use the given function to complete **Table 2.18.**

Age (years)	Computer Value (dollars)
0	3600
1	
2	
3	
4	
5	

Table 2.18

b) Add a third column to Table 2.18 and label it "Depreciation per Year." In this column, show the average rate of change of the value of the computer with respect to age during each year. What observations can be made about the average rate of change of the function?

c) What is the mathematical domain of this function? What is the problem domain?

---

d) Construct a graph of $v = -720t + 3600$.

e) Give the coordinates and interpret the meaning of any intercepts on your graph.

f) Is the function $v = -720t + 3600$ a linear function? Explain.

Solution:

a) See **Table 2.19**.

Age (years)	Computer Value (dollars)
0	3600
1	2880
2	2160
3	1440
4	720
5	0

Table 2.19

b) The third column of **Table 2.20** shows the depreciation per year.

Age (years)	Computer Value (dollars)	Depreciation per Year (dollars/year)
0	3600	0
1	2880	$(2880 - 3600)/(1 - 0) = -720$
2	2160	$(2160 - 2880)/(2 - 1) = -720$
3	1440	$(1440 - 2160)/(3 - 2) = -720$
4	720	$(720 - 1440)/(4 - 3) = -720$
5	0	$(0 - 720)/(5 - 4) = -720$

Table 2.20

The average rate of change (the ratio of $\dfrac{\text{change in value}}{\text{change in age}}$) between any 2 years is constant.

c) Any real number can be used as an input for the function $v = -720t + 3600$, but in the context of this problem, only age in years greater than or equal to 0 and less than or equal to 5 is meaningful.

d) Since age t is the independent variable, it is placed on the horizontal axis and the value of the computer v, the dependent variable, is on the vertical axis. The six pairs of numbers are plotted as points on the coordinate plane and connected with a straight line. (See **Figure 2.51**.) Note that the line is not extended to the left of point (0, 3600) nor to the right of point (5, 0), since those points are not in the domain of the problem.

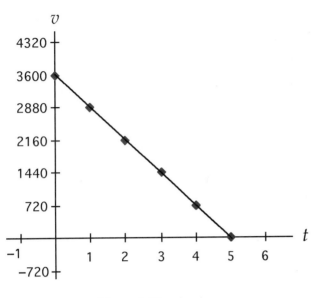

Figure 2.51

e) The v-intercept is the point (0, 3600), and the t-intercept is the point (5, 0). The v-intercept indicates that at time zero, the value of the computer is $3600. The t-intercept indicates that at the end of 5 years, the value of the computer is worth $0.

f) Yes, the function is a linear function. Its equation $v = -720t + 3600$ is in the form $y = mx + b$, where $m = -720$ and $b = 3600$. Its graph is a straight line, and the average rate of change is constant.

Using Tables to Graph Linear Functions

Consider the relationship between the cost in dollars of renting a moving van for one day and the distance driven in miles. For a typical city, the linear equation $c = 0.49d + 30$ might be used to represent this relationship.

A graph of this function can provide a quick summary of the relationship that exists between the two variables. Recall that the graph of an equation involving two variables is the collection of *all* the ordered pairs of numbers that are solutions to the equation. For instance, point (100, 79) is a solution to the equation $c = 0.49d + 30$, so the point (100, 79) is a point on the graph of $c = 0.49d + 30$.

One way to sketch the graph is to create a table of values, plot the ordered pairs, look for a pattern, then connect the plotted points. **Table 2.21** shows three solutions to the equation $c = 0.49d + 30$.

d	Substitute to Find c	c
0	0.49(0) + 30 = 30	30
10	0.49(10) + 30 = 34.9	34.9
20	0.49(20) + 30 = 39.8	39.8

Table 2.21

The graph in **Figure 2.52** shows the three points from Table 2.21 and the line drawn through the points. This line contains an unlimited number of points, all of which satisfy the equation $c = 0.49d + 30$. Note that the line has not been extended to the left of point (0, 30), since it is meaningless in this context for distance to be less than zero.

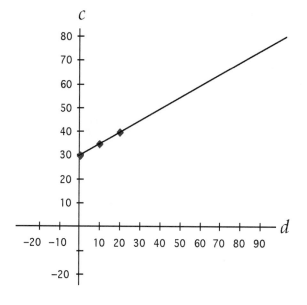

Figure 2.52

Slope of a Line

For the linear functions we have graphed, some graphs slant upward from left to right, whereas others slant downward. We have also noticed that some graphs are steeper than others. This notion of steepness as the line rises or falls can be represented by a number known as the **slope of the line.** The line in **Figure 2.53** has an upward vertical change of 2 units (rise) for each 1 unit of horizontal change (run) as we move from left to right. This indicates that the line has a slope of $\dfrac{\text{rise}}{\text{run}} = \dfrac{2}{1}$ or 2.

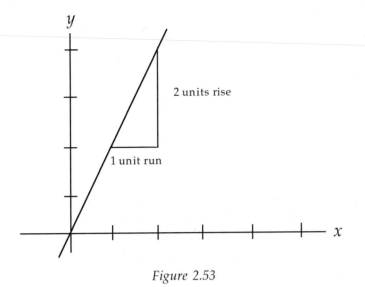

Figure 2.53

Because the slope of a line measures how much the dependent variable y changes with respect to the independent variable x, it is equivalent to the rate of change of the function. Hence, the rate of change of y with respect to x for the function shown in Figure 2.53 is $\frac{2}{1}$ or 2 units change in y per unit change in x.

In general, the slope m of a nonvertical line passing through two points (x_1, y_1) and (x_2, y_2) is $m = \frac{y_2 - y_1}{x_2 - x_1}$. (See **Figure 2.54.**)

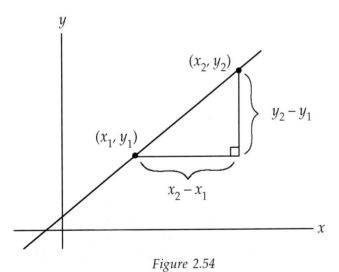

Figure 2.54

Example 18

For (a)–(c), plot the points, sketch the line that passes through the points, and find the slope of the line.

a) $(-2, 5)$ and $(1, -4)$

b) $(5, 4)$ and $(-2, 4)$

c) $(-5, -1)$ and $(-1, 5)$

Solution:

a) See **Figure 2.55.**

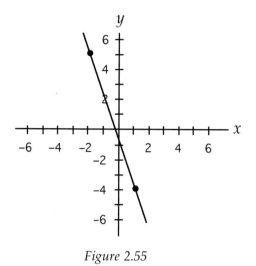

Figure 2.55

$$m = \frac{(-4) - 5}{1 - (-2)}$$

$$= \frac{-9}{3} \text{ or } -3$$

b) See **Figure 2.56.**

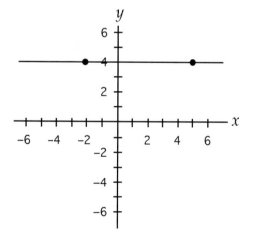

Figure 2.56

$$m = \frac{4 - 4}{-2 - 5}$$

$$= \frac{0}{-7} \text{ or } 0$$

c) See **Figure 2.57.**

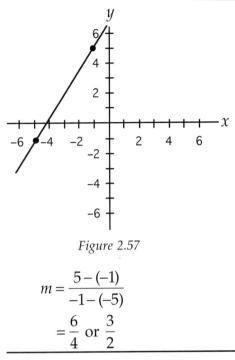

Figure 2.57

$$m = \frac{5-(-1)}{-1-(-5)}$$

$$= \frac{6}{4} \text{ or } \frac{3}{2}$$

In Example 18, note that lines with positive slopes rise from left to right, lines with negative slopes fall from left to right, and horizontal lines have slopes of zero.

Example 19

Consider the linear function $y = -2.5x - 7$.

a) Use the function to complete **Table 2.22.**

x	y
–2	
0	
2	
4	

Table 2.22

b) Use the table of values to sketch the graph of the function.

c) Use any two points on the graph of the function to find the slope of the line.

d) What do you notice about the slope of the line and the equation of the line?

e) Add a third column to Table 2.22. Between each two pairs of values in the table, find the average rate of change of y with respect to x. What do you notice about the average rate of change for the values in the table?

f) Use the equation of the line to find the coordinates of the y-intercept of the line.

Solution:

a) See **Table 2.23.**

x	y
−2	−2
0	−7
2	−12
4	−17

Table 2.23

b) The graph of the function is shown in **Figure 2.58.**

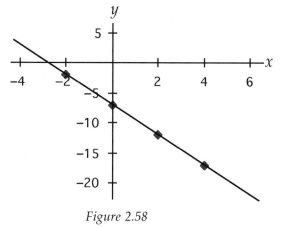

Figure 2.58

c) Using the points (0, −7) and (2, −12), $m = \dfrac{-12-(-7)}{2-0} = -\dfrac{5}{2}$ or −2.5.

d) The coefficient of x in the equation $y = -2.5x - 7$ is the slope of the line.

e) See **Table 2.24.**

x	y	Average Rate of Change of y with Respect to x
−2	−2	0
0	−7	$\dfrac{(-7-(-2))}{(0-(-2))} = \dfrac{-5}{2}$ or −2.5.
2	−12	$\dfrac{(-12-(-7))}{(2-0)} = \dfrac{-5}{2}$ or −2.5.
4	−17	$\dfrac{(-17-(-12))}{(4-2)} = \dfrac{-5}{2}$ or −2.5.

Table 2.24

The average rate of change between any two pairs of values is constant and is the same as the slope of the line.

f) The y-intercept is found by letting $x = 0$ in the equation and solving for y:
$y = -2.5(0) - 7$; $y = -7$. The y-intercept is the point $(0, -7)$.

Slope-Intercept Form of an Equation of a Line

In Example 19 we noticed that the slope of the line is the same as the coefficient of x in the equation $y = -2.5x - 7$. Notice also that -7, the constant term of the equation, is the value of y when $x = 0$ and is equal to the y-intercept of the graph. If we were to examine many different equations written in the form $y = mx + b$, we would notice that the same thing is true.

> If an equation of a line is written in **slope-intercept form,** $y = mx + b$, m is the slope of the line and b is the y-intercept.

Example 20

For each function, find the slope and the coordinates of the y-intercept of the graph.

a) $y = -5x + 6$.

b) $2y - 3x + 8 = 0$.

Solution:

a) The equation is in slope-intercept form. The slope of the line is -5 or $\dfrac{-5}{1}$ and the y-intercept is the point $(0, 6)$.

b) First solve the equation for y.

$$2y - 3x + 8 = 0$$
$$2y = 3x - 8$$
$$y = \frac{3}{2}x - 4$$

The equation is now in slope-intercept form, where $m = \dfrac{3}{2}$ and $b = -4$.

Therefore, the slope of the line is $\dfrac{3}{2}$, and the y-intercept is the point $(0, -4)$.

Using Slope-Intercept Form to Graph a Linear Equation

Once we determine the slope and y-intercept of the graph of a linear function, a quick sketch of the graph can be made. For example, to sketch the graph of the linear function $y = \dfrac{2}{3}x + 1$, first check to make sure the equation is in slope-intercept form, then identify the slope and y-intercept. For this equation, the slope of the line is $\dfrac{2}{3}$ and the y-intercept is 1. (See **Figures 2.59a** and **2.59b**.)

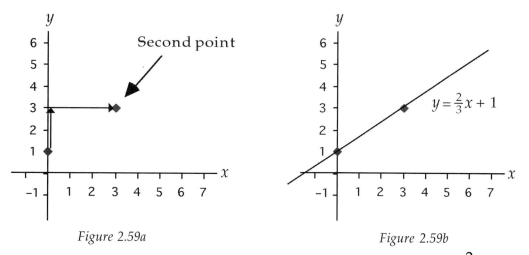

Figure 2.59a   *Figure 2.59b*

In Figure 2.59a, plot the y-intercept, $(0, 1)$. Then use the slope of $\dfrac{2}{3}$ to locate a second point on the graph. From the y-intercept, move up 2 units and to the right 3 units. In Figure 2.59b, draw the line passing through the two points.

Finding Equations of Lines

We can also use our knowledge of the slope-intercept form of an equation to find an equation of a line if we know the slope and y-intercept of the line. For example, an equation for a line with a slope of -7 and y-intercept of 5 is $y = -7x + 5$.

Example 21

When wheat is planted at various depths under good growing conditions, the time when the wheat emerges at the surface of the soil is related to the number of growing degree days (GDD) that have accumulated since the time of planting.

Figure 2.60 shows the relationship for wheat seed between the number of growing degree days G in GDD Celsius before emergence and the depth of planting d in centimeters. Notice that the graph shows only the points that are in the problem domain. In this case, only planting depths of $d > 0$ make sense.

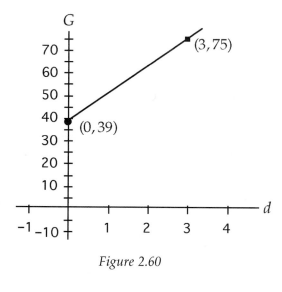

Figure 2.60

---

a) What is the slope of the line in Figure 2.60, including units?

b) What is an equation of the line in Figure 2.60?

Solution:

a) The slope of the line is $\dfrac{75-39}{3-0} = \dfrac{36\ \text{GDD}}{3\ \text{cm}}$ or 12 GDD/cm.

b) Since the y-intercept is equal to 39 and the slope of the line is 12, an equation of the line is $G = 12d + 39$.

> A growing degree day (GDD) is the average of the high and low temperatures for the day, reduced by the freezing temperature of water. So, like temperatures, growing degree days can be measured using either Fahrenheit or Celsius units.
>
> The number of GDD for a day with a temperature high of 20°C and a temperature low of 4°C is
>
> $\dfrac{20+4}{2} - 0 = 12 - 0 = 12$ GDD Celsius.

Exercises 2.5 *(SE pages 188–193)*

I. Investigations

1. In Discovery 2.3 you graphed a linear function relating volume and weight of a liquid. (See **Figure 2.61.**) Although only six pairs of data were plotted, a line was drawn through all the plotted points. The reason for drawing the line is that every point on the line represents a unique volume-weight pair that is physically possible for this situation.

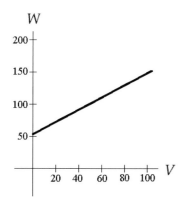

Figure 2.61

a) Recall that in Activity 2.1 you measured the weights of various quantities of nails. **Table 2.25** shows typical data for that activity.

Number of Nails	Weight of Box Plus Nails (g)
0	132.0
1	139.3
2	146.5
3	153.9
4	160.2
5	168.6
6	175.8
7	183.1
8	190.3
9	197.6
10	204.9

Table 2.25

Identify the independent and dependent variables for these data.

1. a) **Number of nails is the independent variable; weight is the dependent variable.**

    b) Construct a graph of these data by plotting points corresponding to each of the pairs of values in the table.

    b)

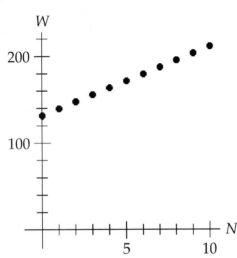

    c) Would it make sense to draw a line through the points? Explain.

    c) **No, the number of nails is measured in integers.**

Variables whose values represent counts, such as the number of nails in Table 2.25, are called *discrete variables* (see Section 1.2). A discrete variable is any variable whose possible values are limited to a countable set of numbers and cannot take on intermediate values. Since fractional parts of nails do not make sense for this data set, the points in the graph in (b) are not connected with a line.

The weight and volume from Figure 2.61 are continuous variables, since all values in a continuous interval are possible. Continuous lines are often drawn on graphs even when variables are discrete, particularly when the overall mathematical relationship is being examined. But it is important to be aware of situations in which a line on a graph does not reflect reality.

For (d)–(g), each of the functions described is linear. Discuss whether it would be appropriate to draw a line through the data points that are plotted for the graph of the function.

    d) The length L of a concrete slab (in meters) changes with temperature T (in °C), according to the function $L = 0.00018T + 15$.

    d) **A line can be drawn, since temperature can change continuously.**

e) A cable television company's monthly charges are given by $C = 45.90 + 3.95m$, where m is the number of movies a customer rents in a month.

e) A line is not appropriate, since the number of movies must be a whole number.

f) The actual length (in inches) of a particular style of women's shoe is related to shoe size as shown in **Table 2.26**.

Size	5	$5\frac{1}{2}$	6	$6\frac{1}{2}$	7	$7\frac{1}{2}$	8	$8\frac{1}{2}$	9	$9\frac{1}{2}$	10	$10\frac{1}{2}$
Length	9	$9\frac{1}{4}$	$9\frac{1}{2}$	$9\frac{3}{4}$	10	$10\frac{1}{4}$	$10\frac{1}{2}$	$10\frac{3}{4}$	11	$11\frac{1}{4}$	$11\frac{1}{2}$	$11\frac{3}{4}$

Table 2.26

f) A line is not appropriate because shoes are made in half-size increments.

g) The amount of light L (in lumen-hours) that passes through the lens of a particular photographic enlarger during printing is given as a function of time t (in minutes) by $L = 0.035t$.

g) A line can be drawn because time changes continuously.

2. Elderly and home-care patients can subscribe to a service that supplies them with a device that can summon an ambulance in case of an emergency. Suppose the fee for this device is $50 for connection plus $27 per month of service.

a) Let t represent the number of months of use and c represent the total cost for the service. Which variable is the independent variable? Which is the dependent variable? Explain.

a) Since the cost c for the service depends on the number t of months of service, time is the independent variable and cost is the dependent variable.

b) Write an equation for the function that represents the relationship between time and cost.

b) $c = 27t + 50$.

c) Plot points for $t = 1, 2, 3,$ and 4 months. Graph the line that goes through these points.

c)

Time (months)	Cost (dollars)
1	77
2	104
3	131
4	158

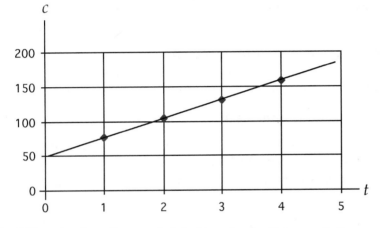

d) What is the slope of this line including units?

d) $27 per month

e) What are the coordinates of the vertical intercept for this line? What does this intercept indicate?

e) (0, 50). At the beginning of the first month of service, the connection charge of $50 is paid.

f) Use your equation or graph to find the cost for 1 year of service.

f) $c = 27(12) + 50; c = \$374.$

g) Suppose that insurance covers up to $1000 for this service. Use your graph to estimate how long insurance will pay for the service.

g) The graph makes it look like 35 or 36 months. The actual value is 35.19 months, which is found by solving 1000 = 50 + 27t.

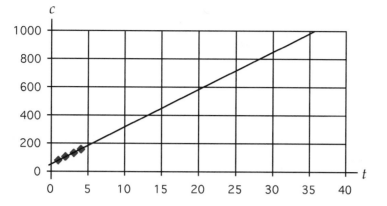

3. The linear functions examined in this section are all characterized by the algebraic form $y = mx + b$. But there are many linear functions for which the value of b is 0. In such cases, the equation has a simpler form, $y = mx$.

For example, consider the recycling of aluminum cans. On the average (allowing for variations in can size), 1 pound of recycled aluminum contains 33 cans. Obviously, 0 cans must weigh 0 pounds.

a) Assuming that every pound of aluminum contains 33 cans, write an equation expressing the number N of cans as a function of the weight w in pounds of recycled aluminum.

3. a) $N = 33w$.

b) In 1998, 1,938,000,000 pounds of cans were recycled. How many cans were recycled?

b) $N = 33(1,938,000,000)$; $N = 63,954,000,000$, or about 64 billion pounds.

c) Sketch a graph of the relationship between weight (in billions of pounds) and number of cans (in billions).

c)

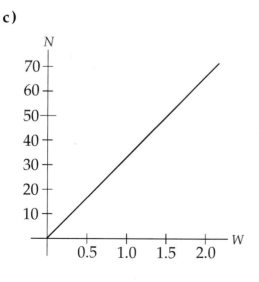

A linear relationship of this type, which includes the ordered pair (0, 0), is called a **direct variation function.** We say that the dependent variable **varies directly** with the independent variable, or sometimes that the variables are **directly proportional.** When two quantities vary directly, their ratio is a constant that is equal to the slope of their graph. The graph of a direct variation function always passes through the origin.

d) What is the constant ratio of the number of cans to the weight of aluminum in pounds?

d) 33 cans/lb

For (e)–(j), consider the following situation.

Henry Ford, the founder and president of the Ford Motor Company, was notorious for understaffing his accounting department. As a result there were not enough people to keep track of requisitions, which were generated at the rate of about 10,000 a day during the 1920s. All the requisitions for supplies that were less than $10 were thus put in huge piles and never recorded.

To determine the total cost of all the requisitions, the company's auditor devised a scheme. A small sample of the requisitions was examined, and the average value of a single requisition was found to be $2.43. Then, rather than count all the requisitions, the employees weighed some requisitions and determined a linear function that computed the approximate total value based on weight.

e) For the linear function in this situation, what are the independent and dependent variables?

e) Weight is the independent variable; total value of requisitions is the dependent variable.

f) Write an equation expressing the total value V of the requisitions as a function of total weight w, with an as yet undetermined slope m.

f) $V = mw$.

g) If 100 requisitions weighed 0.45 pounds, what was the total value contained in that 0.45 pounds of requisitions?

g) (100)($2.43) = $243.

h) Calculate the constant ratio of the value of the requisitions in dollars to the weight of the requisitions in pounds.

h) $\dfrac{243 \text{ dollars}}{0.45 \text{ pounds}}$ = 540 dollars/pound.

i) Since the constant ratio from (h) is equal to the slope m in your equation from (f), write an equation for V as a function of w.

i) $V = 540w$.

j) If all the requisitions for a month weighed 1500 pounds, what was their total value?

j) $V = 540(1500) = \$810{,}000$.

k) A person's red blood cell count can be estimated by placing a drop of blood on a microscope slide and by counting the number of cells within the circular field of the microscope. (See **Figure 2.62.**)

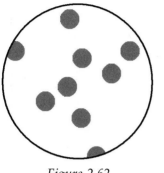

Figure 2.62

If the area of the circle is known, then area can be used as a measure of the number of blood cells. That is, the number of cells varies directly with area.

Assume that a 0.01 mm² viewing field contains 23 red blood cells. Find an equation for the number N of red blood cells as a function of area A.

k) $N = mA$. $N = 23$ **for** $A = 0.01$, **so** $m = 23/0.01 = 2300$ **cells/mm², and** $N = 2300A$.

l) Using your equation from (k), determine how many red blood cells are contained in an area of 50 mm².

l) $N = 2300(50)$; $N = 115{,}000$ **red blood cells.**

4. A quick way to sketch the graph of a linear function is to use the two intercepts.

- First, find the intercepts. (The x-intercept is found by letting $y = 0$ in the equation, and the y-intercept is found by letting $x = 0$.)

- Then plot the two intercepts and draw a line passing through them.

a) Consider the equation $5x + 3y = 30$. Find the x-intercept. Find the y-intercept.

a) **To find the x-intercept: $5x + 3(0) = 30$; $x = 6$. The x-intercept is the point (6, 0). To find the y-intercept: $5(0) + 3y = 30$; $y = 10$. The y-intercept is the point (0, 10).**

b) Use the intercepts to graph the line.

b)

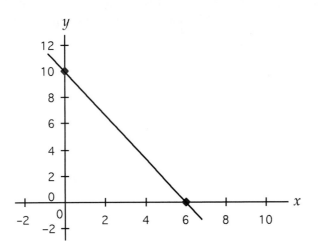

c) Using intercepts, graph the line $y - x = 6$.

c)

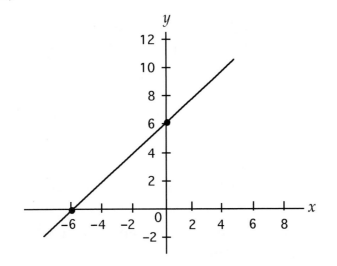

d) The method of using the horizontal and vertical intercepts to obtain a quick graph has its limitations. Describe two types of functions for which the method does not work. Explain why it does not work for these two types of functions. (Hint: Graph $y = 3x$ and $y = 4$ to see two examples.)

d) **It does not work for horizontal lines or lines that go through the origin because you need two different points to draw a line. Horizontal lines have only one intercept, and lines that go through the origin have intercepts that are the same point.**

5. Finding the intercepts of a graph of a linear function is helpful in determining an appropriate scale for a graph if you are graphing by hand or an appropriate viewing window if you are using a graphing calculator to graph a function.

   For example, for the equation $3x - 4y = 72$, the x-intercept is the point $(24, 0)$ and the y-intercept is the point $(0, -18)$. Since it is often advantageous to see the intercepts on a graph, we would want to make sure the points $(24, 0)$ and $(0, -18)$ are included on our axes. The graphing calculator screen in **Figure 2.63** shows the function using a viewing window of $[-10, 30]$ x $[-20, 10]$.

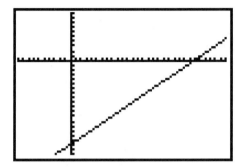

Figure 2.63

a) Write an appropriate viewing window for the linear function $80x + 30y = 2700$.

a) **Sample answer: [0, 40] x [0, 100]. Any window that includes the points (0, 90) and (33.75, 0) is acceptable.**

b) The calculator screen in **Figure 2.64** shows the graph of the linear function $128x - 512 = 32y$.

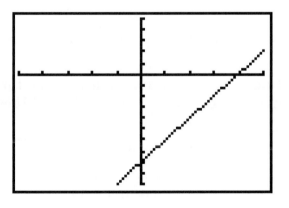

Figure 2.64

Use your knowledge of x- and y-intercepts to find the distance between the adjacent tick marks on the x- and y-axes.

b) **The x-intercept is the point (4, 0), so the distance between the tick marks is 1 unit. The y-intercept is the point (0, –16), so the distance between the tick marks is 2 units.**

6. a) Use the equation $x = 3$ to complete **Table 2.27.**

x					
y	−3	0	1	3	5

Table 2.27

6. a)

x	3	3	3	3	3
y	−3	0	1	3	5

b) Use your completed table to help you graph the equation $x = 3$.

b)

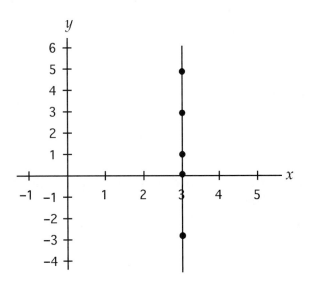

c) Do any of your representations of this relationship (equation, graph, or table) represent a linear function? Explain.

c) No, even though the graph is linear, it is not a function because for the input value 3 in the domain, there are infinitely many output values associated with it.

A vertical line can be represented by the equation $x = a$, where a is the x-intercept.

d) Find the equation of a vertical line passing through the point (−1, 5).

d) $x = -1$.

e) We say that the slope of a vertical line is undefined. Explain why this statement is true. (Hint: Use two points on your graph from (b) to find the slope of the vertical line $x = 3$.)

e) The statement is true because when you try to find the slope of a vertical line, you encounter division by zero, which is undefined.

7. **a)** Use the equation $y = 4$ to complete **Table 2.28**.

x	−3	0	1	3	5
y					

Table 2.28

7. a)

x	−3	0	1	3	5
y	4	4	4	4	4

b) Use your completed table to help you graph the equation $y = 4$.

b)

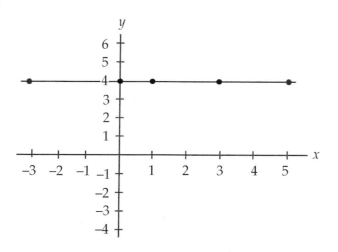

c) Do any of the representations of this relationship (equation, graph, or table) show that it is a function? Explain.

c) Yes, all of them show it is a function because for each value in the input of the domain, there is one and only one output value.

A horizontal line can be represented by the equation $y = b$, where b is the y-intercept.

d) Find the equation of a horizontal line passing through the point (−1, 5).

d) $y = 5$.

e) We say that the slope of a horizontal line is 0. Explain why this statement is true. (Hint: Use two points on your graph from (b) to find the slope of the horizontal line $y = 4$.)

e) The statement is true because when you try to find the slope of a horizontal line, the change in the y-values is 0, while the change in the x-values is some nonzero number. And zero divided by any nonzero number is 0.

II. Projects and Group Activities *(SE pages 194–195)*

8. Making a decision about which cellular phone company to use, or which company's plan to purchase, can be a daunting task. It's often time-consuming, requiring careful research if the consumer hopes to make the wisest choice.

   Suppose that after researching several companies, you've narrowed your choices to one company and now have to make a choice between Plan A and Plan B.

   • Plan A charges $19.99 per month plus 30 cents for each minute of phone use.

   • Plan B charges $14.99 per month plus 40 cents for each minute of phone use.

   To help make a decision as to which plan is better for you, you can use your knowledge of functions and their representations.

   a) If C represents the monthly cost in dollars and t represents the time talked in minutes, write an equation for Plan A that represents the relationship between time and money. Write an equation for Plan B.

8. a) **Plan A: $C = 19.99 + 0.3t$; Plan B: $C = 14.99 + 0.4t$.**

   b) Use your equations from (a) to complete **Table 2.29.**

Time (minutes)	Cost for Plan A (dollars)	Cost for Plan B (dollars)
0		
20		
40		
50		
60		

Table 2.29

b)

Time (minutes)	Cost for Plan A (dollars)	Cost for Plan B (dollars)
0	19.99	14.99
20	25.99	22.99
40	31.99	30.99
50	34.99	34.99
60	37.99	38.99

c) Carefully sketch the graphs of the two equations from (a) on the same coordinate plane.

c)

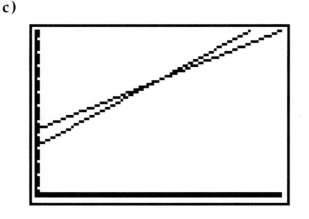

[0, 100] x [0, 50]

d) Notice that the two lines intersect. Use your graph to find the point where the two lines intersect. (If graphing calculators are available, graph each function and use the TRACE or CALC feature on the calculator to find the point of intersection.)

d) (50, 34.99)

Using TRACE:

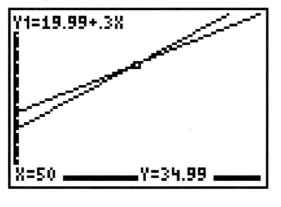

[0, 100] x [0, 50]

e) Explain what the point of intersection in (c) means.

e) If you talk for exactly 50 minutes, the cost for both plans is the same $34.99.

f) Use your graph from (c) to determine which plan is more economical if you talk less than 50 minutes. Determine which plan is more economical if you talk more than 50 minutes. Explain how you used your graph to answer the questions.

f) If you talk less than 50 minutes, Plan B is the more economical. You can see this on the graph because when *t* < 50, the *C*-values for Plan B are "below" those of Plan A. When you talk more than 50 minutes, Plan A becomes more economical.

When two or more linear equations are used to describe a given situation, these equations are referred to as a **system of linear equations.** The **solution to the system** in two variables is the ordered pair that satisfies both equations.

To find the solution to the system of linear equations for the cell phone situation, we graphed each equation and found the point of intersection. This point of intersection lies on both lines. Hence, it is a solution to each equation.

Another way to find the solution to the system of equations is to solve each equation for the same variable and then set the equations equal to each other. For example, we know that $C = 19.99 + 0.3t$ and $C = 14.99 + 0.4t$. Since each equation is already solved for C, we know that

$$19.99 + 0.3t = 14.99 + 0.4t$$

$19.99 + 0.3t - 14.99 = 0.4t$	Subtract 14.99 from each side.
$5.00 = 0.4t - 0.3t$	Subtract 0.3t from each side.
$5.00 = 0.1t$	Multiply each side by 10.
$50 = t$	

Substituting 50 for t in either original equation, we can find the cost C.

$C = 19.99 + 0.3(50)$

$C = 34.99$

So the ordered pair (50, 34.99) is a solution to each equation.

   g) Consider the following two plans:

- Plan I: $C = 0.3t + 10.99$.

- Plan II: $C = 0.35t + 3.99$.

Determine the time when the two plans cost the same. Discuss the times when each plan is the more economical. Explain by showing solutions to equations or by using graphs and/or tables.

   g) Using the graphing calculator's CALC function:

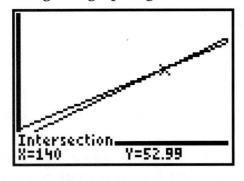

Intersection
X=140   Y=52.99

[0, 200] x [0, 100]

For time less than 140 minutes, Plan II is the more economical. For time greater than 140 minutes, Plan I is better. If exactly 140 minutes are used, the plans cost the same.

h) Solve the following system both graphically and algebraically.
$y = 3x + 7$ and $y = -2x - 11$.

h) Graphically:

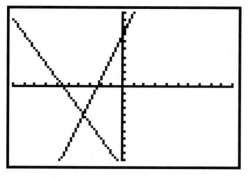

[–10, 10] x [–10, 10]

Algebraically:

$3x + 7 = -2x - 11$

$5x + 7 = -11$	**Add $2x$ to both sides of the equation.**
$5x = -18$	**Subtract 7 from both sides.**
$x = \dfrac{-18}{5}$ or –3.6	**Divide both sides of the equation by 5.**

To find the y-value of the solution, substitute $x = -3.6$ into either equation. This gives $y = 3(-3.6) + 7$; $y = -3.8$.

So, the solution to the system is the ordered pair (–3.6, –3.8).

9. The graph in **Figure 2.65** can be used to relate temperature in degrees Celsius to its equivalent temperature in degrees Fahrenheit.

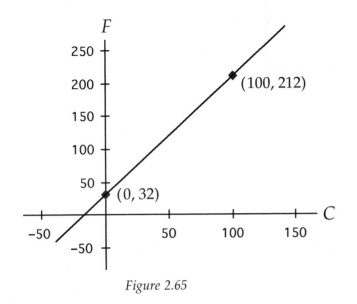

Figure 2.65

a) The coordinates of the point (0, 32) on the vertical axis represent the temperature at which water freezes in degrees Celsius (0) and degrees Fahrenheit (32). What do the coordinates of the point (100, 212) represent?

9. a) **The coordinates represent the temperature at which water boils in degrees Celsius (100) and degrees Fahrenheit (212).**

b) Use the graph in Figure 2.65 to write an equation that relates temperature in degrees Celsius to its equivalent temperature in degrees Fahrenheit.

b) **To write the equation, find the slope and y-intercept of the line.**
    Slope = $\dfrac{(212 - 32)}{(100 - 0)} = \dfrac{9}{5}$. The y-intercept is 32. Hence, an equation for the line is $F = \dfrac{9}{5}C + 32$.

10. In 1999, the exchange rate for Russian rubles was about 25 Russian rubles per 1 American dollar.

a) Write an equation that represents the relationship between a number r of Russian rubles and its equivalent number d of American dollars. Is this relationship linear? Explain.

10. a) $r = 25d$; **yes, the relationship is linear because the equation is of the form** $y = mx + b$, **where** $m = 25$ **and** $b = 0$.

b) What is the rate of change for this function, including units?

b) The rate of change is 25 rubles/dollar.

c) Explain in terms of rubles and dollars why the vertical intercept is zero.

c) The vertical intercept is zero because 0 dollars is exchanged for 0 rubles.

d) Now let d be the dependent variable and r the independent variable. Write a function for d in terms of r.

d) $d = \dfrac{1}{25} r$ **or** $d = 0.04r$.

e) What is its rate of change for the function in (d), including units? What does this rate of change mean?

e) The rate of change is (1/25) dollars per ruble or 0.04 dollars/ruble. This means you get 4 cents for every 1 ruble.

11. Let s be the number of shares of a stock that you are going to buy. The stock is presently selling for \$7.25 per share. Your online broker charges a fee of \$25 per transaction.

a) Write an equation in slope-intercept form for c, the total cost of purchasing s shares of stock.

11. a) $c = 7.25s + 25$.

b) Sketch a graph of the equation in (a).

b)

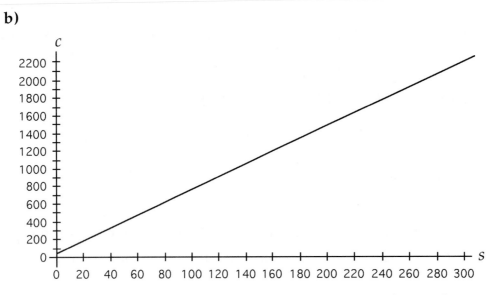

c) What is the slope of the graph, including units? What is the vertical intercept, including units?

c) m = **$7.25/share; the vertical intercept is $25.**

d) Use the equation from (a) or the graph from (b) to determine the cost of purchasing 200 shares of this stock.

d) c = **25 + 7.25(200);** c = **$1475.**

e) Use your graph to estimate the number of shares of this stock you can afford to purchase if you have $2000 available.

e) The graph shows that the number of shares is between 270 and 280.

12. Suppose your computer downloads data at about 20 kilobytes per second. Let n be the number of kilobytes in a file and t the number of seconds it will take to download the file.

a) Find the length of time it will take to download a file that is 1000 kb.

12. a) $\dfrac{1000 \text{ kb}}{20 \text{ kb}/\text{s}} = 50 \text{ s.}$

b) Write an equation for the linear function for t in terms of n.

b) $t = \dfrac{1}{20}n$ **or** $t = \dfrac{n}{20}.$

c) What is the rate of change of this function?

c) $\dfrac{1}{20}$ **seconds per kilobyte**

d) What is the vertical intercept of the graph of this function? What does it mean in this context?

d) 0 seconds. It takes 0 seconds to download a 0 kb file.

e) What is the problem domain for this function?

e) All numbers greater than or equal to 0

f) Graph the function.

f)

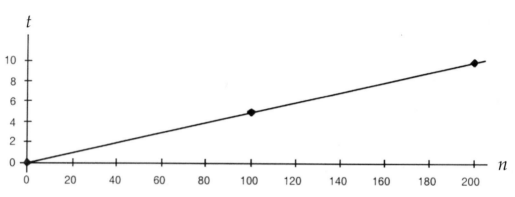

13. Does **Table 2.30** describe a linear relationship? Explain.

x	−2	−1	0	1	2
y	0	0.5	1	1.5	2

Table 2.30

13. Yes, there is a linear relationship. There is a constant average rate of change of 0.5 between any two sets of data pairs.

14. Does **Table 2.31** describe a linear relationship? Explain.

x	−4	−2	0	2	4
y	16	4	0	4	16

Table 2.31

14. No, there is not a linear relationship because the average rate of change is not constant. For example, the average rate of change between points (−4, 16) and (−2, 4) is −12/2 = −6. Between points (0, 0) and (2, 4), the average rate of change is 4/2 = 2.

15. Consider the graphs in **Figures 2.66–2.69.** Determine whether each is a linear function. Explain.

a)

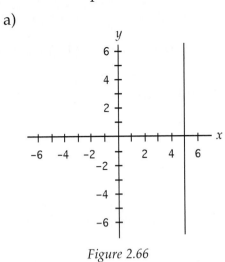

Figure 2.66

b)

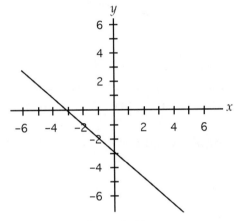

Figure 2.67

c)

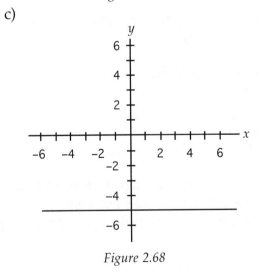

Figure 2.68

d)

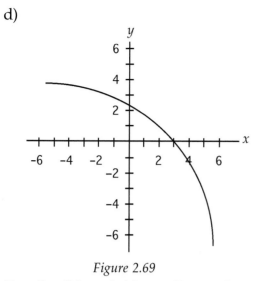

Figure 2.69

15. Graphs (b) and (c) are linear functions, since they are nonvertical straight lines. Graph (a) is not a function, since its only input value (5) has more than one output value associated with it. Graph (d) is a function, but it is not linear, as it is not a straight line.

For 16–20, create a table of values similar to **Table 2.32**. Then use the table to sketch the graph of the linear function.

x	y

Table 2.32

16. $y = 6 - 3x$.

16. Sample table:

x	y
0	6
2	0
4	−6

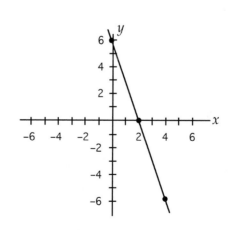

17. $4y - 2x = 8$.

17. Sample table:

x	y
–2	1
0	2
2	3

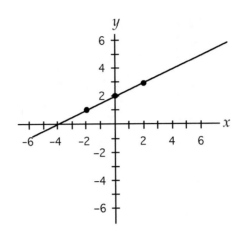

18. $x - y = -2$.

18. Sample table:

x	y
–4	–2
0	2
4	6

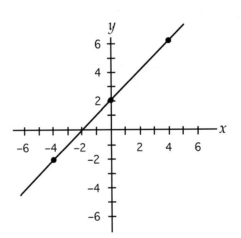

19. $y = \dfrac{3}{4}x - 1$.

19. Sample table:

x	y
–4	–4
0	–1
4	2

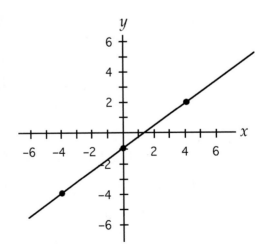

20. $y = -2$.

20. Sample table:

x	y
-2	-2
0	-2
2	-2

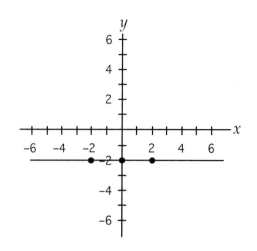

21. Which of the following points lie on the graph of the linear function $3x + 2y = -1$? Justify your decisions algebraically.

    a) $(0, 0)$ b) $(-1, 1)$ c) $\left(0, \dfrac{-1}{2}\right)$ d) $(3, -4)$

21. a) Does not lie on the graph, as $3(0) + 2(0) \neq -1$.

    b) Does lie on the graph, as $3(-1) + 2(1) = -1$.

    c) Does lie on the graph, as $3(0) + 2\left(\dfrac{-1}{2}\right) = -1$.

    d) Does not lie on the graph, as $3(3) + 2(-4) \neq -1$.

22. Find the slope of a line passing through points $(1, 6)$ and $(5, 22)$.

22. $m = \dfrac{22 - 6}{5 - 1}; m = \dfrac{16}{4}$ **or 4.**

23. Find the slope of a line passing through points $(0, 7)$ and $(-2, 4)$.

23. $m = \dfrac{4 - 7}{(-2) - 0}; m = \dfrac{-3}{-2}$ **or** $\dfrac{3}{2}$.

24. Find the slope of a line passing through points $(-3, -5)$ and $(-1, 12)$.

24. $m = \dfrac{12 - (-5)}{(-1) - (-3)}; m = \dfrac{17}{2}$ **or 8.5.**

25. Find x so that a line passing through points $(4, 3)$ and $(12, x)$ will have a slope of 2.

25. $2 = \dfrac{x - 3}{12 - 4}; 2 = \dfrac{x - 3}{8}; x - 3 = 16; x = 19.$

26. For (a)–(c), use the graph in **Figure 2.70.**

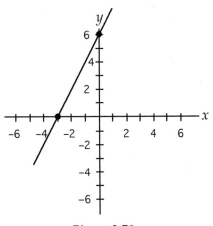

Figure 2.70

    a) What is the slope of the line?

26. a) $m = 2.$

    b) What are the coordinates of the y-intercept? What are the coordinates of the x-intercept?

    b) (0, 6); (–3, 0)

    c) What is the equation of the line?

    c) $y = 2x + 6.$

27. For (a)–(c), use the graph in **Figure 2.71.**

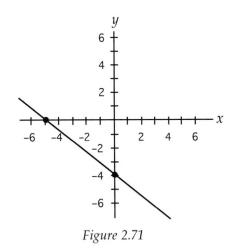

Figure 2.71

    a) What is the slope of the line?

27. a) $m = -\dfrac{4}{5}.$

    b) What are the coordinates of the y-intercept? What are the coordinates of the x-intercept?

    b) (0, –4); (–5, 0)

c) What is the equation of the line?

c) $y = -\dfrac{4}{5}x - 4$ or $5y = -4x - 20$.

For 28–31, write the equation in slope-intercept form. Identify the slope and the y-intercept of the graph of the linear function.

28. $4y - 7x = 42$.

28. $y = \dfrac{7}{4}x + \dfrac{21}{2}$; $m = \dfrac{7}{4}$; $b = \dfrac{21}{2}$ or 10.5.

29. $6x = 72 - 3y$.

29. $y = -2x + 24$; $m = -2$; $b = 24$.

30. $0.5x + 0.2y = -15$.

30. $y = -\dfrac{5}{2}x - 75$; $m = -\dfrac{5}{2}$; $b = -75$.

31. $\dfrac{3}{7}y = -18$.

31. $y = -42$; $m = 0$; $b = -42$.

For 32–35, write the equation in slope-intercept form. Then sketch the graph.

32. $2y = 6x - 2$.

32. $y = 3x - 1$.

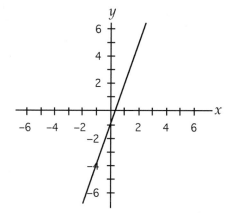

33. $4x + y = -5.$

33. $y = -4x - 5.$

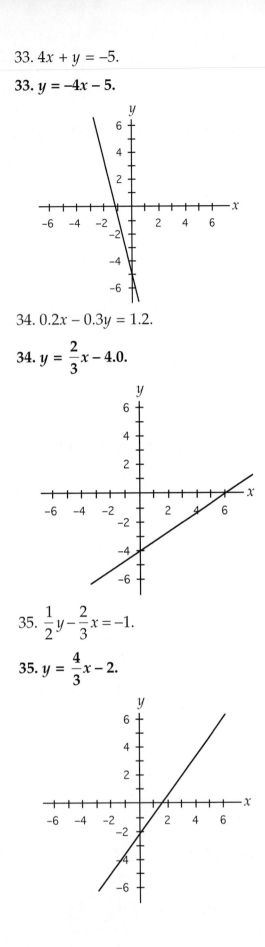

34. $0.2x - 0.3y = 1.2.$

34. $y = \dfrac{2}{3}x - 4.0.$

35. $\dfrac{1}{2}y - \dfrac{2}{3}x = -1.$

35. $y = \dfrac{4}{3}x - 2.$

For 36–42, graph the line passing through the point P and having a slope of m.

36. $P = (2, 4)$; $m = 5$.

36.

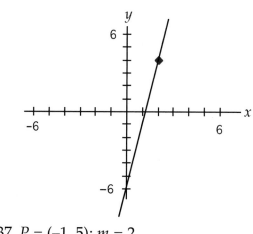

37. $P = (-1, 5)$; $m = 2$.

37.

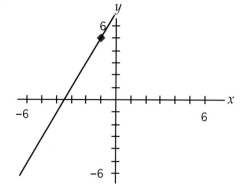

38. $P = (3, -2)$; $m = -4$.

38.

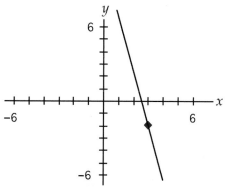

39. $P = (-1, 2); m = -\dfrac{3}{4}.$

39.

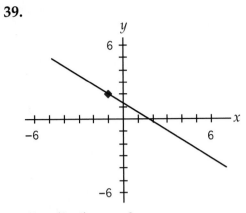

40. $P = (3, 4); m = 0.$

40.

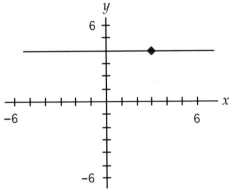

41. $P = (4, 0); m$ is undefined.

41.

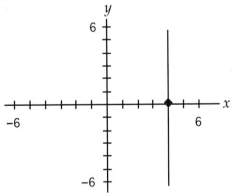

42. $P = (-2, -1)$; m is undefined.

42.

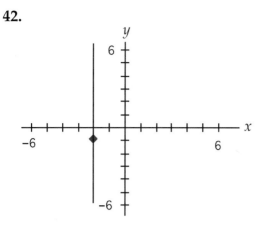

For 43–52, find the equation of the line.

43. The slope is 6; the y-intercept is -2.

43. $y = 6x - 2$.

44. The slope is $-\dfrac{2}{5}$; the y-intercept is 0.

44. $y = -\dfrac{2}{5}x$.

45. Use **Table 2.33.**

x	-2	0	2	4
y	12	6	0	-6

Table 2.33

45. $m = -3$; $b = 6$. The equation: $y = -3x + 6$.

46. Use **Table 2.34.**

x	-3	0	3	6
y	-5	-3	-1	1

Table 2.34

46. $m = \dfrac{2}{3}$; $b = -3$. The equation: $y = \dfrac{2}{3}x - 3$ or $3y = 2x - 9$.

47. See **Figure 2.72.**

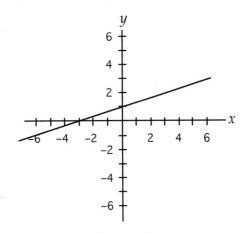

Figure 2.72

47. $y = \dfrac{1}{3}x + 1$ or $3y = x + 3$.

48. See **Figure 2.73.**

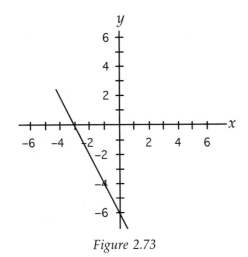

Figure 2.73

48. $y = -2x - 6$.

49. See **Figure 2.74.**

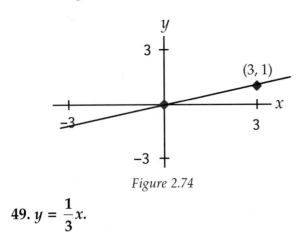

Figure 2.74

49. $y = \dfrac{1}{3}x$.

50. See **Figure 2.75.**

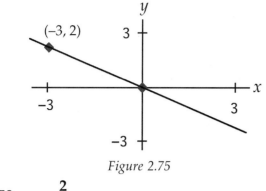

Figure 2.75

50. $y = -\dfrac{2}{3}x.$

51. See **Figure 2.76.**

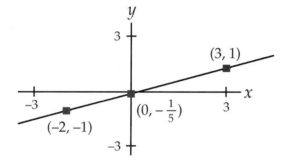

Figure 2.76

51. $y = \dfrac{2}{5}x - \dfrac{1}{5}.$

52. See **Figure 2.77.**

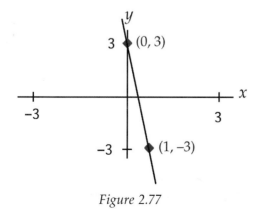

Figure 2.77

52. $y = -6x + 3.$

53. If two lines have the same slope and different x-intercepts, can they have the same y-intercept? Explain.

53. No, if two lines have the same slope and different x-intercepts, they are distinct, parallel lines. If two lines are distinct and parallel, they must have different y-intercepts.

54. Is it possible for a graph not to have a y-intercept? Explain.

54. Yes, if the line is vertical.

55. Is it possible for a graph not to have an x-intercept? Explain.

55. Yes, if the line is horizontal.

56. Is it possible for a graph to have no intercepts? Explain.

56. No, not to have an x-intercept means that the line is horizontal, and not to have a y-intercept means that the line is vertical. It is impossible for a line to be both horizontal and vertical.

Section 2.6 Creating Linear Models

What You Need to Know

- How to find the slope of a line

- How to find an equation for a line given its slope and y-intercept

- How to graph the equation of a line

What You Will Learn

- To find an equation of a line given its slope and one of its points

- To find an equation of a line given two of its points

- To find an equation of a line given its graph

- To identify parallel and perpendicular lines by examining their slopes

Materials

- None

In Section 2.5 we learned about linear functions and some of their uses. We also learned how to find an equation for a line when the slope and the y-intercept were known. But there are times when we need to know an equation and the slope and the y-intercept are not given. This section provides us with additional means of finding equations of lines.

For years people throughout our country have been obsessed with reaching some ideal weight and body size. For some it is simply a matter of looking good, but for others it is a health concern. Tables and graphs showing weight and height relationships seem to be everywhere. You can find them in magazines, newspapers, books, and manuals. These tables may be constructed for a variety of reasons. For example, a doctor may use them for health purposes, an insurance company may use them to help assess risk, and organizations such as the armed forces and police departments may use them to help determine fitness.

The graph in **Figure 2.78** reflects an old rule of thumb used for finding ideal weight from a given height.

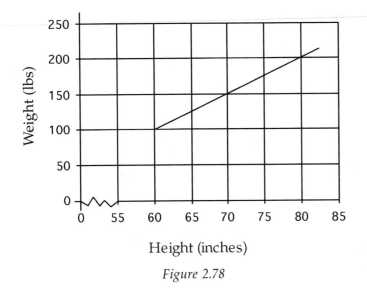

Figure 2.78

Discovery 2.4 Modeling a Height-Weight Relationship with an Equation *(SE page 205)*

1. With a partner, use the graph in Figure 2.78 to find the ideal weight for a person who is 6'8". Explain how you found your answer.

1. **Convert the height into inches: 80". Find 80" along the horizontal axis; move up to find the graph. The ideal weight is the *y*-coordinate of that point: 200 lb.**

2. Find the ideal weight of a person who is 5'8", of a person who is 5'3.5", and of a person who is 7'4". Explain any problems you encountered in finding these ideal weights.

2. **5'8" = 68 inches. You can only approximate the weight. It looks close to 140 lb.**

   5'3.5" = 63.5". Again, you can only approximate the weight, which looks close to 120 lb.

   7'4" = 88". The graph does not extend that far. If you extend it and guess, the weight would be about 220 lb.

   The problems encountered deal with accuracy and the limitations of the graph.

The problems that arose in item 2 can be resolved if you find an equation for the line.

3. Find the slope of the line in Figure 2.78. What does the value of the slope in this equation tell you about the relationship between a person's height and his or her ideal weight?

3. **Using the two points shown on the graph, (60, 100) and (70, 150):**

   $$m = \frac{150 - 100}{70 - 60} = 5.$$ **This means that for every 1-inch change in height, there is a corresponding 5-pound change in weight. So if you grow an inch, you can gain 5 more pounds and still be ideal.**

4. Find the *y*-intercept of the graph. For this context, what does the *y*-intercept tell you? (Note: The zigzag along the *x*-axis indicates that a portion of the graph is missing.)

4. **The *y*-intercept is –200. This tells you that for a person with height 0 inches, his or her ideal weight is –200 pounds. Of course, this makes no sense.**

5. Now that you have found the *y*-intercept and the slope of the line, find an equation for the line.

5. **$m = 5$; *y*-intercept = –200: $w = 5h - 200$.**

The equation you found in item 5 is a **linear model** that relates a person's height and weight. In this model, we say that weight is linearly related to height.

6. Use your equation from item 5 to predict the ideal weight of a person who is 5'6.5", of a person who is 4'10", and of a person who is 7'7".

6. **Using the equation $w = 5h - 200$, a person 5'6.5" should weigh 132.5 pounds, a person 4'10" should weigh 90 pounds, and a person who is 7'7" should weigh 225 pounds.**

7. Your equation from item 5 expresses weight as a function of height. The domain of this function, considered in a purely mathematical sense, includes all real numbers. What is a reasonable problem domain for this function?

7. **Answers will vary: This model seems to break down for people with heights under 5 ft. It also does not work well for people who are very tall. A possible answer for the problem domain might be 4 ft $\leq h \leq$ 7 ft.**

8. Do you think the line shown in Figure 2.78 provides a good model for predicting ideal weight for any given height? Explain. If you feel that it is not a good model, what would you do to improve it?

8. **Answers will vary, but most students should agree that this is not a good model. It does not take into account the person's sex, age, bone structure, or frame size. For tall people, the ideal weight seems to be too low.**

A better model might curve upward as height increases. For example:

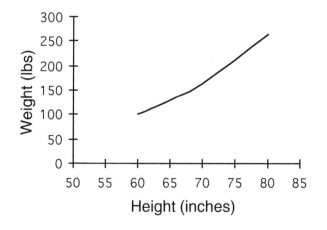

Point-Slope Form

One of the challenges in Discovery 2.4 was accurately finding the *y*-intercept so that you could find an equation for the line. There are times that we need to find an equation of a line and do not have its graph, slope, or *y*-intercept; but we do have other information, such as the slope of the line and a point on the line, or just two points on the line.

Most insurance companies provide their customers with height and weight tables. The information in **Table 2.35** comes from one such chart.

Men (maximum weight)	
Height (inches)	Small Frame (pounds)
61	113
64	122

Table 2.35

Assume that the relationship between weight and height is linear and we want to find an equation of the line. We can find an equation of the line that passes through the two points given in the table by using the **point-slope equation of a line.**

> **Point-Slope Equation of a Line**
>
> An equation of a line with slope *m* containing the point (h, k) is $y - k = m(x - h)$.

This equation can be derived by using the definition for slope, $m = \dfrac{y_2 - y_1}{x_2 - x_1}$. If we replace the point (x_1, y_1) with the coordinates of the given point on the line (h, k) and (x_2, y_2) with the coordinates of any point on the line (x, y), we get $m = \dfrac{y - k}{x - h}$ or $y - k = m(x - h)$.

To use point-slope form for the equation of a line when two points are given, first determine the slope of the line through the two points:

$$m = \frac{122 \text{ lb} - 113 \text{ lb}}{64 \text{ lb} - 61 \text{ lb}} = \frac{9 \text{ lb}}{3 \text{ lb}} = 3 \text{ lb} / \text{in.}$$

Now substitute the coordinates of either point, $(64, 122)$ or $(61, 113)$, for (h, k) and 3 for *m* in the equation $y - k = m(x - h)$:

$$y - 122 = 3(x - 64)$$
$$y = 3x - 70.$$

Does this equation seem reasonable? How does it compare with the equation in Discovery 2.4? The equation seems reasonable, since the slope is positive, but the slope is smaller than the slope of the line in Discovery 2.4. Which model is best? We will not know until Chapter 3, where we learn more about the modeling process and how to analyze data.

Example 22

Use the point-slope equation of a line to find an equation for a line that contains the point (5, 1) and has a slope of –4.

Solution:

Substitute (5, 1) for (h, k) and –4 for m in the equation $y - k = m(x - h)$:

$$y - 1 = -4(x - 5)$$
$$y = -4x + 21$$

Example 23

Find an equation of the line that passes through the points (–2, 7) and (3, –8).

Check your equation by seeing if the two given points satisfy the equation.

Solution:

Find the slope of the line:

$$m = \frac{(-8) - 7}{3 - (-2)} = -3$$

Substitute the coordinates of one of the points for (h, k) and –3 for m in the equation $y - k = m(x - h)$.

$$y - 7 = -3(x - -2)$$
$$y = -3(x + 2) + 7$$
$$y = -3x + 1$$

At $x = -2$, $y = 7$,　　　$y = -3x + 1$

　　　　　　　　　　$7 = -3(-2) + 1$ ✓

At $x = 3$, $y = -8$,　　　$y = -3x + 1$

　　　　　　　　　　$-8 = -3(3) + 1$ ✓

Parallel and Perpendicular Lines

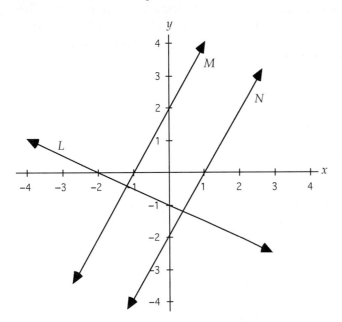

Figure 2.79

If and Only If

The phrase "if and only if" is a mathematical way of writing two converse statements as one single statement. In the statement about parallel lines, it means: If two distinct nonvertical lines are parallel, then they have the same slope; and if two distinct nonvertical lines have the same slope, then they are parallel.

Parallel lines are lines that do not intersect. Are the lines M and N in **Figure 2.79** parallel? One way to tell is to examine the slope of each line.

Parallel Lines

Two distinct, nonvertical lines are parallel if and only if they have the same slope.

The slope of line M is 2, and the slope of line N is 2, so the two lines are parallel.

Example 24

Line A contains the points (1, 5) and (2, 9). An equation for line B is $y = 4x - 2$. Are the two lines parallel? Why or why not?

Solution:

Find the slope of each line:

$$m_A = \frac{9-5}{2-1} = 4; \ m_B = 4.$$ The slopes are equal, so the lines are parallel.

In Figure 2.79, lines L and M appear to be **perpendicular,** which means that the two lines intersect to form right angles (90°). As we did with parallel lines, we can examine the slopes of the two lines to tell if they are perpendicular. (See Exercise 7.)

Perpendicular Lines

Two distinct nonvertical lines are perpendicular if and only if their slopes are negative reciprocals of each other.

The slope of line M is 2, and the slope of line L is $-\frac{1}{2}$. Since 2 and $-\frac{1}{2}$ are negative reciprocals, we know that the lines M and L are perpendicular.

Negative Reciprocals

Two numbers are negative reciprocals of each other if you multiply the two numbers together and the product is -1. For example, $\frac{2}{5}$ and $-\frac{5}{2}$ are negative reciprocals because

$$\left(\frac{2}{5}\right)\left(-\frac{5}{2}\right) = -1.$$

Example 24

Find an equation of a line that is perpendicular to the line $y = \frac{1}{7}x - 4$.

Solution:

The slope of the given line is $\frac{1}{7}$, so any line with a slope of -7 is perpendicular to the given line. One possible equation is $y = -7x + 2$.

Interpreting Graphs

As we read through the daily paper or leaf through a book, frequently we just glance at the graphs provided. Often that quick look is not good enough. It is easy to be deceived by what looks like a simple graph. For example, **Figures 2.80a** and **2.80b** show graphs of straight lines A and B, respectively. Which line has the greatest slope?

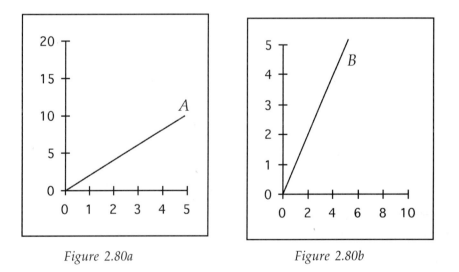

Figure 2.80a   Figure 2.80b

If we only glance at the lines, line B in Figure 2.80b looks steeper than line A in Figure 2.80a. But when we graph both lines on the same set of axes, we see something that looks very different. (See **Figure 2.81**.)

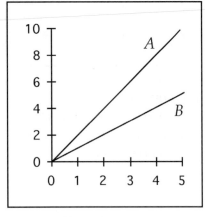

Figure 2.81

It is easy to see by looking at the two lines on the same graph that line *A* has the greater slope. The deception, purposeful or not, was caused when different scales were chosen for the two graphs.

Example 25

Figures 2.82 and **2.83** show the values of two different investments over time.

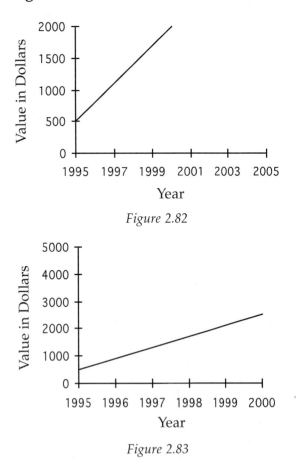

Figure 2.82

Figure 2.83

1. Look quickly at the two graphs. Which investment appears to be growing more rapidly? Explain.

2. Find equations of the lines representing Investment A and Investment B.

3. What do the slopes of these lines mean in this context?

4. Why are the graphs deceiving?

Solution:

1. With just a quick glance, the value of Investment A appears to be increasing faster because the line looks steeper.

2. Investment A: Slope = $300/year; y-intercept is $500; equation of the line: $y = 300x + 500$.

   Investment B: Slope = $400/year; y-intercept is $500; equation of the line: $y = 400x + 500$.

3. The slope in each case gives the number of dollars increase in value per year of investment.

4. The graphs are deceiving in that, with a quick glance, Investment A appears to be increasing faster, but in reality, upon examination of the slope of each line, Investment B is growing at a faster rate.

Exercises 2.6 (SE pages 212–215)

I. Investigations

1. According to Baby Bag Online, the average weight for an 8-year-old girl is 60-3/4 pounds. The average weight for a 12-year-old girl is 94 pounds.

   a) Use this information to create a linear model. Let w represent weight and a represent age.

1. a) Using the ordered pairs (8, 60.75) and (12, 94):

$$m = \frac{94 - 60.75}{12 - 8} = \frac{33.25}{4} \approx 8.3; \ w - 94 = 8.3(a - 12) \text{ or } w = 8.3a - 5.6.$$

   b) Express your model in slope-intercept form, $y = mx + b$. What does the slope of the line mean in this context?

b) $w = 8.3a - 5.6$; the slope 8.3 indicates that for each increase of one year of age, an average girl will gain 8.3 pounds.

   c) Does the y-intercept have any meaning in this context? Explain.

c) The y-intercept –5.6 indicates that a person with age zero would have a weight of –5.6 pounds. This makes no sense in this context.

   d) Use your model from (a) to predict the average weight of a 9-year-old girl.

d) Substitute 9 for the girl's age a: $w = 8.3(9) - 5.6$. The average weight is 69.1 pounds.

2. A diode is a common device that is used to create electronic temperature-sensing instruments because its voltage in a circuit is related linearly to temperature when the current is held constant. The data on diode voltage V_D in **Table 2.36** were collected experimentally.

Temperature	Voltage
27° C (room temperature)	588 mV
35° C (skin temperature)	570 mV

Table 2.36

   a) Use these two sets of values to draw a graph of voltage V_D as a function of temperature T. Assume that you are interested in the temperature range 0°C – 100°C (the range of liquid water).

2. a)

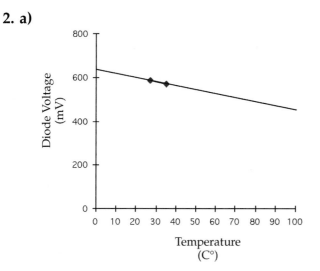

b) Find an equation of the line.

b) $m = \dfrac{570 - 588}{35 - 27}$; $V_D - 588 = -2.25(T - 27)$ or $V_D = -2.25T + 649$.

c) What does the slope of the line indicate?

c) The slope indicates that for every 1°C change in temperature, there is a –2.25-millivolts change in voltage.

d) Use the equation from (b) to complete **Table 2.37**.

Temperature (°C)	80	15		
Diode Voltage (mV)			460	600

Table 2.37

d)

Temperature (°C)	80	15	84	22
Diode Voltage (mV)	469	615	460	600

3. Measurement can be used to make predictions for the past, present, or future. Archaeologists are scientists who study ancient human life. They learn about early humans by studying their bones, fossilized footprints, and other artifacts. Often unable to find a complete skeleton intact, they must gather information from only a few bones.

One example of how an archaeologist might collect information about a specimen is by using a general rule about proportions. In modern times, for instance, a typical female has a forearm length that is 16% of her total height.

a) Write an equation that expresses forearm length f in terms of the height h of an individual. Then write a second equation that expresses height in terms of forearm length.

3. a) $f/h = 0.16$. So $f = 0.16h$ and $h = 6.25f$.

b) What does the slope of each equation from (a) indicate?

b) In the equation $f = 0.16h$, the slope 0.16 indicates that for each 1-inch change in height, there is a 16/100-inch change in the forearm length. In the equation $h = 6.25f$, the slope 6.25 indicates a 6.25-inch change in height for each 1-inch change in forearm length.

c) Use the height–forearm length relationship to complete **Table 2.38.**

Forearm Length (in)	11.0	12.5	10.5		
Height (in)				75.0	62.0

Table 2.38

c)

Forearm Length (in)	11.0	12.5	10.5	**12.0**	**9.9**
Height (in)	**68.8**	**78.1**	**65.6**	75.0	62.0

d) If the length of the forearm of a typical female is 16% of her height, do you think this is true for males? Explain.

d) Sample answer: Probably not, as the body structure for males and females is different. So the ratio of height to forearm length may be different for males and females.

e) Do you think that this relationship between a person's height and forearm length was the same long ago as it is today? Explain.

e) Sample answer: Probably not, as the body structure of people has changed over time.

4. According to anthropologists, the relationship between a person's height and the length of his or her tibia is linear.

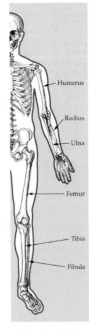

Humerus

Radius

Ulna

Femur

Tibia

Fibula

Tibia Length (cm)	Height (cm)
42	184
40	179

Table 2.39

Figure 2.84

a) Use the data in **Table 2.39** to create a linear model. Let H represent height and T represent the length of the tibia. Let T be the independent variable.

4. **a)** $H - 179 = \dfrac{5}{2}(T - 40); H = 2.5(T - 40) + 179; H = 2.5T + 79.$

b) Express your model in slope-intercept form, $y = mx = b$. What does the slope of the line indicate in this context?

b) $H = 2.5T + 79$; **the slope 2.5 indicates that each increase of 1 cm in the length of the tibia would correspond to a 2.5-cm increase in height.**

c) Does the y-intercept have any meaning in this context? Explain.

c) **The y-intercept 79 indicates that a person with tibia length 0 would have a height of 70 cm. This makes no sense in the context.**

d) What is a reasonable problem domain for this function?

d) **Answers will vary. A tibia of a young person might be 20 cm, whereas the tibia of a very tall person could be as long as 60 cm.**

e) Use your model from (a) to predict the height of a person whose tibia is 45 cm long.

e) **Substitute 45 cm for T: $H = 2.5(45) + 79 = 192$ cm.**

f) Use your model to predict the length of your tibia.

f) **Answers will vary. Most likely students will need to convert their heights into cm. To do so, multiply the height in inches by 2.54 cm/in.**

Sample answer: A person who is 5'8" tall: 68 in = 173 cm. Use the model to find the tibia length: $173 = 2.5T + 79$; $T = 37.6$ cm.

5. Although linear functions are useful in modeling many situations, there are times when the rate of change varies for certain values in the domain. Sometimes these situations can be modeled by what are called **piecewise linear functions,** whose graphs consist of two or more rays or line segments joined together.

Consider the following cellular phone situation. One company with nationwide long distance service offers a plan that costs $69.99 per month, which includes 500 free minutes plus 25 cents for each minute of use over 500. **Table 2.40** shows the cost c in dollars for t minutes of phone use.

Time (min)	100	200	300	400	500	501	550	600	650	700
Cost (dollars)	69.99	69.99	69.99	69.99	69.99	70.24	82.49	94.99	107.49	119.99

Table 2.40

The points from Table 2.40 are shown in the graph in **Figure 2.85.**

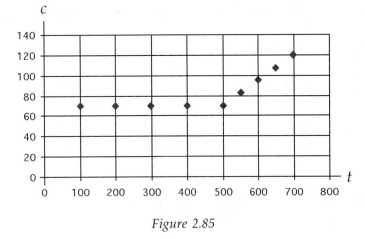

Figure 2.85

a) Notice that when $t \leq 500$, the points lie on the horizontal line. Write an equation for this line.

5. **a)** $c = 69.99$.

b) Also notice that when $t > 500$, this pattern changes. These points continue to exhibit a linear pattern, but the pattern is no longer horizontal. Find an equation for the line that passes through these points.

b) Using the ordered pairs (600, 94.99) and (700, 119.99), $m = \dfrac{119.99 - 94.99}{700 - 600} =$ 0.25 cents/minute. Using point-slope form, an equation for the line is $c - 94.99 = 0.25(t - 600)$ or $c = 0.25t - 55.01$.

c) To describe this piecewise function, we generally combine the equations into one expression. Complete the following expression.

$$c = \begin{cases} ? \text{ if } 0 \leq t \leq 500 \\ ? \text{ if } t > 500 \end{cases}$$

c) $c = \begin{cases} \textbf{69.99 if } 0 \leq t \leq 500 \\ \textbf{0.25}t - \textbf{55.01 if } t > 500 \end{cases}$

d) Sketch the graph of the piecewise function from (c).

d)

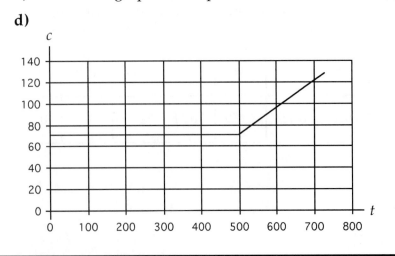

e) For local service only, the same company offers a plan that costs $24.99 per month, which includes 100 free minutes plus 19 cents for each minute of use over 100. Write an equation for a piecewise linear function that models this plan. (Hint: If needed, create a table and draw a graph.)

e) **The horizontal portion of this function can be modeled with the equation $c = 24.99$. To find an equation when $t > 100$, first find a solution point that lies on that portion of the graph, for example, (200, 43.99). Using point-slope form, $c - 43.99 = 0.19(t - 200)$ or $c = 0.19t + 5.99$.**

Hence, $c = \begin{cases} 24.99 \text{ if } 0 \le t \le 100. \\ 0.19t + 5.99 \text{ if } t > 100. \end{cases}$

f) Graph the following piecewise linear function:

$$y = \begin{cases} x + 2 \text{ if } x < 0. \\ 2 \text{ if } 0 \le x \le 3. \\ x - 1 \text{ if } x > 3. \end{cases}$$

f)

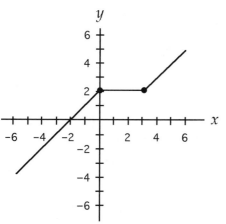

6. As you will see in this exercise, graphs created by the graphing calculator can also be deceptive.

a) Use your calculator to sketch the graph of $y = x$ using the following viewing window: Xmin = –20, Xmax = 20, Xscl = 1, Ymin = –5, Ymax = 5, Yscl = 1. Repeat using the window Xmin = –5, Xmax = 5, Xscl = 1, Ymin = –20, Ymax = 20, Yscl = 1. What do you notice about the appearance of the line in the two different viewing windows?

6. a) The first graph appears much steeper than the second graph, even though both graphs are of the same equation.

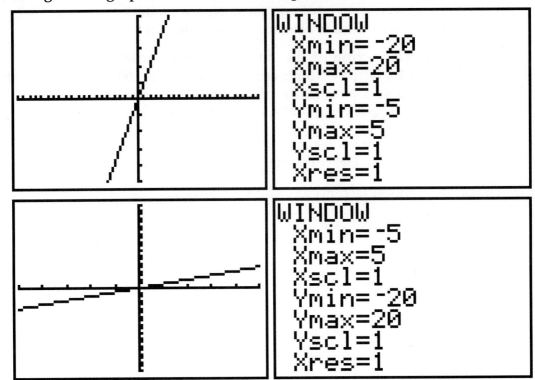

b) Care must be taken to get an undistorted view of the slope of a line on graphing utilities because of the rectangular viewing screen. What happens when you graph the function $y = x$ using a window where the Xmax and Xmin are equal to the Ymax and Ymin? For example, try the window Xmin = –5, Xmax = 5, Xscl = 1, Ymin = –5, Ymax = 5, Yscl = 1. Does this window give an undistorted view? Explain.

b) The view is still distorted because of the rectangular screen. One unit on the *x*-axis is not the same size as one unit on the *y*-axis.

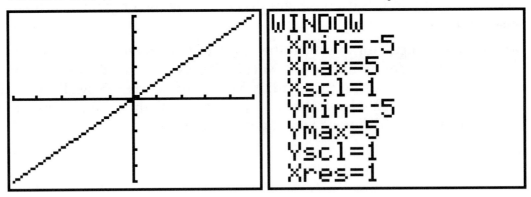

To avoid this distortion, the window of the calculator must be adjusted so that the screen will be square. On many calculators a built-in function such as Zsquare automatically squares the screen. If this is not the case with your calculator, consult your manual to find the setting ratio of x to y that will accomplish a square screen.

c) The line $y = x$ bisects the first and third quadrants. Find a window on your calculator that makes it appear that $y = x$ does so.

c) Sample answer: Using Zsquare, the window is [–15.16, 15.16] x [–10, 10].

d) Test your undistorted screen by graphing the following two functions: $y = 2x + 6$ and $y = -0.5x - 2$. First graph them on a standard window of [–10, 10] x [–10, 10] and then on a square screen. What do you notice about the relationship between the two lines?

d) The two lines appear perpendicular.

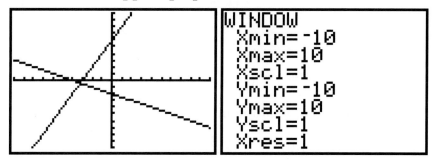

Standard window

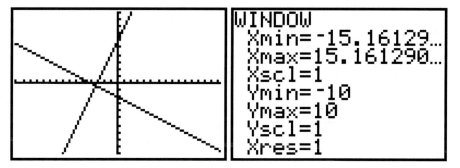

Square screen

II. Projects and Group Activities *(SE page 216)*

7. As stated in this section, two lines are perpendicular if and only if their slopes are negative reciprocals of each other. You can see why if you examine a particular pair of lines. Consider lines *A* and *B* in **Figure 2.86.** Three points on these lines are labeled: *P*(1, 2), *Q*(2, 5), and *R*(4, 1).

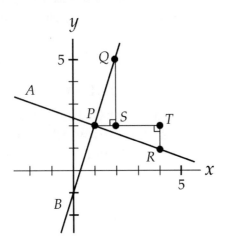

Figure 2.86

a) Find the slopes of lines *A* and *B*.

7. **a) Using the points *P* and *R*, the slope of line *A* is $\dfrac{1-2}{4-1} = -\dfrac{1}{3}$. Using the points *P* and *Q*, the slope of line *B* is $\dfrac{5-2}{2-1} = 3$.**

b) How are the slopes of lines *A* and *B* related?

b) They are negative reciprocals.

c) Examine the two right triangles *QPS* and *PRT*. How are they related to each other?

c) They are congruent, meaning that they have identical size and shape, although they are rotated with respect to each other.

d) In triangle *QPS*, what is the sum of angle *QPS* and angle *PQS*? Explain how you know.

d) 90°; the sum of the angles of a triangle is 180°. Hence, angle *PQS* + angle *QPS* + 90° = 180°. So angle *PQS* + angle *QPS* = 90°.

e) What is the sum of angle *QPS* and angle *TPR*? Explain your reasoning.

e) 90°; from (d) we know that angle *PQS* + angle *QPS* = 90°. We also know that angle *TPR* is equal in measure to angle *PQS* (congruent triangles). Therefore, angle *TPR* + angle *QPS* = 90°.

---

f) Based on your answer to (e), what can you say about the relationship between line *A* and line *B*?

f) They are perpendicular because they meet to form 90°angles.

8. Look in newspapers and magazines and on the Internet for graphs of lines. Based on what you know, write a report on the equations of the lines and the interpretations of the slope of the lines as well as the *y*-intercepts. Also look for possible deceptive graphs. If you find one, indicate what makes the graph deceptive and whether you think it is intentional or not. (Be sure to include copies of the graphs in your report.)

III. Additional Practice *(SE pages 217–219)*

For 9–12, find an equation for each line. Express your answer in the form $y = mx + b$ (slope-intercept form).

9. See **Figure 2.87.**

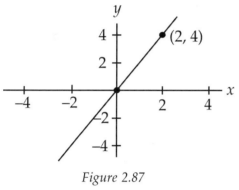

Figure 2.87

9. $y = 2x$.

10. See **Figure 2.88.**

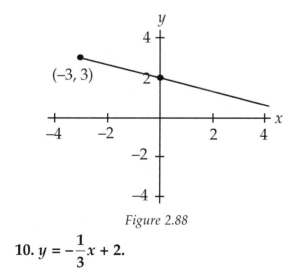

Figure 2.88

10. $y = -\dfrac{1}{3}x + 2$.

11. See **Figure 2.89.**

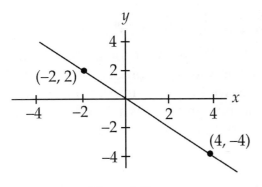

Figure 2.89

11. $y = -x.$

12. See **Figure 2.90.**

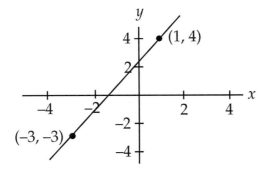

Figure 2.90

12. $y = \dfrac{7}{4}x + \dfrac{9}{4}$ **or** $y = 1.75x + 2.25.$

For 13–17, find an equation of the line that passes through the two given points.

13. (5, 2), (4, 8)

13. $m = \dfrac{2-8}{5-4} = -6;\ y - 8 = -6(x-4);$ **or** $y = -6x + 32.$

14. (−1, 5), (−3, 9)

14. $m = \dfrac{9-5}{-3+1} = -2;\ y - 5 = -2(x+1)$ **or** $y = -2x + 3.$

15. (−3, 8), (3, 8)

15. $m = \dfrac{8-8}{3+3} = 0;\ y - 8 = 0(x+3);\ y = 8.$

16. (−5, −1), (3, 7)

16. $m = \dfrac{7+1}{3+5} = 1;\ y + 1 = 1(x+5)$ **or** $y = x + 4.$

17. (−4, 2), (4, 4)

17. $m = \dfrac{4-2}{4+4} = \dfrac{1}{4};\ y - 2 = \dfrac{1}{4}(x+4)$ **or** $y = \dfrac{1}{4}x + 3.$

18. Find an equation that relates temperature in degrees Fahrenheit (*F*) and Kelvin (*K*). The following facts are known: the relationship is linear, 273*K* corresponds to 32°F, and 373*K* corresponds to 212°F.

18. If you choose *K* as the independent variable and *F* as the dependent variable and use the points (273, 32) and (373, 212), $m = \dfrac{9}{5}$. You get the equation $F - 32 = \dfrac{9}{5}(K - 273)$ or $F = \dfrac{9}{5}K - \dfrac{2297}{5}$. If you choose *F* for the independent variable, $m = \dfrac{5}{9}$, you get the equation $K - 273 = \dfrac{5}{9}(F - 32)$ or $K = \dfrac{5}{9}F + \dfrac{2297}{9}$.

For 19–28, find an equation for the line with the given properties.

19. Slope = –2 passing through point (1, 2)

19. $y = -2x + 4$.

20. Slope = 5 passing through point (–2, –13)

20. $y = 5x - 3$.

21. Passing through points (2, 5) and (– 3, –5)

21. $m = \dfrac{-5 - 5}{-3 - 2} = 2$; $y - 5 = 2(x - 2)$ or $y = 2x + 1$.

22. Passing through points (–2, 5) and (3, –5)

22. $m = \dfrac{-5 - 5}{3 + 2} = -2$; $y - 5 = -2(x + 2)$ or $y = -2x + 1$.

23. *x*-intercept = 5, *y*-intercept = 1

23. $m = \dfrac{0 - 1}{5 - 0} = -\dfrac{1}{5}$; $y = -\dfrac{1}{5}x + 1$.

24. *x*-intercept = –2, *y*-intercept = 4

24. $m = 2$; $y = 2x + 4$.

25. Slope = 0; *y*-intercept = –6

25. $y = -6$.

26. Slope is undefined, *x*-intercept = 3

26. $x = 3$.

27. *y*-intercept = –3, parallel to the line $y = 4x + 8$

27. $y = 4x - 3$.

28. Passing through point (2, 8), perpendicular to the line $y = 0.5x - 1$

28. $y = -2x + 12$.

For 29–32, tell whether the two lines are parallel, perpendicular, or neither. Justify your answer.

29. Line 1: $3y = 2x - 6$

   Line 2: the line passing through points $(1, 5)$ and $(-2, 3)$

29. The two lines are parallel. Both lines have a slope of $\dfrac{2}{3}$.

30. Line 1: $6y = 2x - 5$

   Line 2: $y + 3x = 1$

30. The lines are perpendicular. The slope of line 1 is $\dfrac{1}{3}$. The slope of line 2 is –3. The slopes are negative reciprocals of each other, so the lines are perpendicular.

31. Line 1: the line passing through points $(-2, 7)$ and $(1, -2)$

   Line 2: a line parallel to the line $y = 7x - 3$

31. Neither; the slope of line 1 is –3, and the slope of line 2 is 7. The lines are neither parallel nor perpendicular.

32. Line 1: x-intercept is 4 and y-intercept is 4

   Line 2: the line passing through points $(1, 2)$ and $(2, 3)$

32. Perpendicular; the slope of line 1 is –1, and the slope of line 2 is 1. The slopes are negative reciprocals of each other, so the lines are perpendicular.

For 33–34, find an equation of the line that contains the points in the table. Use the equation to find the missing values.

33. See **Table 2.41.**

x	y
1	2
2	9
3	16
4	
20	
50	
100	
–5	

Table 2.41

33. $y = 7x - 5.$

x	y
1	2
2	9
3	16
4	**23**
20	**135**
50	**345**
100	**695**
−5	**−40**

34. See **Table 2.42.**

x	y
−20	
−10	
10	−10
20	−30
30	−50
	−90
100	
200	

Table 2.42

34. $y = -2x + 10.$

x	y
−20	**50**
−10	**30**
10	−10
20	−30
30	−50
50	−90
100	**−190**
200	**−390**

Chapter 2 Summary

Writing and evaluating algebraic expressions

Distributive property

Order of operations guidelines for expressions

Modeling with equations

Identifying terms, factors, and coefficients

Solving equations

Functions

Representations of functions

Linear functions

Slope and intercepts

Equations of lines

Parallel and perpendicular lines

Chapter 2 Review

1. Write a summary of the important mathematical ideas found in Chapter 2.

1. Answers will vary. Following are some of the important ideas that should be listed:

Algebraic expressions can be used to represent real-world situations.

Algebraic expressions can be evaluated by replacing variables in the expression with numbers.

The distributive property can be used when evaluating expressions that contain parentheses.

The order of operation guidelines must be followed when evaluating expressions.

Equations can be used to model real-world situations.

Solving an equation means to find numbers that make the equation true.

When two variables are related in such a way that there is exactly one output value for each input value, the relationship is called a *function*.

Functions can be represented in many different ways such as verbal descriptions, arrow diagrams, graphs, equations, and tables.

Functions of the form $y = mx + b$ are called *linear functions*.

The graph of a linear function is a straight line.

A linear function has a constant rate of change that is equal to the slope of its graph.

When given certain information about a linear function, such as the slope and y-intercept or two points on the graph, an equation for the function can be found.

Graphs of functions can be deceptive. Care must be taken when drawing conclusions from a graph.

The slopes of parallel lines are equal in value. The slopes of perpendicular lines are negative reciprocals of each other.

For 2–3, evaluate the algebraic expression.

2. $5c - 3$ when $c = 7$.

2. 32

3. $12(p - 3q) - 4(1 - pq)$ when $p = 1.7$ and $q = 2.46$.

3. −55.432

4. An average size person burns about 2500 calories of energy each day doing normal activities. In addition to this amount, walking at a fast pace burns 5.6 calories per minute, running burns 15 calories per minute, and bicycling burns 11 calories per minute.

   a) Write an expression for the total number of calories burned in a day by an average size person who walks fast for w minutes, runs for r minutes, and bicycles for b minutes.

4. a) $2500 + 5.6w + 15r + 11b$

   b) How many calories will be burned in a day by an average size person who walks fast for 45 minutes, runs for 20 minutes, and bicycles for 32 minutes.

b) 3404

5. Write an expression for the perimeter of the hexagon in **Figure 2.91.**

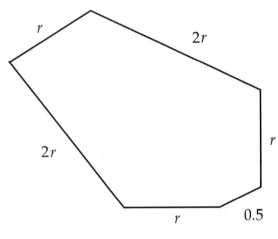

Figure 2.91

5. $r + 2r + r + r + 2r + 0.5 = 7r + 0.5.$

6. Exercise 28 (b) in Section 2.2 stated a rule of thumb that a hospital should have four and one-half beds for every 1000 people in the community it serves. The equation $b = \dfrac{4.5p}{1000}$, where b is the number of beds and p is the population of the community, can be used to model this relationship. How large a population would a community have to have in order to require a hospital with 200 beds?

6. 44,444, or about 44,000 people

7. The shear force V (in pounds) at any point along a 12-foot-long beam that carries a uniform load of 100 pounds per foot is given by the equation $V = 600 - 100x$, where x is the distance from the left end (in feet). How far from the left end is the shear force equal to 350 pounds?

7. 2.5 ft

For 8–11, solve the equation for the value of the variable.

8. $3(7h - 2) = 18$.

8. $h = \dfrac{8}{7}$.

9. $\dfrac{n+2}{7} - 1 = 3$.

9. $n = 26$.

10. $6x + 2(x - 3) = 5 - (1 - 10x)$.

10. $x = -5$.

11. $358d - 80.3(0.9 - 4.2d) = 21.3$.

11. $d = 0.1345\ldots$; $d \approx 0.13$.

12. The equation $I = I_c + \dfrac{wd^2}{g}$ is a formula for the moment of inertia of an object about any axis. Solve for the object's weight w.

12. $w = \dfrac{g}{d^2}(I - I_c)$ or $w = \dfrac{Ig - I_c g}{d^2}$.

13. Consider the following situation: A temperature of a hot cup of coffee sitting in a cool room.

a) Identify two quantities that vary.

13. a) Time and temperature

b) Which is the independent variable? Which is the dependent variable?

b) Time is the independent variable; temperature is the dependent variable.

14. Consider the graphs in **Figures 2.92** and **2.93**. Determine whether each is the graph of a function. Explain your reasoning.

a)

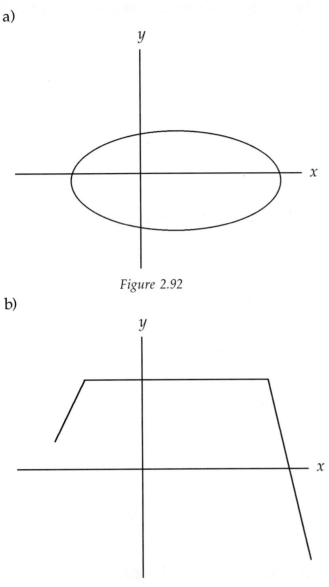

Figure 2.92

b)

Figure 2.93

14. **Graph (b) is a function; graph (a) is not, because at least one input value of its domain has more than one output value.**

For 15–16, determine (a) the value of y when $x = -2$ and (b) the value(s) of x when $y = -5$.

15. $y - 3 = -4(x - 1)$.

15. a) $y - 3 = -4(-2 - 1) = 15.$

   b) $-5 - 3 = -4(x - 1) = 3.$

16. See **Figure 2.94.**

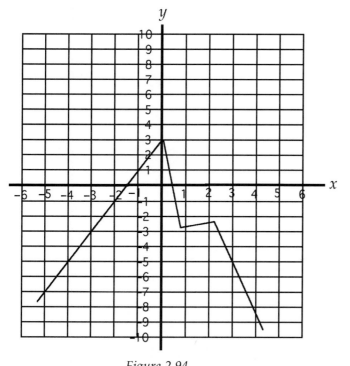

Figure 2.94

16. a) When $x = -2$, $y = -1$.

   b) When $y = -5$, $x = -4$ and 3.

17. Write an equation for the function that is represented by the arrow diagram in **Figure 2.95.**

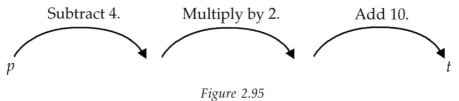

Subtract 4.　　　Multiply by 2.　　　Add 10.

p t

Figure 2.95

17. $t = 2(p - 4) + 10$.

18. Consider the function $y = \dfrac{3x}{x - 4}$.

   a) What is the domain of the function?

18. a) All real numbers except $x = 4$

   b) Is the point $(1, 4)$ on the graph of the function?

   b) No.

   c) Is the point $(8, 6)$ on the graph of the function?

   c) Yes.

19. For (a)–(c), use the graph in **Figure 2.96.**

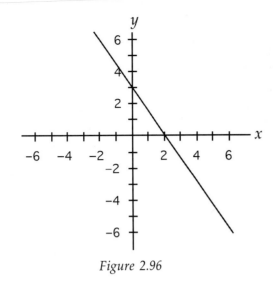

Figure 2.96

    a) What is the slope of the line?

19. a) $m = -\dfrac{3}{2}$.

    b) What are the coordinates of the *y*-intercept? What are the coordinates of the *x*-intercept?

b) (0, 3); (2, 0)

    c) What is the equation of the line?

c) $y = -\dfrac{3}{2}x + 3$ **or** $2y = -3x + 6$.

20. Solid plastic rod is sold wound on large spools. **Figure 2.97** shows a graph of the total weight W of the spool (in pounds) as a function of the length L of $\dfrac{1}{4}$-inch rod wound on it (in feet).

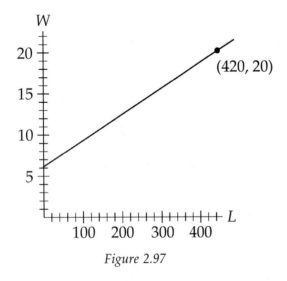

Figure 2.97

    a) Find the slope of the graph including units, and interpret its meaning.

20. a) $\dfrac{20\ \text{lb} - 6\ \text{lb}}{420\ \text{ft} - 0\ \text{ft}} = \dfrac{1}{30}$ pounds per foot. The slope indicates a 1/30-lb increase in weight for each 1-ft increase in length.

   b) What is the meaning of the vertical intercept?

   b) The weight of the spool by itself (with 0 ft of rod on it) is 6 lb.

21. Describe the graph of each of the following:

   a) A linear function, $y = mx + b$, where $m > 0$

   21. a) A straight line that is increasing from left to right

   b) A linear function, $y = mx + b$, where $m < 0$

   b) A straight line that is decreasing from left to right

   c) A linear function, $y = mx + b$, where $m = 0$

   c) A horizontal line

22. **Table 2.43** shows the average amount of savings that can be expected on a $100 gas bill by turning down the thermostat in a house by various amounts. The data shown are for locations at the latitude of Chicago.

Setback Amount (°F)	Savings ($)
1	4
2	8
3	12
4	16
5	20
6	24
7	28

Table 2.43

   Is this a linear relationship? Explain.

   22. Yes, it is a linear relationship. There is a constant average rate of change of $4 per degree Fahrenheit between any two data pairs in the table.

23. Write the equation $3x - 5y = 10$ in slope-intercept form. Identify the slope and the y-intercept.

   23. $y = \dfrac{3}{5}x - 2$. The slope is $\dfrac{3}{5}$, and the y-intercept is –2.

24. Create a table of values for the function $y = 4 - 2x$, similar to **Table 2.44**. Then use the table to sketch the graph of the linear function.

x	y

Table 2.44

24. Sample table:

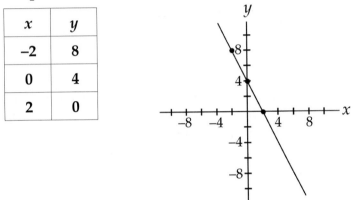

x	y
–2	8
0	4
2	0

For 25–31, find an equation of the line with the given characteristics. Express your answer in the form $y = mx + b$.

25. The slope is $-\dfrac{2}{3}$, and the y-intercept is –1

25. $y = -\dfrac{2}{3}x - 1$.

26. Slope $= \dfrac{1}{2}$; passes through the point (1, 4)

26. $y = \dfrac{1}{2}x + \dfrac{7}{2}$.

27. Contains points (2, 5) and (3, 2)

27. $y = -3x + 11$.

28. See **Figure 2.98.**

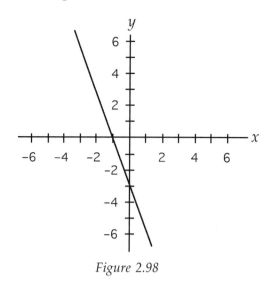

Figure 2.98

28. Because $m = -3$ and $b = -3$, an equation for the line is $y = -3x - 3$.

29. Slope undefined; passes through the point $(-2, -4)$

29. $x = -2$.

30. x-intercept $= 6$; y-intercept $= -3$

30. $y = \dfrac{1}{2}x - 3$.

31. Passes through the points $(-2, 7)$ and $(3, -3)$

31. $y = -2x + 3$.

For 32–33, tell whether the two lines are parallel, perpendicular, or neither. Justify your answer.

32. Line 1: $5y - 2x = 5$

  Line 2: $4y + 10x + 1 = 0$

32. The two lines are perpendicular. The slope of line 1 is $\dfrac{2}{5}$. The slope of line 2 is $\dfrac{-5}{2}$. The slopes are negative reciprocals of each other, so the lines are perpendicular.

33. Line 1: $2y - 6x = 12$

  Line 2: the line passing through points $(1, 1)$ and $(-1, -5)$

33. The lines are parallel. Both have a slope of 3.

Chapter 3—Modeling Behavior from Data

Goals of the Chapter

- To explore two-variable data analysis

- To further understanding of linear relationships

Preparation Reading

In Chapters 1 and 2 we used several different mathematical models to help simplify real-world situations. For example, in Chapter 2 we used an equation $W = V + 52$ to explain the relationship between the weight (W) of a particular liquid and its volume (V).

When building models, people often use accumulated knowledge to help them find a relationship between variables. After creating the model, they gather data to check its accuracy.

There are times when it is not possible for the modeler to explain a certain behavior, but predictions are needed anyway. For example, we may not be able to build a model for the number of students who will be attending a particular college. But the college needs to make estimates each year in order to plan for faculty, facilities, and materials such as books. In such cases, data are collected and examined. If a pattern in the data is observed, an attempt is made to capture the trend of the pattern with a model. In turn, the resulting model may give hints as to why the variables are related as they are.

Thus, data are collected and examined for at least two distinct purposes. One is to check the accuracy of a proposed model. The other is to look for a pattern in collected data in hopes of creating a model based on that pattern. In the first instance, the model is **theory-driven,** and in the second the model is **data-driven.**

$$\text{Theory} \longrightarrow \text{Model} \longrightarrow \text{Data}$$
$$\text{Data} \longrightarrow \text{Model} \longrightarrow \text{Theory}$$

Both theory-driven and data-driven models are useful. Each has its advantages and disadvantages. In this chapter we will explore the construction of some data-driven models and use them to make predictions.

Reflect and Discuss *(SE page 229)*

1. Name some fields of work where data collection is important.

1. **Sample answer: Medicine, weather, health research, business, etc.**

2. What type of job might require employees to create mathematical models?

2. **Sample answer: Any job where predictions need to be made. For example, weather forecasters, building and trades personnel, wildlife managers, engineers, and economists are just a few of many possibilities.**

Section 3.1 Collecting Data and Determining a Model

What You Need to Know

- How to plot points in the coordinate plane

- How to find the slope of a line

- How to find the equation of a line given two points on the line

What You Will Learn

- To create a scatter plot from collected data

- To examine a scatter plot for linear patterns

- To estimate a line of best fit to model data in a scatter plot

Materials

- Tape measures or meter sticks

- Graph paper

Dr. Mildred Trotter had a long, distinguished career as a physical anthropologist. She worked as a special consultant to the U.S. government during World War II. Her task during the war involved the identification of skeletal remains of servicemen. At the time, she realized that bone size and proportions vary based on age, sex, and racial/ethnic background. Forensic scientists and law enforcement agencies are still using Trotter's formulas for estimating a person's stature based on the lengths of their bones. (Conroy, Glenn, et al. 1992)

National Anthropological Archives, Smithsonian Institution

Figure 3.1

In the workplace as well as in our everyday lives, we probably know of an equation that models some mathematical relationship between two variables. For example, we know that the equation $C = \dfrac{5}{9}(F - 32)$ describes the relationship between temperature C measured in degrees Celsius and temperature F measured in degrees Fahrenheit.

We also know that for a car traveling at a constant rate of 60 mph, the equation $d = 60t$ provides a model of the relationship between distance d and time t. This equation can be used to predict how far we will travel if we know how long we plan to drive.

Sometimes we do not know of a specific mathematical relationship between two variables and only suspect that one exists. For example, forensic scientists are often called upon to solve crimes in which only skeletons or parts of skeletons are available as evidence. Sometimes, in attempting to identify a body, these scientists are asked to determine the height of the individual from the remaining bones.

Activity 3.1 Determining a Model *(SE pages 231–232)*

Materials: tape measures or meter sticks; graph paper

Look around the class. Do you think there might be a relationship between the length of a person's forearm and his or her height? Would a person with a very long forearm more likely be taller or shorter than a person with a short forearm?

1. Break into groups and measure the length of the forearm and height of each member in your group.

    Note: Before the data are collected, the class needs to establish a method for measuring forearm lengths and heights. Remember, the usefulness of your model depends on the quality of the data collected. An agreement should be reached on exactly what will be measured and how the measurements will be made.

    Collect your data in a table similar to **Table 3.1.**

Forearm Length (cm)	Height (cm)

Table 3.1

1. **Sample answer:**

Forearm Length (cm)	Height (cm)
27	167
24	164
30	185
26.5	173

2. Combine the data from all the groups so that each person has data for the entire class.

2. **Sample answer:**

Forearm Length (cm)	Height (cm)
23.0	161
24.0	157
24.0	164
24.5	166
25.5	176
26.0	162
26.0	175
26.5	172
26.5	173
27.0	163
27.0	167
27.0	174
27.0	177
27.5	163
28.0	175
28.0	172
28.5	166
29.0	180
30.0	178
30.0	185
31.0	192
32.0	184

3. A forensic scientist might suggest that if a person's forearm length is known, his or her height could be predicted from it. Would forearm length be the independent variable or the dependent variable in this relationship?

3. **Forearm length is the independent variable.**

4. On a piece of graph paper, draw a set of axes. Label the horizontal axis with the independent variable and the vertical axis with the dependent variable. Include the units of measurement and construct a reasonable scale for each variable.

Think of your data as sets of ordered pairs (forearm length, height). Plot the data obtained for your entire class from item 2. A graph of ordered pairs of data is called a **scatter plot.**

Do you notice any pattern or trend to your data?

4. **Sample scatter plot:**

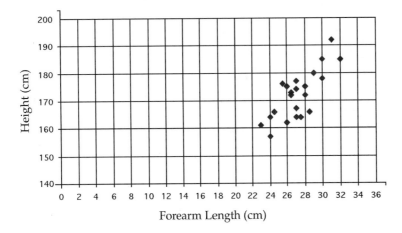

Generally, as the forearm length increases, so does the height of the individual.

5. On your scatter plot, use a ruler to draw a straight line that you think describes the pattern in your data reasonably well.

5. **Sample graph:**

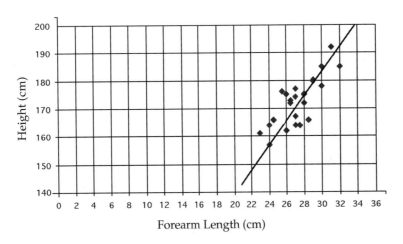

6. What is the approximate slope of your line? How did you determine the slope? What does the slope of the line indicate in this context?

6. **Answers will depend on data collected and the line each student drew. Sample answer: Slope is approximately 5. Slope was determined by finding two points on the line and computing $\dfrac{y_2 - y_1}{x_2 - x_1}$ (here x represents forearm length and y represents height). This means that for every increase of 1 cm in forearm length, there is a corresponding increase of 5 cm in height.**

7. Determine the coordinates of two points that are on your line.

7. Sample answer: (28, 175) and (24, 157).

8. Now use your answers to item 7 to find an equation that describes your line.

8. Sample answer: $y - 157 = \dfrac{9}{2}(x - 24)$.

9. Rewrite your equation from item 8 in slope-intercept form.

9. Sample answer: $y = \dfrac{9}{2}x + 48$.

10. If your slope in item 9 differs from your slope in item 6, explain how this might have happened.

10. When finding an equation of the line, it may have been difficult to find points exactly on the line. Also, the slope from item 6 was an approximation.

Extend the Activity (SE page 232)

11. Interpret the value of the y-intercept in your equation to item 9. Does it make sense in this context? Explain.

11. Sample answer: The value of the y-intercept indicates that a person with a forearm length of 0 cm would have a height of (in the sample answer) 49 cm. The y-intercept does not make sense. A height of 49 cm is too short for anyone but a newborn baby. Even in that case, a forearm would have to have a positive length.

12. The data in **Table 3.2** was taken from a group of adults.

Forearm Length (cm)	Height (cm)
26.5	173
27.0	177
27.0	174
31.0	192
28.0	172
29.0	180
27.0	174
28.0	175
32.0	185
30.0	185
30.0	178

Table 3.2

a) Make a scatter plot of the data.

12. a) Sample answer:

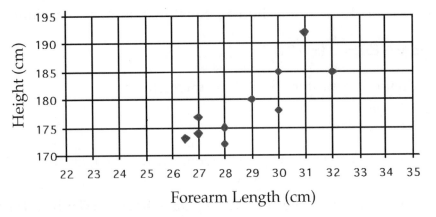

b) On your scatter plot, use a ruler to draw a straight line that best describes the data.

b) Sample answer:

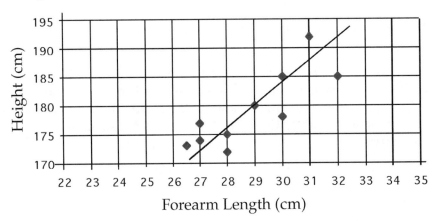

c) Find an equation for your line.

c) Sample answer: The line contains the point (29, 180) and has a slope of about 4 cm of height per 1 cm of forearm length. The equation, using point slope form, is $y = 4x + 64$.

d) Compare the data and the equation from (c) with the data and the equation you found for your class in Activity 3.1. Are they different? If so, why do you think the data and lines are not the same? If they are similar, why do you think this happened?

d) The data, and therefore the equations, are probably not the same. This could be because of the amount of data used. In this exercise, only 10 data points are in the set; for the class, there are probably more data points. It could be that the populations of people measured are quite different. For example, the group measured in the activity could be shorter than average or taller than average. If the data and the equations are similar, it would be because the populations from which both sets of data were collected are quite similar.

13. Use a calculator or a computer graphing program to produce a scatter plot of your class's data from item 2 of the activity. Then graph your equation from item 9 along with the scatter plot.

13. Sample answer:

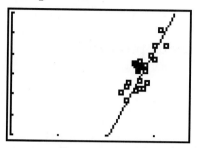

[–1, 35] x [140, 200]

Section 3.2: Scatter Plots and Data-Driven Models

What You Need to Know

- How to create a scatter plot from given data
- How to find the equation of a line when given various properties

What You Will Learn

- To examine scatter plots for linear patterns
- To use trial and error to create linear models describing data in scatter plots
- To use linear models to make predictions

Materials

- Tape measure
- CBL and motion detector or CBR (optional)

Scatter Plots

As we analyze situations in hopes of understanding them, it is helpful to collect data, make scatter plots, and look for patterns in the graphs.

As was noted in Chapter 2, mathematicians refer to the variables in a function as independent and dependent. Statisticians often refer to them as explanatory and response variables. The explanatory variable is the variable on which a prediction is based. It often "explains" the behavior of the response variable. In turn, the response variable "responds" to changes in the explanatory variable.

In Activity 3.1 we graphed forearm length on the horizontal axis and height on the vertical axis. Because of this choice, we can say that we created a scatter plot of height **versus** forearm length. Here the placement of the word "versus" indicates that height is the dependent variable and forearm length is the independent variable.

A scatter plot is useful in helping us determine whether a relationship exists between two variables. If one does seem to exist, the scatter plot helps determine the type of relationship. Then we can build a model in an attempt to explain the relationship mathematically.

We can create such a model in a manner similar to the method we used in Activity 3.1. Here are some suggestions for building linear models from data.

- Collect two-variable data and organize it in an input/output table.
- Examine the data to see if they exhibit a pattern. A scatter plot is often helpful in revealing patterns in data. If there is a pattern, see if it appears to be linear.

- If a linear pattern exists, then draw a straight line that appears to fit the data reasonably well.

- Determine an equation for the line that was drawn.

If the linear equation determined by this process is a good model for the data, it can be used to make predictions. The linear model will be most useful if it is written in slope-intercept form. Values of the independent variable that were not included in the data can be substituted in the linear function. The resulting values of the dependent variable should be good estimates of what would result if more data were collected.

Example 1

A scatter plot is shown in **Figure 3.2.** A line is drawn through the scatter plot in the general direction of the pattern of dots.

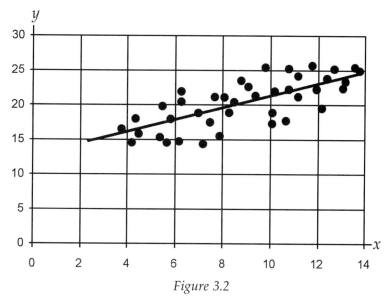

Figure 3.2

a) Approximately what is the slope of the line in the figure?

b) Determine an equation for the line.

c) Write the equation from (b) in slope-intercept form.

Solution:

a) To determine an equation for the line, select two points on the line as far apart as possible. These two points do not have to be data points. For example, the points (4, 16) and (12, 23) appear to be on the line. Using these points, the slope of the line is $\dfrac{23-16}{12-4} = \dfrac{7}{8}$ or 0.875.

b) Using the point (4, 16) and the slope of $\dfrac{7}{8}$, we have $y - 16 = \dfrac{7}{8}(x - 4)$ or $y - 16 = 0.875(x - 4)$.

c) In slope-intercept form, the equation is $y = \dfrac{7}{8}x + \dfrac{25}{2}$ or $y = 0.875x + 12.5$.

Using Data to Make Predictions

Once a model has been found that describes a data set, it can be used to predict the value of one variable from the other.

Example 2

Understory trees are the short trees among much taller trees in a forest or jungle. Although understory trees are shorter than other trees, their crowns (the leafy top part of the tree) can be very wide. The scatter plots in **Figures 3.3a** and **3.3b** show the crown width versus the height of two different species of trees.

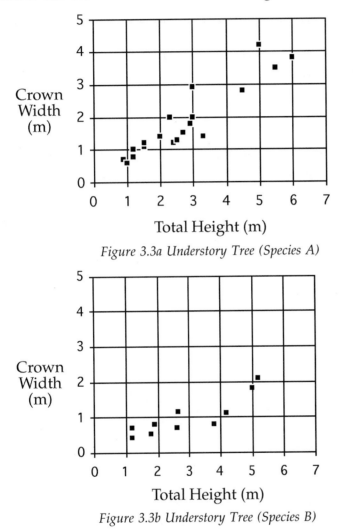

Figure 3.3a Understory Tree (Species A)

Figure 3.3b Understory Tree (Species B)

a) Describe any patterns or trends in Figures 3.3a and 3.3b.

b) Draw lines that best describe the general patterns of the data in Figure 3.3a and Figure 3.3b.

c) For each species, use the line drawn in (b) to predict the crown width when the tree height is 4 meters.

d) Find equations for the two lines from (b).

e) For each species, use an equation from (d) to predict the crown width when the tree height is 4 meters. Compare the results with the answers to (c).

f) For each species, use the equations from (d) to predict the crown width when the tree height is 8 meters.

Solution:

a) In both figures, as the height of the tree increases, the crown width increases.

b) **Figures 3.4a** and **3.4b** show lines that could be drawn.

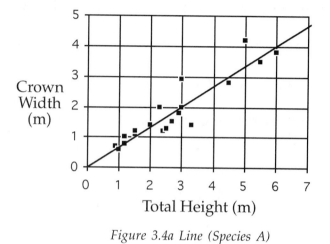

Figure 3.4a Line (Species A)

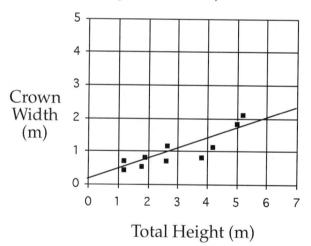

Figure 3.4b Line (Species B)

c) Species A: When tree height is 4 meters, the crown width appears to be about 2.7 meters.

Species B: The crown width appears to be about 1.4 meters.

d) Species A: Let x represent total height, and y represent crown width. The line from (b) contains the origin, and the approximate value for m is $\frac{2}{3}$. Using slope-intercept form, an equation for the line is

$$y = \frac{2}{3}x \text{ or } y = 0.67x.$$

Species B: From the graph, the slope of the line appears to be about $\frac{2}{7}$. The point (6, 2) is on the line. Using point-slope form, an equation of the line is $y - 2 = \frac{2}{7}(x - 6)$, which simplifies to $y = \frac{2}{7}x + \frac{2}{7}$ or $y = 0.29x + 0.29$.

e) Using the equation $y = \frac{2}{3}x$ for Species A: When the height is 4 meters, the crown width will be $y = \frac{2}{3}(4)$ or $\frac{8}{3} \approx 2.7$ meters.

Using the equation $y = \frac{2}{7}x + \frac{2}{7}$ for Species B: The crown width will be $y = \frac{2}{7}(4) + \frac{2}{7}$ or $\frac{10}{7} \approx 1.4$ meters.

Both results are in agreement with the answers to (c).

f) Species A: When the height is 8 meters, the crown width will be $y = \frac{2}{3}(8)$ or $\frac{16}{3} \approx 5.3$ meters.

Species B: The crown width will be $y = \frac{2}{7}(8) + \frac{2}{7}$ or $\frac{18}{7} \approx 2.6$ meters.

Linear models were used in Example 2 to make predictions. The predictions made in (c) and (e) should be fairly reliable, as long as the models are good ones. This is because the values of the independent variable that are used for prediction are within the range of the data.

The predictions made in (f) may or may not be reliable, however. Because no data are available for trees with heights greater than 6 meters, we cannot be confident that the pattern on which the linear model is based will continue up to tree heights of 8 meters. Using a data-driven model to make predictions outside the range of the data is called **extrapolation.** When using extrapolation, it is important to be very cautious.

The Shape of the Scatter Plot

A scatter plot does not always exhibit a pattern. In such a case, there may not be any relationship between the variables that allows us to make predictions. Or a relationship may exist, but it may be so weak that it is hidden by other factors that influence the data.

Frequently there is a pattern, but it is not linear. Then a linear model is not appropriate. Other kinds of models, however, may work, and some of these will be examined in later chapters.

Example 3

Examine each scatter plot and indicate whether it contains a pattern. If it does, decide whether the pattern appears to be linear.

   a) See **Figure 3.5.**

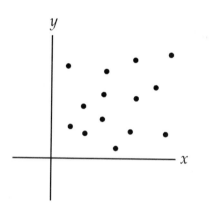

Figure 3.5

   b) See **Figure 3.6.**

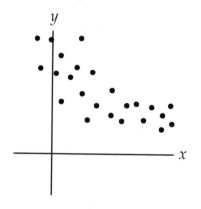

Figure 3.6

c) See **Figure 3.7.**

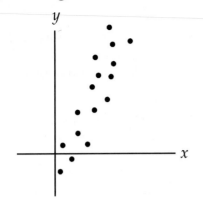

Figure 3.7

Solution:

    a) The points in the scatter plot are randomly scattered. There is no apparent pattern.

    b) There is a pattern in the scatter plot, but it is not linear.

    c) There is a linear pattern in the scatter plot.

Exercises 3.2

I. Investigations *(SE pages 240–242)*

1. Doctors look at many factors when assessing the health of a newborn. They observe the baby's color, listen to its heartbeat, measure the length of the baby, and check the size of the baby's head relative to the length of its body.

   As you may expect, body length and head circumference measurements of newborns vary from baby to baby. So how do doctors determine what is normal?

   Tables 3.3 and **3.4,** taken from a reference book for pediatricians, contain body-length and head-circumference data on male and female babies.

Males		Females	
Length (in)	Head circumference (in)	Length (in)	Head circumference (in)
18.25	12.75	17.75	12.75
18.75	13.00	18.25	13.00
19.25	13.25	19.00	13.25
20.00	13.75	19.75	13.50
20.50	14.00	20.00	13.75
21.00	14.50	20.50	14.00
21.50	14.75	20.75	14.25

Table 3.3   *Table 3.4*

   a) Why do you think the data are separated by gender?

1. **a) The relationship between head circumference and body length may not be the same for males and females. In other words, what is normal for males may not be normal for females.**

b) For each data set, draw a set of axes and label each axis with the appropriate variable. Represent the data with scatter plots.

b) Sample answer:

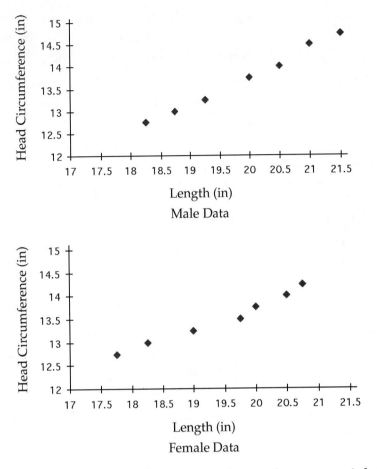

Male Data

Female Data

c) For each scatter plot, use a ruler to draw a straight line that you think describes the pattern in your data reasonably well.

c) Sample answer:

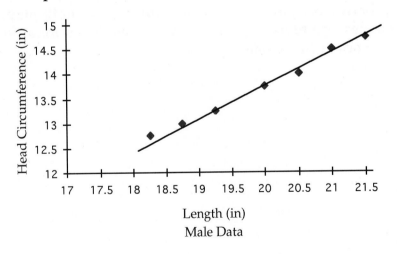

Male Data

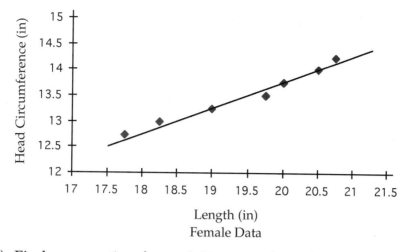

Length (in)
Female Data

d) Find an equation for each line you drew from (c).

d) **Sample answer: Let x represent length and y represent head circumference.**

Male data: Using the points (19.25, 13.25) and (20, 13.75),

$$y - 13.75 = \frac{13.25 - 13.75}{19.25 - 20}(x - 20).$$

$$y - 13.75 = \frac{2}{3}(x - 20).$$

Female data: Using the points (19, 13.25) and (20, 13.75),

$$y - 13.75 = \frac{13.75 - 13.25}{20 - 19}(x - 20).$$

$$y - 13.755 = \frac{1}{2}(x - 20).$$

e) What does the slope of your lines from (d) tell you about babies?

e) **In general, the slope indicates the increase of head circumference per unit increase of length. In the sample answer for males, the head circumference increases 2/3 inch per inch increase in length or 2 inches per 3-inch increase in length. For females, the head circumference increase is about 1/2 inch per inch increase in length or 1 inch per 2-inch increase in length.**

f) Compare the model you chose to describe the male data with the one for the female data. Do the relationships between head circumference and body length appear to be different for male babies and female babies? If so, how do they differ?

f) **They do appear to be different. The slope of the line for the males is steeper than the slope of the line drawn for the females.**

g) Use your models to predict the head circumferences of a female baby who is 21 inches long and of a male baby who is 22 inches long.

g) **Female prediction:** $y - 13.75 = \dfrac{1}{2}(21 - 20)$; $y = 14.25$ **inches.**

Male prediction: $y - 13.75 = \dfrac{2}{3}(22 - 20)$; $y = 15.08$ **inches.**

2. In Section 2.6 Exercise 1, you found a model ($w = 8.3a - 5.6$) that related the average weight and age of female children. Now it is time to test your model by using additional data.

a) Make a scatter plot of the data in **Table 3.5.**

Age	Weight (lb)
6	47.50
7	53.50
8	60.75
9	69.00
10	77.00
11	87.50
12	94.00
13	103.00

Table 3.5

2. a)

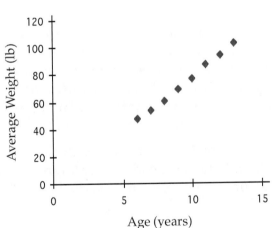

b) Draw a graph of the model $w = 8.3a - 5.6$ on your scatter plot.

b)

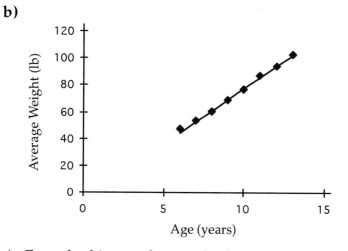

c) From looking at the graph, do you feel that your model is still a good model or that it could be improved? Explain.

c) Answers will vary. Some students will want to move the line upward slightly, others will say that the model is good because it appears that the line comes close to most of the points. It does appear that the data are fairly linear in form.

3. **Table 3.6** contains data on the number of doctors in the United States for a 30-year period.

Year	Total Number of Physicians (in thousands)	Number of Women Physicians (in thousands)
1970	330	25
1975	390	36
1980	470	55
1985	550	80
1990	620	100
1995	720	150
1999	800	190

Table 3.6 (Source: St. Louis Post-Dispatch*)*

a) For the years given in the table, make a scatter plot of total number of physicians versus year. Indicate whether the scatter plot has a linear pattern, and if it does, draw a line that describes the data. Find an equation for the line.

3. a) The scatter plot appears to have a linear pattern.

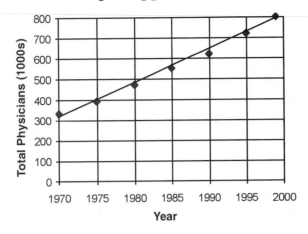

A sample line is shown. Two points on this line are (1970, 310) and (1995, 730). An equation for this line is $P = 16.8y - 32{,}786$. Here, P represents the total number of physicians and y represents the calendar year.

b) Repeat (a), but use the data on the number of women physicians.

b) The scatter plot does not have a linear pattern. It appears to curve upward in recent years.

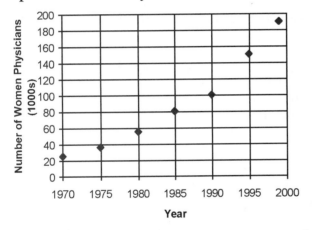

c) Compute the percent of physicians in each year that are women. Construct a table similar to **Table 3.7** that summarizes the results.

Year	% Women
1970	
1975	
etc.	

Table 3.7

c)

Year	% Women
1970	8%
1975	9%
1980	12%
1985	15%
1990	16%
1995	21%
1999	24%

d) Again repeat (a), but this time use the data from (c) to graph and analyze the data on percent of women physicians versus year.

d) The scatter plot has a linear pattern.

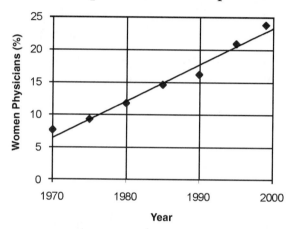

One possible line is drawn. It contains the points (1970, 7) and (2000, 23). Using these points, an equation is $W = 0.533y - 1044$. Here, W represents the percent of physicians who are women.

4. **Figure 3.8** shows a scatter plot of data on cigarette demand versus retail price per pack. A line has been drawn to describe the data.

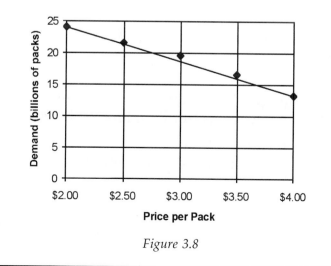

Figure 3.8

a) Find an equation for the line.

4. **a) Sample answer: The points (2.00, 24) and (4.00, 13.5) appear to be on the line. The resulting equation is $D = -5.25p + 34.5$, where D represents demand and p represents price.**

b) Use your answer to (a) to predict the demand for cigarettes for a retail price of $3.20. Do you think your answer would be an accurate prediction of cigarette demand for that price?

b) Substitute 3.20 for p. The predicted demand is 17.7 billion packs. Yes, the prediction should be fairly accurate because the price of $3.20 is within the range of the collected data.

c) Use your answer to (a) to predict the demand for cigarettes for a retail price of $4.50. Do you think your answer would be an accurate prediction of cigarette demand for that price?

c) Substitute 4.50 for p. The predicted demand is 10.9 billion packs. The price of $4.50 is slightly outside the range of the data, so this is an extrapolated value. But because this price is only slightly beyond the range of the data, the prediction may still be reasonably accurate.

d) Use your answer to (a) to predict the demand for cigarettes for a retail price of $7.00. Do you think your answer would be an accurate prediction of cigarette demand for that price?

d) Substitute 7.00 for p. The predicted demand is -2.25 billion packs. This makes no sense, as there cannot be a negative demand for cigarettes. A price of $7.00 involves extrapolation too far outside the range of the data.

e) What are the coordinates of the y-intercept of the graph of your equation from (a)? What is the meaning of the y-intercept in this context?

e) The coordinates of the y-intercept are (0, 34.5). They imply that when cigarettes are free, the demand is 34.5 billion. But this value involves extrapolation too far outside the range of the data for it to have any real meaning.

II. Projects and Group Activities *(SE page 243)*

5. Materials: CBL or CBR attached to a graphing calculator (If a CBL is used, a program such as Hiker will be needed—see CBL or CBR manual for set-up instructions.)

In this activity, one member in the group will walk in front of the motion detector or CBR in such a way that the data collected has a linear pattern.

a) Use the CBL and motion detector (or the CBR) to create at least three linear graphs: one with a positive slope, one with a negative slope, and one with a slope of zero.

5. **a)** To create a line with a positive slope, the person should walk away from the detector at a steady pace. To create a line with a negative slope, the person should walk toward the detector at a steady pace. To create a line with zero slope, the person should stand still in front of the detector.

b) Have each member of the group record the data from one of the graphs. Make a scatter plot of at least 10 of the collected data points. What is the independent variable? What is the dependent variable?

b) **The independent variable is time; the dependent variable is distance.**

c) Fit a line to the data in the scatter plot and find a linear equation that fits the data.

c) **Answers will vary with the data collected.**

d) Explain what the slope of the line means for each of the groups' graphs.

d) **The slopes of the lines indicate the rate at which the person is walking. That is, it indicates distance-per-unit time duration. (The unit used for distance will vary by the program used. It may be meters, or it may be feet.)**

6. Repeat Activity 3.1, only this time measure the length of a person's head and his or her height.

a) Collect the data, make a scatter plot of the data, and draw a straight line that best describes the pattern in the data.

6. **a)** **Answers will vary depending on the data collected. Data should have a linear pattern.**

b) Find an equation of the line.

b) **Answers will vary depending on the scatter plot constructed in (a).**

c) Compare this model for determining height with the model created in Activity 3.1. Which model do you think would be more reliable in predicting a person's height?

c) **Answers will vary depending on the data collected. The model that would be considered better for predicting height would be the one with the stronger relationship between the two variables (i.e., the one whose points on the scatter plot are closer to the line).**

For 7–10, draw a scatter plot of the given data.

7. Use **Table 3.8,** which shows the number of cases of diabetes diagnosed in the United States in selected years since 1958.

Year	Diagnosed Cases of Diabetes (millions)
1958	1.6
1960	1.6
1963	2.1
1966	2.7
1968	3.2
1973	4.2
1975	4.7
1978	5.2
1980	5.5
1983	5.6
1986	6.6
1988	6.2
1990	6.2
1993	7.8
1995	8.7
1998	10.3

Table 3.8 (Source: National Institutes of Health)

7. **Sample scatter plot:**

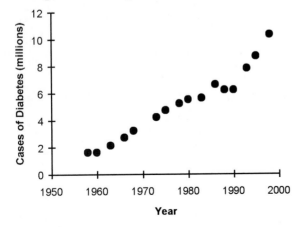

8. Use **Table 3.9,** which shows how the average number of changes of pitchers in major league baseball games has varied since 1909.

Year	Average Number of Pitching Changes per Game
1909	1.39
1919	2.16
1929	2.71
1939	2.93
1949	3.28
1959	3.79
1969	4.20
1979	4.04
1989	4.75
1999	6.05

Table 3.9 (*Source:* Sports Illustrated)

8. Sample scatter plot:

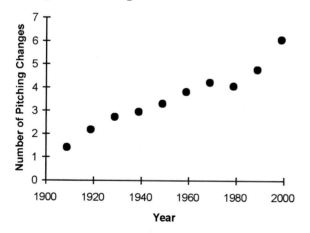

9. Use **Table 3.10.**

x	y
3	27
6	16
5	21
2	36
8	40
5	12

Table 3.10

9. Sample scatter plot:

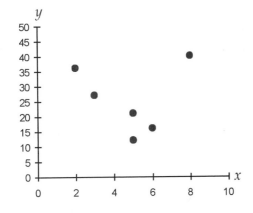

10. Use **Table 3.11.**

x	y
0	19
5	17
10	9
15	18
20	19
25	20
30	18
35	12
40	16
45	16
50	15
55	12

Table 3.11

10. Sample scatter plot:

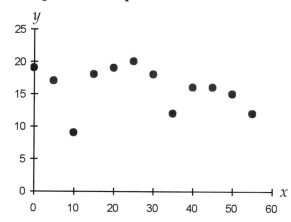

For 11–15, a scatter plot of data is given.

a) Find a line that appears to describe the data.

b) Find an equation for your line, in slope-intercept form.

11. Use the scatter plot in **Figure 3.9,** which shows the percent of the U.S. female population in the workforce from 1940 to 1997.

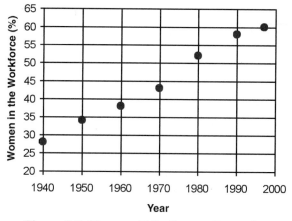

Figure 3.9 (Source: U.S. Census Bureau)

11. a) Sample line:

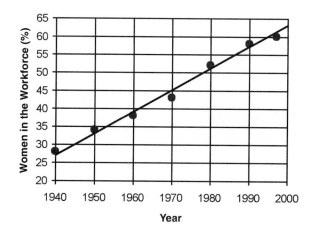

b) The points (1940, 27) and (2000, 63) are on the line. The slope-intercept equation is $W = 0.6y - 1137$.

12. Use the scatter plot in **Figure 3.10**, which shows the number of deaths by fire in the United States from 1979 to 1999.

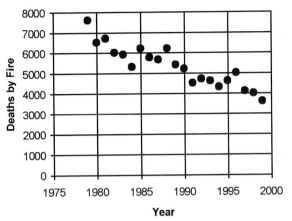

Figure 3.10 (Source: National Fire Protection Association)

12. a) Sample line:

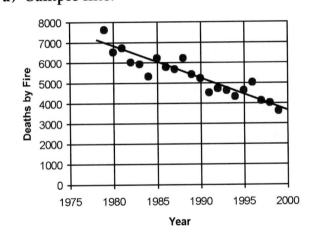

b) The points (1980, 6800) and (2000, 3700) are on the line. The slope-intercept equation is $D = -155y + 313{,}700$.

13. Use the scatter plot in **Figure 3.11,** which shows the relationship between available zinc in cold lozenges taken by cold sufferers and the number of days the colds were shortened. (Negative zinc availability means that conditions were used that removed zinc from the bloodstream.)

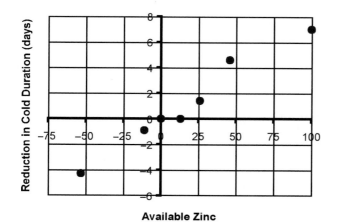

Available Zinc

Figure 3.11 (Source: George Eby Research)

13. a) Sample line:

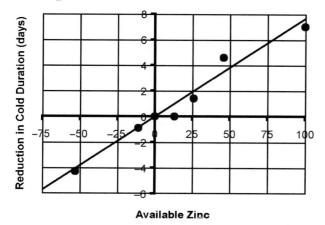

Available Zinc

b) The points (0, 0) and (100, 7.6) are on the line. The slope-intercept equation is $R = 0.076Z$.

14. Use the scatter plot in **Figure 3.12.**

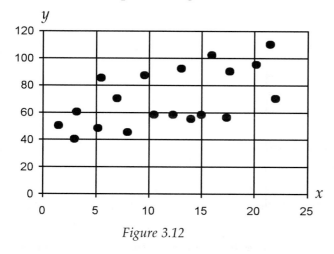

Figure 3.12

14. a) Sample Line:

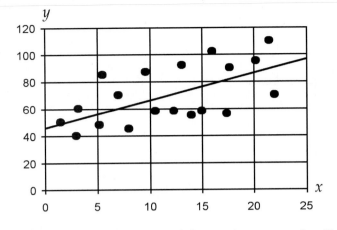

b) The points (5, 56) and (20, 85) are on the line. The slope-intercept equation is $y = 1.9x + 46$.

15. Use the scatter plot in **Figure 3.13.**

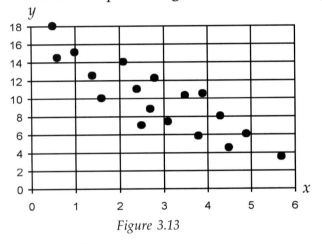

Figure 3.13

15. a) Sample line:

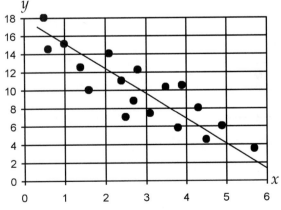
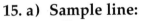

b) The points (1, 15) and (5, 4) are on the line. The slope-intercept equation is $y = -\dfrac{11}{4}x + \dfrac{71}{4}$ or $y = -2.75x + 17.75$.

16. **Figure 3.14** shows a scatter plot of the electrical resistance of an induction coil versus temperature. A line that describes the data is drawn on the scatter plot.

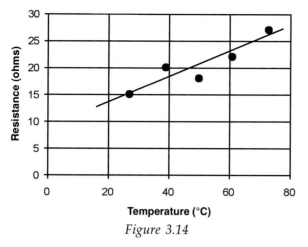

Figure 3.14

a) Find a slope-intercept equation for the line.

16. a) Sample answer: The points (20, 13.5) and (67, 25) appear to be on the line. The slope-intercept equation is R = 0.24T + 8.6.

b) Use your answer to (a) to predict the resistance of the coil for a temperature of 65°C.

b) When T = 55, R = 21.8, so the resistance is about 22 ohms for a temperature of 55°C.

17. **Figure 3.15** shows a line that is drawn on a scatter plot.

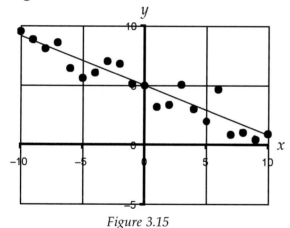

Figure 3.15

a) Find a slope-intercept equation for the line.

17. a) The points (0, 5) and (5, 3) appear to be on the line. The equation of the line is y = −0.4 + 5.

b) Use your answer to (a) to predict the value of y when x is –6.5.

b) Substitute –6.5 for x. The value of y is 7.6.

18. The data shown in **Table 3.12** are for AT&T direct-dialed domestic calls made in the Midwest.

Duration of Calls (min)	1	2	2	3	2	1	4
Cost of Calls (cents)	13	44	32	78	52	26	104

Table 3.12

a) Make a scatter plot of the given data. If the data has a linear pattern, draw a straight line that best describes the data.

18. a) Sample answer:

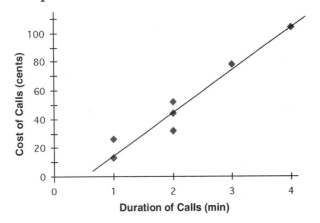

b) Find an equation of the line.

b) Using the points (2, 44) and (4, 104), the equation is $y = 30x - 16$.

c) What is the slope of the line? What is the meaning of the slope of the line?

c) 30 cents per minute; the slope gives the cost in cents per minute of call time.

d) Use your equation to predict the cost of a 5-minute call.

d) Using $y = 30x - 16$, $y = 30(5) - 16 = 134$ cents.

e) Will this line be a good predictor of call cost for calls having a long duration?

e) Sample answer: Probably not, because most calls get cheaper per minute as they get longer.

For 19–22, examine each scatter plot. Indicate whether it contains a pattern. If it does, decide whether the pattern appears to be linear.

19. See **Figure 3.16.**

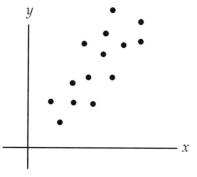

Figure 3.16

19. Linear pattern; as the values of the independent variable increase, the values of the dependent variable appear to increase at a constant rate.

20. See **Figure 3.17.**

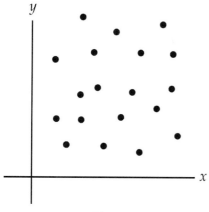

Figure 3.17

20. There is no pattern.

21. See **Figure 3.18.**

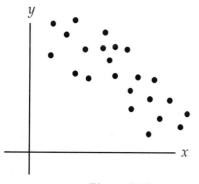

Figure 3.18

21. Linear pattern; as the values of the independent variable increase, the values of the dependent variable appear to decrease at a constant rate.

22. See **Figure 3.19.**

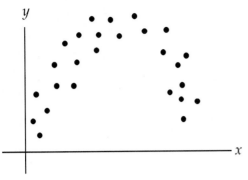

Figure 3.19

22. There is a pattern, but it is nonlinear.

23. See **Figure 3.20.**

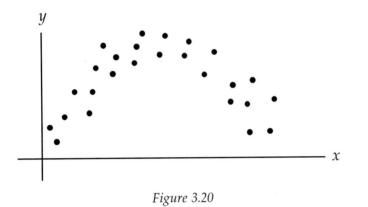

Figure 3.20

a) On the scatter plot in Figure 3.20, draw a line so that half of the data points are above the line and half are below the line.

23. a) Answers will vary. Sample answer:

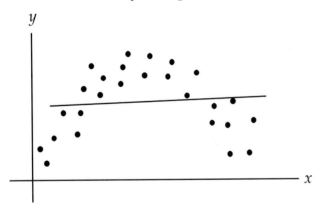

b) Explain why the line drawn is not a good model for the data and would not be useful in making predictions.

b) Even though an equal number of points are above and below the line, a line simply does not capture the pattern of the data. As x gets larger, the data increases to a maximum and then looks as if it will continue to decrease. The line, in this case, slowly increases as x gets larger.

Section 3.3 Lines of Best Fit

What You Need to Know

- How to recognize linear patterns in scatter plots

- How to create linear models that describe data in scatter plots

- How to use linear models to make predictions

What You Will Learn

- To describe the direction, form, and strength of scatter plots

- To calculate residuals

- To use a calculator or spreadsheet to determine an equation of the least-squares line

- To use the least-squares equation to make predictions

Materials

- Circular objects such as lids, plates, hula-hoops

- Tape measures, rulers, and yardsticks

In Activity 3.1 we fit a line to the height versus forearm data by drawing a line that appeared to describe the pattern in the data reasonably well. However, our work raises several questions about using scatter plots and lines to analyze data. Should we fit a line to our data? If so, what line? What method should we use to get the "best-fitting" line? Does every set of data have a best-fitting line? How precise are the predictions made based on the line?

Our previous work has answered the first question. We should try to fit a line to data only if the scatter plot appears to have a linear pattern.

In this section we will begin to answer the other questions.

Direction, Form, and Strength

When examining scatter plots for insight into possible relationships, it is helpful to check the direction of the relationship. In Activity 3.1 we noted that as the lengths of the forearms of individuals increased, their heights also increased. When the independent variable and the dependent variable increase together, we say that the two variables are **positively related.** If, instead, one variable decreases while the other increases, then the variables are **negatively related.** See **Figures 3.21a** and **3.21b.**

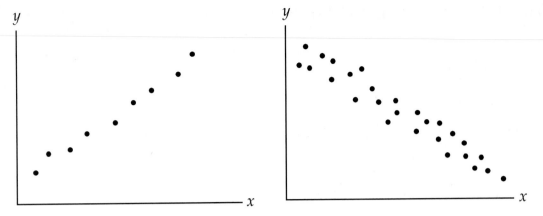

Figure 3.21a Positively Related Variables   Figure 3.21b Negatively Related Variables

So far, most of the scatter plots we have drawn have a **linear form.** When a scatter plot has a linear form, it is possible to draw a line that describes the general trend of the data. However, sometimes the data do not fall along a straight line. In that case, the scatter plot has a **nonlinear form.** See **Figures 3.22a, 3.22b,** and **3.22c.**

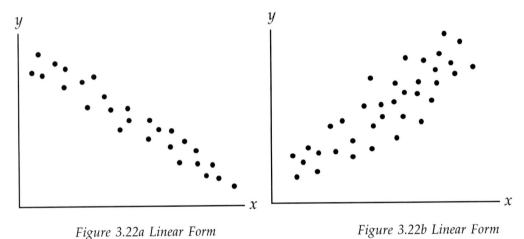

Figure 3.22a Linear Form   Figure 3.22b Linear Form

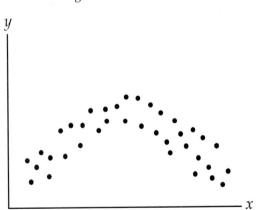

Figure 3.22c Nonlinear Form

When the points on a scatter plot fall very close to a line, we say that the variables have a **strong** (linear) **relationship.** In contrast, if the data do not lie as close to a line (the data are more scattered), the variables have a **weak** (linear) **relationship.**

The scatter plots in **Figures 3.23a** and **3.23b** show relationships between human height and the forearm bone length. Both relationships have a linear form. Figure 3.23b shows a stronger linear relationship than Figure 3.23a because the data appear to lie in a narrower band about the line.

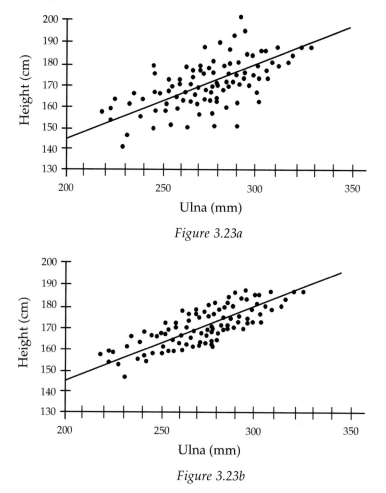

Figure 3.23a

Figure 3.23b

When the data in a scatter plot form a narrow band about the linear model, the predictions are more accurate than when the data form a wide band about the model. That is, we can make more accurate predictions when we deal with stronger relationships rather than weaker ones.

Figure 3.24

On the coast of Florida live the manatee, a large, gentle marine mammal. Unfortunately, the slow-moving Florida manatee is one of the most endangered marine mammals in the United States. The deaths of manatee have steadily increased over the last 20 years. About one-third of all manatee deaths are from human-related causes. **Table 3.13** shows the number of powerboat registrations and the number of manatee deaths due to accidents with powerboats in the state of Florida from 1977 to 1990.

Year	Powerboat Registrations (thousands)	Manatees Killed
1977	447	13
1978	460	21
1979	481	24
1980	498	16
1981	513	24
1982	512	20
1983	526	15
1984	559	34
1985	585	33
1986	614	33
1987	645	39
1988	675	43
1989	711	50
1990	719	47

Table 3.13

1. Have each person in the group create a scatter plot of the data in Table 3.13. Think about which variable is the independent variable and which is the dependent variable. Label the scatter plot appropriately.

1. Sample scatter plot:

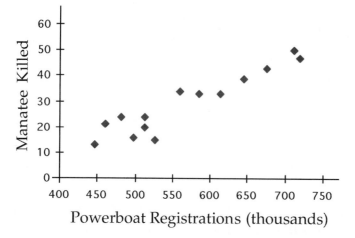

2. In your group, answer the following questions about the scatter plots: What is the independent variable in the scatter plot? What is the dependent variable? Describe the form of the scatter plot. Are the variables positively or negatively related? Do the variables have a strong or weak linear relationship?

2. The number of powerboat registrations is the independent variable, and the number of manatee killed is the dependent variable. The scatter plot has a linear form. The variables are positively related. The relationship seems to be relatively strong, especially for the latter years in the period.

3. Have each individual in the group draw a line that best describes the data displayed in his or her scatter plot. Find an equation for the line.

3. Sample answer:

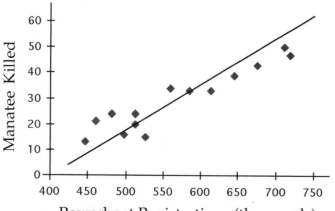

The line passes through the points (512, 20) and (585, 33).

$$m = \frac{33 - 20}{585 - 512} = 0.18.$$

An equation of the line is $y - 20 = 0.18(x - 512)$ or $y = 0.18(x - 512) + 20$.

Once manatee data were released, the state of Florida realized that the plight of the manatee was tied directly to the increased development in the state. As population increased and more and more time was spent in boats on the water, the state began to consider ways to protect the manatee and their young.

Speed limits have been imposed in key areas (manatee zones), and protection plans such as limiting the number of boat docks have been considered. Has it helped? Data after 1990 tell the story.

4. Examine each of the lines drawn by the members of the group. Have each member explain why he or she drew the line that they did. Did everyone draw the same line? Did everyone find the same equation?

4. Most likely, not everyone drew the same line, in which case the equations will not be the same.

5. Compare the lines drawn by each member of the group. Which line provides the best model of the data? That is, which line fits the data the best? What criteria did you use when you made the decision about which line was best?

5. Answers will vary here, with each group making its own decision. Possible criteria: the line hits as many points as possible, the line has as many points above the line as below the line, or the line is most influenced by the data near the middle. Some students may even start to quantify the errors at this point by minimizing the distances from the points to the line.

Residuals

Unless the data in the scatter plot lie perfectly on a line, picking a good line may not be as easy as it seems. Simply "eyeballing" a line may not be the best method of finding a good line from which to make predictions.

We are well aware that most of the points in our scatter plots do not lie on the lines we draw. But how close are they? One way to answer this question is to examine the differences between the actual values and the predicted values ($y_{actual} - y_{predicted}$). This difference in y-values is called the error or **residual.** In the case of the manatee data, the residuals are the differences between the actual number of manatee deaths and the predicted number of deaths.

Example 4

x	y
1	2
1	4
3	3
3	6.2
5	4.2
5	6.8
8	5.5
8	7.5

Table 3.14

a) Plot the data in **Table 3.14** either by hand or with a calculator or spreadsheet. Check to see that the scatter plot has a linear form and that a line is an appropriate model.

b) Add a line that seems to fit reasonably well. Then indicate the residuals on your scatter plot.

c) Find an equation for the line in (b). Use the equation to complete **Table 3.15.**

x	y	Predicted y	Error (Actual − Predicted)
1	2		
1	4		
3	3		
3	6.2		
5	4.2		
5	6.8		
8	5.5		
8	7.5		

Table 3.15

Solution:

a) The scatter plot appears to have a linear form. (See **Figure 3.25**.)

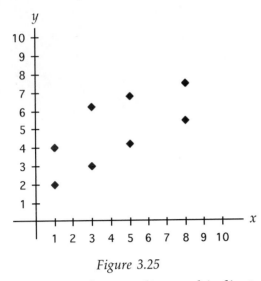

Figure 3.25

b) **Figure 3.26** shows a line and indicates the residuals.

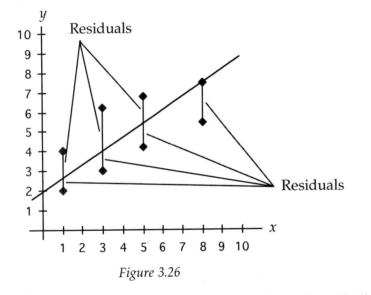

Figure 3.26

c) The line drawn in (b) goes through the points (0, 2) and (8, 7.5). An equation of the line is $y = \dfrac{5.5}{8}x + 2$ or $y = 0.6875x + 2$.

Table 3.16 shows the completed table.

x	y	Predicted y	Error (Actual − Predicted)
1	2	2.69	−0.69
1	4	2.69	1.31
3	3	4.06	−1.06
3	6.2	4.06	2.14
5	4.2	5.44	−1.24
5	6.8	5.44	1.36
8	5.5	7.5	−2.0
8	7.5	7.5	0

Table 3.16

Linear Least Squares

It is impossible to answer the question about which line is best without discussing what we mean by "best." Statisticians, who have worked on this problem longer than we, have developed several criteria. The **least-squares line** results from one of the most widely used criteria.

The **least-squares criterion** suggests that the best-fitting line is the one with the smallest possible total of the squared errors (residuals). Why square the residuals? *Error* is defined as actual value minus predicted value. Therefore, some errors are positive and some are negative. One way to eliminate negative values is to take the absolute value of the error. Another way is to square the error. The least-squares method uses the latter.

Table 3.15 in Example 4 can now be expanded to include a column for squared residuals. (See **Table 3.17**.)

x	y	Predicted y	Error (Actual − Predicted)	Squared Errors
1	2	2.69	−0.69	0.476
1	4	2.69	1.31	1.716
3	3	4.06	−1.06	1.124
3	6.2	4.06	2.14	4.580
5	4.2	5.44	−1.24	1.538
5	6.8	5.44	1.36	1.850
8	5.5	7.5	−2.0	4.0
8	7.5	7.5	0	0

Table 3.17

To find the sum of the squared errors (known to statisticians as the **SSE**), simply add the squared errors in the last column to get a sum of 15.284.

We could try finding a different line that might fit our data better by completing another table similar to Table 3.17 and again summing the squared errors. The better of the two lines would be the one with the smallest SSE.

Spreadsheets and geometric drawing utilities such as the Geometer's Sketchpad or Cabri provide two dynamic ways of comparing lines using the least-squares criterion.

Figures 3.27–3.29 show three screens from a geometric drawing utility such as the Geometer's Sketchpad or Cabri. The script used to create these figures allows the user to move the line by clicking on it and dragging it to a new position. As the line moves, the software finds an equation of the new line and recalculates the sum of the residuals and the SSE. To find the best line, the user moves the line to a position where the SSE has the smallest value.

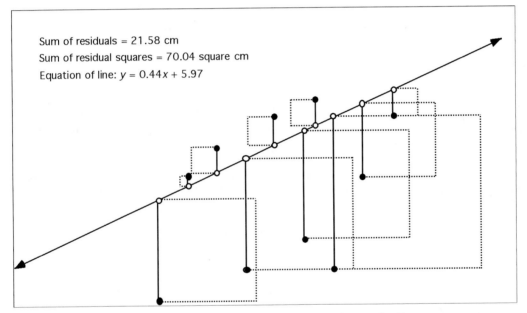

Sum of residuals = 21.58 cm
Sum of residual squares = 70.04 square cm
Equation of line: $y = 0.44x + 5.97$

Figure 3.27 A First Attempt at Fitting a Line to the Data

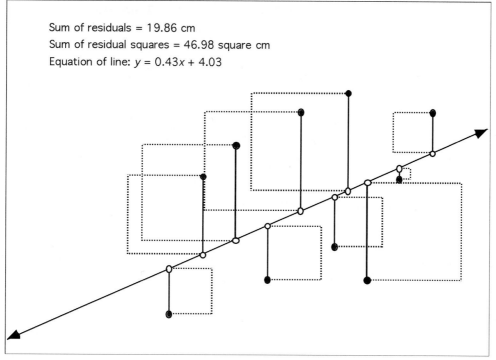

Sum of residuals = 19.86 cm
Sum of residual squares = 46.98 square cm
Equation of line: $y = 0.43x + 4.03$

Figure 3.28 A Line with a Smaller SSE

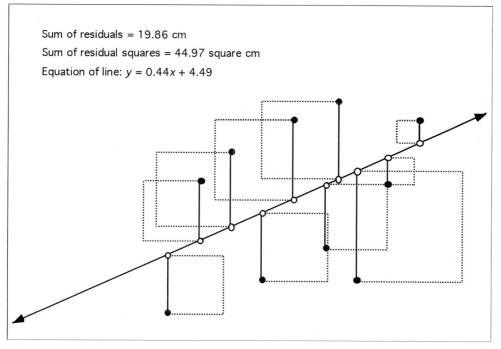

Sum of residuals = 19.86 cm
Sum of residual squares = 44.97 square cm
Equation of line: $y = 0.44x + 4.49$

Figure 3.29 The Line with the Smallest SSE

Finding the Least-Squares Prediction Equation

The obvious question now is how do we find the least-squares line? Because finding the least-squares line by hand requires mathematics beyond the scope of this course, we will do what most people do—that is, we will use a calculator or computer to calculate the slope and y-intercept of the line.

Graphing calculators (as well as most scientific calculators and spreadsheet programs) have built-in commands that calculate an equation of the least-squares line. However, you probably will not see the term "least-squares line" anywhere on your calculator. The general name for determining an equation that fits the data is **regression.** The technique used in fitting the best line to data with a linear pattern is called **linear regression.**

Example 5

   a) Use a calculator or computer to determine an equation of the least-squares line for the manatee data in Table 3.13 in Discovery 3.1.

   b) What do the slope and y-intercept tell us about boats and manatee?

Solution:

   a) First enter into the calculator lists or two columns of a spreadsheet the data from the last two columns of the table. (See **Figure 3.30.**)

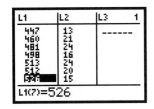

Figure 3.30

Then use a calculator (or spreadsheet) to determine the values of the slope and y-intercept of the least-squares line. (See **Figures 3.31–3.33.**)

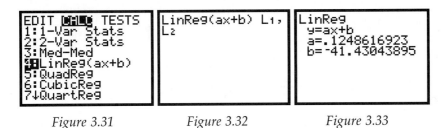

    Figure 3.31   *Figure 3.32*   *Figure 3.33*

An equation of the least-squares line is $y = 0.125x - 41.4$. Note that the values for slope and y-intercept have been rounded.

   b) The slope tells us that each additional 8 (thousand) boats tend to add 1 more manatee death. The y-intercept indicates that if there were no boats, manatee deaths would be –41.4 per year. But "negative deaths" make no sense.

Now that we have used technology to find an equation of the least-squares line, we will turn our efforts to assessing the appropriateness of our linear models.

Exercises 3.3

I. Investigations *(SE pages 263–265)*

1. We are constantly aware of the frictional force that opposes the motion of one surface in contact with another surface. We put sand on our icy roads to increase the friction in the wintertime. We also lubricate machines to reduce friction. Depending upon the circumstances, either too much or too little friction can be a problem.

   The data in **Table 3.18** were collected during an investigation on the effects of friction. In the experiment, the force necessary to move varying numbers of bricks uniformly along a surface was measured.

Number of Bricks	Force (newtons)
1	2.5
2	5.1
3	7.8
4	10.2
5	12.3

Table 3.18

   a) Make a scatter plot of the data in Table 3.18. Which variable is the independent variable and which is the dependent variable? Do your data have a linear form?

1. **a) The independent variable is the number of bricks; the dependent variable is force in newtons. The data do have linear form.**

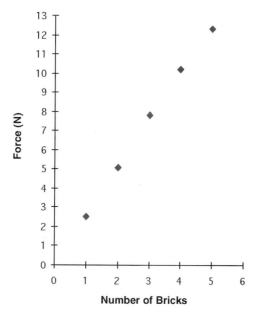

b) On your scatter plot, draw a line that best describes the data. Indicate the residuals on your scatter plot.

b) The residuals are the vertical distances between the points and the line.

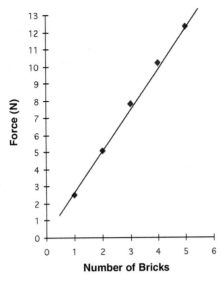

c) Find an equation for your line. Use the equation to complete **Table 3.19**.

x	y	**Predicted y**	**Error (Actual − Predicted)**
1	2.5		
2	5.1		
3	7.8		
4	10.2		
5	12.3		

Table 3.19

c) Sample answer: Using a line that passes through the points (5, 12.3) and (2, 5.1), an equation of the line is $y = 2.4x + 0.3$.

Predicted y	**Error**
2.7	−0.2
5.1	0
7.5	0.3
9.9	0.3
12.3	0

d) Could you move 7 bricks with a force of 16.6 newtons? Explain.

d) No. Sample answer: Using the equation $y = 2.4x + 0.3$, it would take 17.1 newtons to move 7 bricks.

> **For Your Information:**
> A golf score is the number of strokes required to complete the course; the lower the score, the better.

2. The 10 members of a college women's golf team play a practice round, then the next day play a round in competition on the same course. Their scores are shown in **Table 3.20.**

Player	1	2	3	4	5	6	7	8	9	10
Practice Score	89	90	87	95	86	81	83	88	91	79
Competition Score	94	85	89	89	81	76	87	91	88	80

Table 3.20

a) Which variable is the independent variable and which is the dependent variable? Make a scatter plot of the data given in Table 3.20 and label it appropriately.

2. a) The independent variable is the practice score; the dependent variable is the competition score.

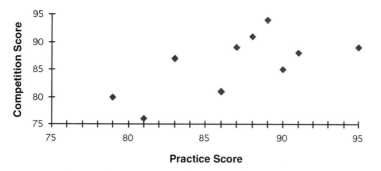

b) Use a calculator or spreadsheet to determine the values of the slope and y-intercept of the least-squares line. Write an equation of the least-squares line and draw it on the scatter plot.

b) $y = 0.75x + 20$.

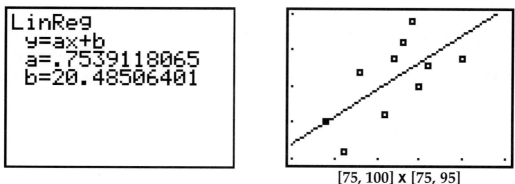

[75, 100] x [75, 95]

c) What does the slope of your line tell you? What would a slope of 1.0 indicate?

c) The slope of 0.75 indicates that for each stroke in the practice round, the player only takes approximately 3/4 of a stroke in the competition. A slope of 1.0 (strokes in competition per strokes in practice) would indicate that the scores were about the same for practice and competition.

d) Use the equation of the least-squares line to complete **Table 3.21.**

Player	1	2	3	4	5	6	7	8	9	10
Practice Score	89	90	87	95	86	81	83	88	91	79
Actual Competition Score	94	85	89	89	81	76	87	91	88	80
Predicted Competition Score										
Error (Actual − Predicted)										

Table 3.21

d)

Player	1	2	3	4	5	6	7	8	9	10
Practice Score	89	90	87	95	86	81	83	88	91	79
Actual Competition Score	94	85	89	89	81	76	87	91	88	80
Predicted Competition Scores	86.8	87.5	85.3	91.3	84.5	80.8	82.3	86.0	88.3	79.3
Error (Actual − Predicted)	7.2	−2.5	3.7	−2.3	−3.5	−4.8	4.7	5.0	−0.3	0.7

e) Use the equation from (b) to predict the score of a player who scored 93 in practice. Based on the information you have gathered, how accurate do you think your prediction is? Explain.

e) $y = 0.75x + 20$; $y = 0.75(93) + 20 = 89.8$, or a golf score of 90 strokes. The prediction is probably not very good because the prediction errors are large (−4.8–7.2 strokes).

3. **Table 3.22** shows the average ocean wave heights for different years over three decades.

Year	Wave Height (ft)
1962	6.9
1968	7.6
1970	7.4
1972	8.6
1973	6.9
1974	7.7
1976	7.9
1977	8.2
1979	9.3
1981	9.6
1983	9.9
1984	8.9

Table 3.22 (Source: Nature *4/7/88)*

a) Which variable is the independent variable and which is the dependent variable? Make a scatter plot of the data give in Table 3.22 and label it appropriately. (Hint: Take care in numbering the years because they are not consecutive.)

3. **a) The independent variable is the year; the dependent variable is the wave height.**

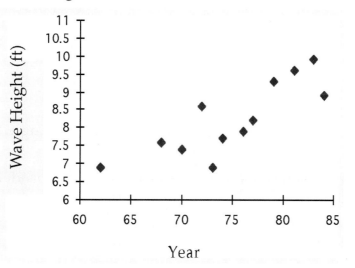

b) Use a calculator or spreadsheet to determine the values of the slope and y-intercept of the least-squares line. Write an equation of the least-squares line and draw it in the scatter plot.

b) $y = 0.130x - 1.462.$

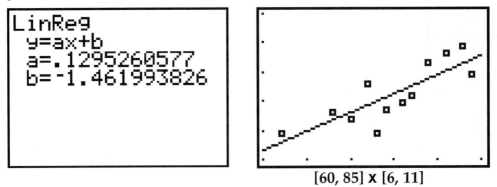

[60, 85] x [6, 11]

c) Use the equation from (d) to predict the wave height in 1990.

c) $y = 0.130x - 1.462; y = 0.130(90) - 1.462; y = 10.2$ **feet.**

II. Projects and Group Activities (SE pages 266–267)

4. Materials: circle-shaped items of various diameters such as lids, plates, and hula-hoops; tape measures and rulers

   a) Have the members of the group measure the diameters and circumferences of several (at least 5) different circular items. Record your data in a table similar to **Table 3.23.** You may choose to measure in inches or centimeters. (Make sure that all members of the group use the same units.)

Diameter (?)	Circumference (?)

Table 3.23

   b) Write a short report about your investigation. Give details telling what you did as well as dependents to the following items:

   - Make a scatter plot of your data using diameter as the independent variable and circumference as the dependent variable.

   - Use a calculator or spreadsheet to determine the values of the slope and y-intercept of the least-squares line. Write an equation for your model.

   - Pay special attention to the slope of your line. What does it tell you? Do you notice anything about the number itself?

   - Explain how you can use your model to make predictions.

5. a) Use the manatee information from Table 3.13 to predict the number of manatee deaths in 1993.

5. a) **Sample answer: An equation for the least-squares line for deaths versus year (using 1997 as year zero) is $y = 2.629x + 12.34$. Using this equation, the number of deaths for 1993 (year 16) is $2.629(16) + 12.34 = 54.40$, or approximately 54 deaths.**

b) As noted in the sidebar in Discovery 3.1, Florida has taken stronger measures to protect the manatee. In 1991, there were 716,000 powerboat registrations and 53 manatee deaths. In 1992, there were 716,000 registrations and 38 deaths. In 1993, there were 716,000 registrations and 35 deaths, and in 1994, there were 735,000 registrations and 49 deaths. How accurate was your prediction from (a)? Explain.

b) **The model did not predict very well. Extrapolating from the data (predicting outside the range of the data) does not always produce accurate predictions.**

c) Use the Internet or other sources to find data from 1994 to the present. Do you see evidence that Florida's effort succeeded?

c) **There should be some evidence that the increase in the number of manatee deaths has slowed.**

6. In Exercise 3 you examined the increase in wave height over time and created a linear model to predict future wave heights. Do you think that the wave height continued to increase during the 1990s as it did in the 1960s, 1970s, and 1980s?

Use the Internet or other sources to find wave height information for the 1990s. Did the heights continue to grow as your model predicted? If not, refine your model to take into account the new data.

6. **Answers may vary.**

III. Additional Practice *(SE pages 267–269)*

For 7–10, assess each scatter plot for form (linear or nonlinear) and strength (strongly or weakly related). If the form is linear, tell whether the variables are positively or negatively related. (These plots do not show either the scales or the variables represented.)

7. See **Figure 3.34.**

Figure 3.34

7. Linear in form; weakly related, negatively related

8. See **Figure 3.35.**

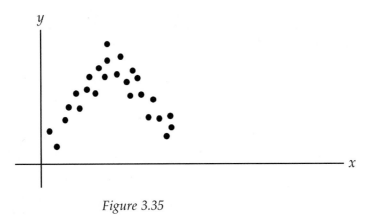

Figure 3.35

8. Nonlinear in form; rather strongly related

9. See **Figure 3.36.**

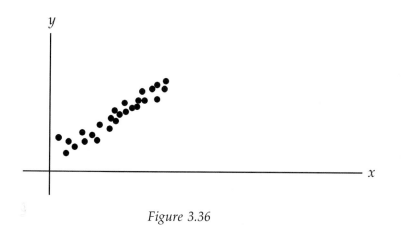

Figure 3.36

9. **Linear in form; strongly related, positively related**

10. See **Figure 3.37.**

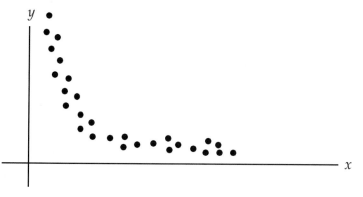

Figure 3.37

10. **Nonlinear in form; strongly related**

11. Suppose the pattern in a scatter plot moves from the upper left to the lower right. Are the two variables in the scatter plot positively or negatively related? Explain.

11. **Negatively related. If the pattern starts in the upper left and moves to the lower right, the value of the dependent variable is decreasing, whereas the value of the independent variable is increasing.**

12. Draw two scatter plots, one that has a linear form and the other a nonlinear form.

12. Sample answer:

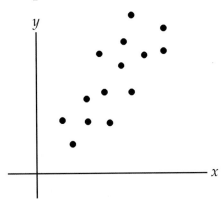

Scatter plot with a linear form

Scatter plot with a nonlinear form

13. Consider the following scenarios:

- For nine weeks, the number of umbrellas sold and the hours that it rained were measured.

- For nine weeks in the summer, the amount of ice cream sold and the amount of rainfall were measured.

a) For each scenario, specify which variable is the independent variable and which is the dependent variable.

13. a) First bullet: Hours of rain is the independent variable and number of umbrellas sold is the dependent variable.

Second bullet: Amount of rain is the independent variable and amount of ice cream sold is the dependent variable.

b) For each scenario, state whether you suspect that the relationship between these two variables is positive or negative. Explain.

b) First bullet: The variables are most likely positively related. The more it rains, the more umbrellas will be sold.

Second bullet: The variables are most likely negatively related. The more it rains, the less ice cream will be sold.

14. Consider the following scenarios:

- Over several years, speed limits in the Florida coastal waters are monitored and the number of manatee deaths are recorded.

- Human population and manatee population data along the Florida coast are gathered over several years.

a) For each scenario, specify which variable is the independent variable and which is the dependent variable.

14. a) First bullet: Power boat speed is the independent variable and the number of manatee deaths is the dependent variable.

Second bullet: Human population is the independent variable and manatee population is the dependent variable.

b) For each scenario, state whether you suspect that the relationship between these two variables is positive or negative. Explain.

b) First bullet: The variables are most likely positively related. The faster the boats are moving, the more likely they are to hit the manatee.

Second bullet: The variables are most likely negatively related. The greater the number of people in and around the manatee habitat, the more likely there will be a decrease in manatee population for whatever reason.

15. The solubility of potassium chloride (KCl) at certain temperatures is shown in **Table 3.24**. Use a calculator or spreadsheet to determine an equation of the least-squares line for the data in the table. Then use the equation to predict the solubility of KCl in water at 70°.

Temperature (°C)	Grams of KCl/100 Grams of Water
10	30
19	32
30	36
43	40
50	42
59	45

Table 3.24

15. $y = 0.31x + 27$. Assuming continued linearity, the solubility of KCl at 70°C will be about 49 grams.

16. It is often desirable to know the volume of liquid (gasoline, propane, fertilizer, etc.) that remains in a large tank. Because the volume of the liquid in the tank cannot be measured without removing it, a dipstick along with a calibration table, graph, or equation is used to find the volume.

Table 3.25 gives the heights and volumes in a given tank.

Height (feet)	Volume (gallons)
1	211
2	423
3	635
4	846
5	1057

Table 3.25

Use a calculator or spreadsheet to determine an equation of the least-squares line for the data in the table. Then use the equation to predict the volume of liquid in the tank when the height on the dipstick is 27 inches.

16. $y = 211.5x - 0.1$; because 27 inches = 2.25 feet, the volume of liquid in the tank = (211.5 gallons/foot)(2.25 feet) − 0.1 gallons ≈ 476 gallons.

Section 3.4 Using Models to Make Predictions

What You Need to Know

- How to use a calculator or spreadsheet to determine an equation of the least-squares line

- How to identify patterns in a scatter plot

What You Will Learn

- To apply the modeling process in order to refine mathematical models

- To develop criteria for assessing the quality of fit of a model

- To use residual plots to assess whether a model is adequate to describe given data

- To use the correlation coefficient as a measure of strength and direction of a linear relationship

- To recognize the influence of outliers

Materials

- Spring

- Hook

- Various weights

- Tape measures or rulers

As discussed in the preparation reading in this chapter, the process of building a mathematical model can begin one of two ways: from theory or from data. In Sections 3.2 and 3.3, we looked mainly at data-driven models and will continue to do so in this section. Keep in mind that both theory-driven and data-driven models are useful, and each has its advantages and disadvantages.

Taking a closer look at the modeling process will help us as we continue to search for good mathematical models.

The Modeling Process

Whether a model is driven by data or theory, the process of modeling can be summarized in the following steps:

Step 1. *Problem Identification:* What is it you would like to do or find out? Make some general observations. Pose a well-defined question asking exactly what you wish to know.

Step 2. *Simplify and Make Assumptions:* Identify the factors that will be used in building a model. Generally, you must simplify to get a manageable set of factors.

Step 3. *Build the Model:* Interpret in mathematical terms the features and relationships you have chosen. Analyze the model to find answers to the questions originally posed.

Step 4. *Evaluate, Revise, and Interpret:* Your conclusions at this point apply to your mathematical model. Verify your conclusions by collecting data. Does your model yield results that are accurate enough? If not, refine the model by reexamining your assumptions. Based on the accuracy of your model, relate the mathematical conclusions to the real world.

The diagram in **Figure 3.38** is useful in describing the modeling process:

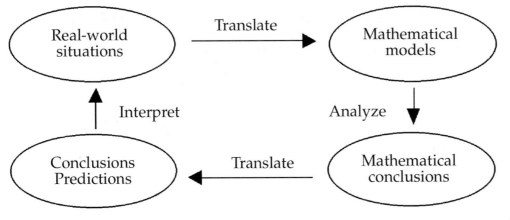

Figure 3.38

The process begins with a real-world situation. But after a model is built, analyzed, and tested, it is often necessary to revise the model to better explain the problem. Therefore, to find a model that adequately describes the situation, more than one trip around the modeling diagram may be needed. The real-world situation can provide the feedback needed to help us refine our model.

Assessing the Quality of Fit

In previous sections we created mathematical models, some of which were quite simple. We examined them carefully, refined them, and, in some cases, refined them even further.

For example, in Section 2.6 we started with a simple model in which a person's forearm length equals 16% of a person's height. In Activity 3.1 we collected data and created a better model, at least for our class. In Section 3.3 we developed criteria as we searched for the best line. This led to our exploration of the least-squares line as a linear model that minimizes the sum of the squares of the errors or residuals. Our trial-and-error searches for the best line could then be abandoned.

We still have one question to answer: How well does our best-fitting line model the data? If we determine that the line models the data well, then we can use it to make predictions. If it does not, our model will not do a good job of predicting.

In assessing whether a linear regression model is adequate to describe the relationship shown by a scatter plot, statisticians routinely ask if the line meets the following criteria:

1. The errors (residuals) should be small relative to the data.

2. The pattern of data in the scatter plot should be randomly scattered above and below the line.

> **Take Note:**
> If the line provides a good fit to the data, then the residual plot looks like a bunch of dots thrown haphazardly at a piece of paper. The dots should appear randomly scattered around the *x*-axis. If the dots do not look randomly scattered around the *x*-axis but instead form a clear pattern, then another model, one that better describes the data, should be sought.

To check these criteria, it is helpful to use a **residual plot,** a scatter plot of the residuals versus the independent variable. This residual plot gives us information about how well our model describes the data. It is especially helpful when we look to see if the data are randomly scattered above and below the line.

For example, packages of light bulbs contain information about the rate at which energy is used (in watts) and the rate of light production (in lumens). **Table 3.26** shows data taken from several different light bulb packages, all from the same brand.

Energy Use (watts)	50	60	60	95	100	140
Light Production (lumens)	640	890	800	1300	1245	1840

Table 3.26

Suppose we are interested in predicting the rate of light production for a 150-watt bulb. To do so, we could create a mathematical model.

Our first step is to examine the data for patterns. One way to do this is to create and examine a scatter plot of the data. **Figure 3.39** shows a scatter plot of the rate of light production versus the rate at which energy is used.

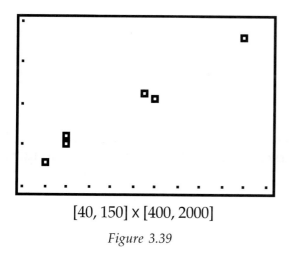

[40, 150] x [400, 2000]

Figure 3.39

Because the data appear to be linear, it would be appropriate to find an equation of the least-squares line for this relationship. **Figure 3.40** shows a calculator's linear regression output. **Figure 3.41** shows the graph of the regression line $y = 12.68217609x + 51.75017895$ and the scatter plot.

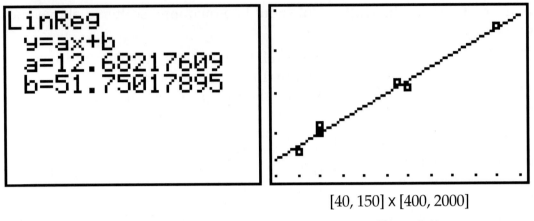

[40, 150] x [400, 2000]

Figure 3.40   *Figure 3.41*

We now ask ourselves if the model is good enough to use to make a prediction. To help us make this decision, we can create a residual plot.

In this situation, the residuals (errors) are the actual rates of light production minus the predicted rates of light production. Hence, the value of a residual is $y_{actual} - y_{predicted}$. These calculations can be done using calculator lists or a spreadsheet. **Figure 3.42** shows the x-values in L1, the actual y-values in L2, and the residuals in L3.

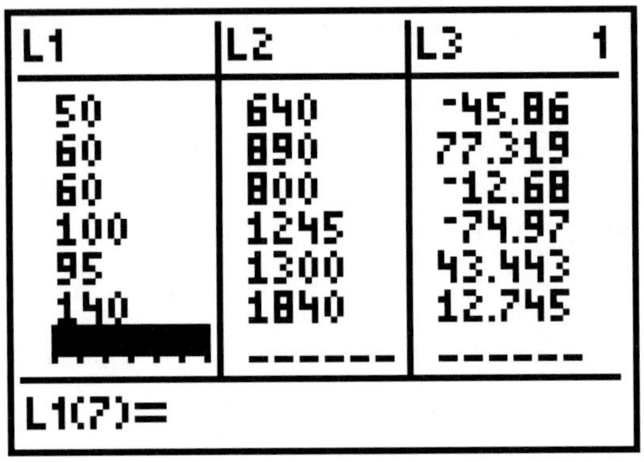

L1	L2	L3	1
50	640	-45.86	
60	890	77.319	
60	800	-12.68	
100	1245	-74.97	
95	1300	43.443	
140	1840	12.745	
▬▬▬	------	------	
L1(7)=			

Figure 3.42

After we find the residual values, we can create and examine a residual plot. This scatter plot of the residuals can be done by hand or on a calculator or spreadsheet. **Figure 3.43** shows the x-values along the horizontal axis and the residuals along the vertical axis.

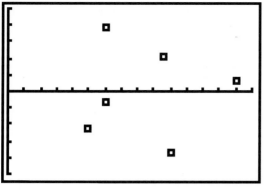

[9, 150] x [−100, 100]

Figure 3.43

Looking at the residual plot in Figure 3.43, we can see that the residuals are randomly scattered above and below the *x*-axis. This tells us that the data are randomly scattered above and below our regression line. Looking at the values of the residuals, we see that they are relatively small in comparison to the data.

Our conclusion, therefore, is that our line seems to provide a good model for the data. We can use it to make predictions as long as we limit our independent variable to values close to the range of our data (50 and 140 watts). To predict the light produced by a 150-watt bulb, we substitute 150 for *x* in the least-squares equation. We find that the light produced is approximately 1960 lumens.

Discovery 3.2 Comparing Models (SE pages 274–275)

There are times when it is possible to make predictions using two or more models, each based on a different independent variable. In this discovery, we will experiment with choosing the model that results in the most reliable predictions.

Consider the data in **Table 3.27.** The asterisks (*) indicate missing data.

Stride Length (cm)	Forearm Length (cm)	Height (cm)
58.2	28.5	166.0
55.9	27.2	164.5
59.1	28.6	175.0
68.9	30.5	184.0
72.5	26.5	161.0
*	28.2	164.0
*	28.4	171.0

Table 3.27

1. Working in groups of two, have one person in the group make a scatter plot of height versus stride length and the other person make a scatter plot of height versus forearm length. (Be sure that both people use the same scaling on the vertical axis for their plots.) Which of the two scatter plots shows the stronger relationship. How can you tell?

1. **Height versus forearm length is the stronger of the two relationships. The points in the height-forearm scatter plot fall closer to fitting on a line than the points in the height-stride scatter plot.**

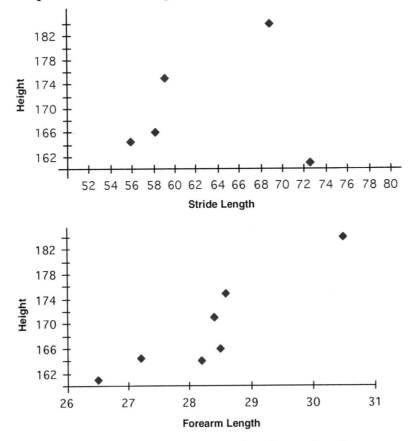

2. What are the least-squares lines for these data?

2. $y = 0.17x + 159.5.$ $y = 5.76x + 6.57.$

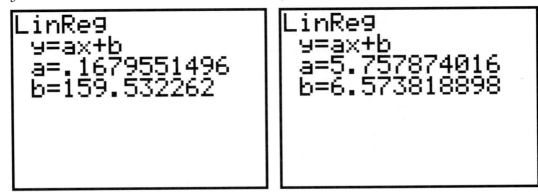

3. Use your calculator to make a residual plot for each model. Based on the residual plot, explain why you would expect the stronger relationship to be the one associated with the smaller residuals.

3. **The residuals are smaller in the height-forearm plot. This indicates that these data have a stronger relationship.**

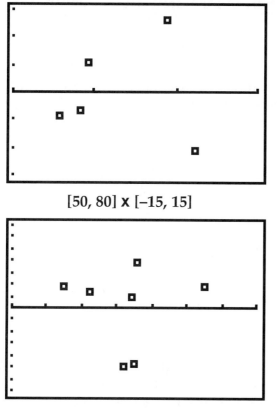

[50, 80] x [–15, 15]

[25, 32] x [–7, 7]

4. Use your two least-squares equations to predict the height of a person whose stride is 73 cm and whose forearm is 27 cm. Which of the two estimates is more reliable? Explain.

4. **Height-forearm model: Height = 10.9 + 5.76(27) = 162.1 cm.**

   Height-stride model: Height = 160 + 0.167(73) = 172.2 cm.

   The first estimate is more reliable because the relationship between height and forearm length is stronger than the relationship between height and stride.

5. State in your own words how you would choose between two different models for predicting the same quantity.

5. **Sample answer: If you have to pick one or the other, choose the one with the smallest residuals because this indicates the strongest relationship.**

Correlation Coefficient

In Discovery 3.2, an examination of the residual plot gave us valuable information about the quality of our model. Also helpful in assessing the goodness of fit is the Pearson's **correlation coefficient**, r, which is a feature available on some calculators. It is often part of the output from a linear regression. (See **Figure 3.44**.)

If $r = 1$, the data are perfectly linear with a positive slope. If $r = -1$, the data are perfectly linear with a negative slope. If $r = 0$, the data are not linear. Hence, r is a measure of the strength and direction of a linear relationship and has a value $-1 \leq r \leq 1$. However, judging the goodness of fit should begin with examining the graphs of the original data and of the residual plot.

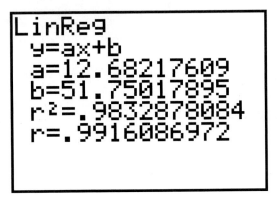

Figure 3.44

Figure 3.44 shows the correlation coefficient for our regression line for the light bulb data in Table 3.26. Notice that it is very close to 1, which indicates a strong linear relationship. This agrees with the conclusions we reached from examining the residuals.

Exercises 3.4

I. Investigations *(SE pages 276–279)*

1. **Tables 3.28–3.31** present four sets of data prepared by statistician Frank Anscombe.

x	10	8	13	9	11	14	6	4	12	7	5
y	8.04	6.95	7.58	8.81	8.33	9.96	7.24	4.26	10.84	4.82	5.68

Table 3.28 Data Set A

x	10	8	13	9	11	14	6	4	12	7	5
y	9.14	8.14	8.74	8.77	9.26	8.10	6.13	3.10	9.13	7.26	4.74

Table 3.29 Data Set B

x	8	8	8	8	8	8	8	8	8	8	10
y	6.58	5.76	7.71	8.84	8.47	7.04	5.25	5.56	7.91	6.89	12.50

Table 3.30 Data Set C

x	10	8	13	9	11	14	6	4	12	7	5
y	7.46	6.72	12.74	7.11	7.81	8.84	6.08	5.39	8.15	6.42	5.73

Table 3.31 Data Set D

a) Enter into a calculator or spreadsheet each of the four sets of data.

1. **a) See (c).**

b) Determine an equation of the least-squares line for each of the data sets. Compare the equations for the various sets of data.

b) All the equations are approximately $y = 0.5x + 3$.

c) Make a scatter plot for each of the four sets and draw the regression line on each of the plots.

c)

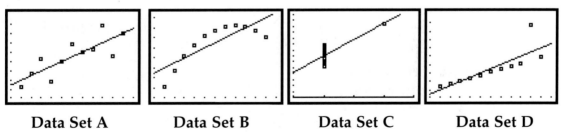

| Data Set A | Data Set B | Data Set C | Data Set D |

d) In which of the four cases would it be a good idea to use the fitted regression line to predict *y* given that $x = 14$? Explain.

d) The only data set that has a linear form is Data Set A. It is not a good idea to try to fit a line unless the data set appears to have a linear form. So for Data Set A, it would be okay to predict that *y* = 10 when *x* = 14.

e) What are the *r*-values (correlation coefficients) for each of the linear regressions?

e) For each data set, the *r*-values are approximately the same, 0.816.

f) What did Anscombe want students to learn from the four sets that he created?

f) He wanted students to see the dangers of not checking to see if the data has linear form before determining the least-squares equation or of using just the *r*-values to analyze the goodness of fit.

2. Your analysis of the manatee data in Discovery 3.1 strongly indicated that the number of manatee killed by powerboats increases as the number of registered boats increases. It seems natural to ask whether you could also use a linear model to predict the number of powerboat registrations in future years. That is, how are powerboat registrations related to year? (See **Table 3.32**.)

Year	1977	1978	1979	1980	1981	1982	1983
Registrations (**x** 1000)	447	460	481	498	513	512	526
Year	1984	1985	1986	1987	1988	1989	1990
Registrations (**x** 1000)	559	585	614	645	675	711	719

Table 3.32

Instead of entering the year data directly into your calculator (1977, 1978, etc.), renumber the years: represent 1977 by a 1, 1978 by a 2, and so forth.

a) Determine a model to predict the number of boat registrations for a given year. Which is the independent variable and which is the dependent variable? What will the slope mean if the data are linear?

2. a) Independent variable: year; dependent variable: number of registrations; the slope indicates the increase in boat registrations per year.

b) Make a scatter plot of the data. Does the scatter plot appear to have a roughly linear form?

b) Answers will vary. Typical answer: The pattern is a bit wavy, but it looks rather straight.

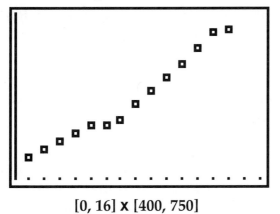

[0, 16] x [400, 750]

c) Determine the least-squares line. Write its equation.

c) $y = 21.6x + 405.5$. (Numbers are rounded to the nearest tenth.)

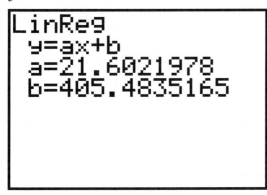

```
LinReg
 y=ax+b
 a=21.6021978
 b=405.4835165
```

d) Use your calculator to make a residual plot for the least-squares line. From examining the residual plot, determine if the least-squares line is adequate to describe the pattern of these data. Explain why or why not.

d) The residuals do not look randomly scattered. Instead, they form a strong V-pattern. This leads us to believe that the least-squares equation is not a good model for predictions.

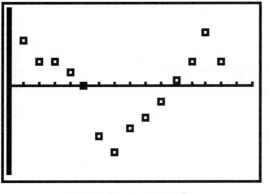

[0, 16] x [−40, 35]

e) Your residual plot in (d) should have appeared V-shaped. Trace along the points in the residual scatter plot until you reach the point at the bottom of the V. What year is associated with this point?

e) Year 7

f) Divide your data on powerboats and years into two sets. In the first set, use the data that corresponds to the year identified in (e) and earlier. In the second set, use the data after the identified year.

Enter the data from Set 1 into lists 1 and 2 of the calculator. Enter the data from Set 2 into lists 3 and 4. Determine the least-squares line for each of these two sets of data. Write the equations.

f) Set 1: $y = 13.32x + 437.7$. Set 2: $y = 28.32x + 332.5$.

g) Now plot the data and graph the lines. (Remember, the first line applies to the domain of the first data set and the second line to the domain of the second data set.) Make a sketch of the scatter plot and the graphs of these lines.

g)

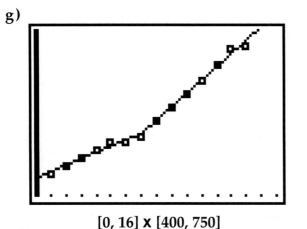

[0, 16] x [400, 750]

h) Does the model consisting of the two half-lines pieced together appear to fit the data better than the single regression line?

h) Yes.

3. Scientists have found that, by collecting data, the number of chirps a cricket makes in a minute is related to the cricket's surrounding temperature. (See **Table 3.33.**)

Temperature (degrees Fahrenheit)	70	92	81	68	72	78	88
Number of chirps (per minute)	116	197	164	108	180	148	187

Table 3.33

a) Make a scatter plot of the data in Table 3.33. Describe in words the features of the plot.

3. a) The pattern in the data looks relatively linear except for one point.

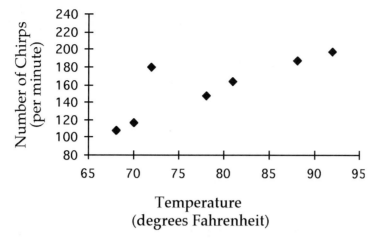

b) Use your calculator or computer to find the least-squares equation, write the equation, and draw the graph of the line on the scatter plot.

b) $y = 3.1x − 85.8$ (rounded to the nearest tenth).

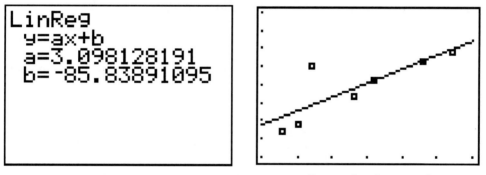

[65, 95] X [80, 240]

c) How well does the line appear to describe the data? Explain. Would the model give accurate predictions?

c) The line does not appear to fit the data very well because most of the points lie below the prediction line. It would not give very good predictions, as they would probably be too large.

d) Statisticians use the term **outlier** when referring to an individual point that falls outside the general pattern of the other data. Find the outlier among the data in Table 3.33. How does the outlier affect the least-squares line?

d) Yes, there appears to be an outlier, the point (72, 180). Its effect on the line is to pull it upward from the rest of the data.

e) Remove the outlier from the data. Recalculate the slope and y-intercept of the least-squares line. Write the equation and graph the line on the scatter plot.

e) $y = 3.8x - 149.0$.

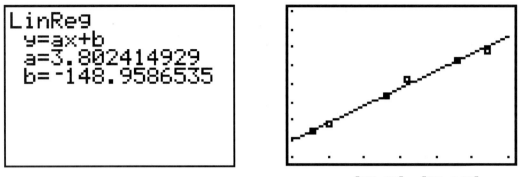

[65, 95] x [80, 240]

f) Does this line appear to fit the data better than the line found in (b)? Which model would give more accurate predictions? Explain.

f) The line without considering the outlier does appear to fit the data better. Most likely, this line would be a better prediction line, as it appears to capture the trend of the data better.

4. Selecting a line according to the least-squares criterion often produces a line with good properties. That is why selecting a line using this criterion is so popular. However, sometimes this line does a poor job in describing the pattern of the data.

A food industry group seeking a relationship between the number of calories a food actually has and the number of calories people think it has surveyed 3368 people. The results of the survey are shown in **Table 3.34**.

Is it possible to predict a person's caloric guess from the actual number of calories in an item?

Food	Actual Calories	Guessed Calories
8 oz whole milk	159	196
5 oz spaghetti with tomato sauce	163	394
5 oz macaroni with cheese	269	350
One slice of wheat bread	61	117
One slice of white bread	76	136
2 oz candy bar	260	364
Saltine cracker	12	74
Medium-size apple	80	107
Medium-size potato	88	160
Cream-filled snack cake	160	419

Table 3.34 (USA Today, 10/12/83)

a) Enter the data into the calculator and make a scatter plot of the number of guessed calories versus the number of actual calories. Describe in words the most important features of the scatter plot.

4. a) **There is a positive relationship between the variables. However, there are two points that appear to be outliers. The pattern for the remaining points appears to have a linear form.**

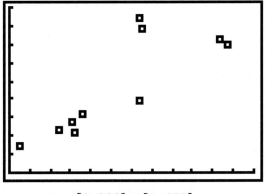

[0, 300] x [0, 450]

b) Find the regression line for predicting guessed calories from actual calories. Write the equation of the line. Add the graph of the line to the scatter plot. Does the regression line appear to adequately describe these data? Why or why not?

b) **$y = 1.30x + 58.6$. The regression line does not appear to fit the data well, as all the points except two are below the line.**

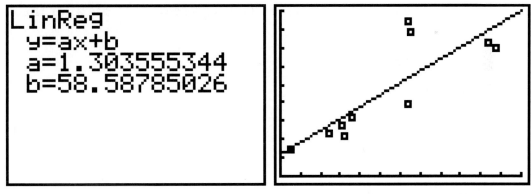

[0, 300] x [0, 450]

c) Make a residual plot. Does this plot confirm the answer given in (b) concerning how well the line describes the data? Explain.

c) The residual plot confirms that the line does not adequately describe the data. The points in the residual plot are not randomly scattered, as all but two are below the x-axis.

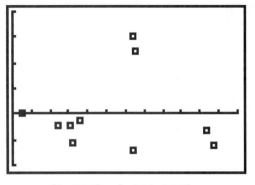

[0, 300] x [−100, 200]

d) Would you classify any of the data as outliers? If so, identify them. What do they indicate?

d) The two points (163, 394) and (160, 419) appear to be outliers. They indicate that people assume cream-filled snack cakes and spaghetti have more calories than they actually do.

e) If you found outliers, remove them and recalculate the regression line. Compare your new equation to the one from (b).

e) New equation: $y = 1.15x + 43.88$. The regression line fits after the outliers are removed.

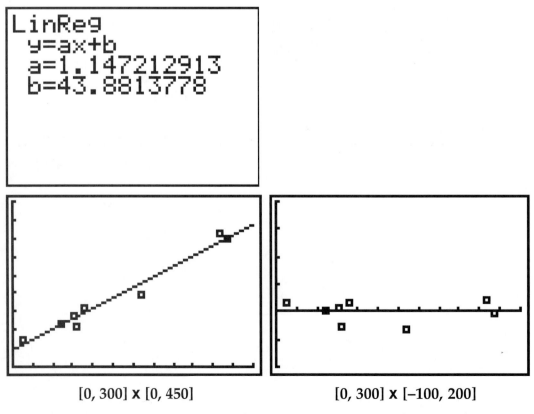

[0, 300] x [0, 450]   [0, 300] x [−100, 200]

f) Do the actual calories in a food item enable you to accurately predict what people will guess? Explain.

f) The size of the largest error once the outliers were removed was approximately 30 calories. The line appears to do a good job in predicting the guessed calories from the actual calories.

g) Interpret the meaning of the slope of your model for predicting guessed calories from actual calories. What would the slope indicate if it were a number between 0 and 1?

g) The slope was 1.15 guessed calories/actual calories. This means that the guessed calories will increase by 1.15 each time the actual number of calories increases by 1.

A slope between 0 and 1 would indicate that people were guessing lower than the actual number of calories.

II. Projects and Group Activities *(SE page 280)*

5. Materials: spring, hook, various weights, tape measures or rulers

    Hang a spring from a vertical hook. Conduct an experiment to measure the stretch of the spring when different masses (measured as weights) are placed on the end of the spring. Take several different measurements, recording the mass added to the end of the spring and the resulting stretch.

    - Make a scatter plot of vertical stretch versus mass. If the scatter plot appears to have a linear form, fit a line to it.

    - Investigate Hooke's law. (A visit to the physics teacher or a search on the Internet might prove helpful.) Does your experiment support Hooke's law? Explain.

6. Have each member of your group collect data from a different pizza place. Find the dimensions (diameters if circular or length and width if rectangular) and the price for the different sizes of one variety of pizza (e.g., cheese). Calculate the area for each pizza.

    Write a short group report that includes the following:

    - Scatter plots of each data set (price versus area)

    - The least-squares line for each data set

    - A discussion of what the slope and *y*-intercepts of the equations of the least-squares lines mean

    - Conclusion(s) as to what these equations and scatter plots might mean to you as a consumer (avoid personal preference, quality, etc., in your conclusions)

For 7–9, do the following:

   a) Make a scatter plot of the data. If the scatter plot has a linear form, find the least-squares line and make a residual plot.

   b) Use the residual plot of the data with linear form to decide whether the equations of the least-squares lines appear to adequately describe the data. Explain.

7. Use **Table 3.35.**

Year	1960	1965	1970	1975	1980	1985	1990
Population (millions)	180	194	205	215	227	238	249
Solid Waste (millions of pounds/year)	87	106	122	127	149	161	190

Table 3.35 (Source: U.S. Statistical Abstract)

7. a) The scatter plot has a linear form.

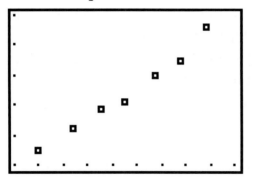

[170, 260] **x** [75, 200]

Scatter plot of data

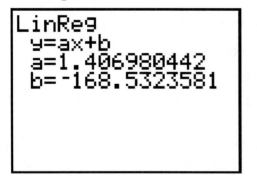

```
LinReg
 y=ax+b
 a=1.406980442
 b=-168.5323581
```

An equation of the least-squares line is $y = 1.41x + 168.5$.

Residual plot

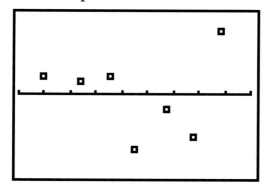

[170, 260] x [10, −10]

b) The equation of the least-squares line appears to adequately describe the data because the residuals seem to be relatively small and randomly scattered.

8. Use **Table 3.36.**

City	Latitude N (°)	Average August Temperature (°F)
San Antonio, TX	29.3	85
Chicago, IL	41.9	74
St. Louis, MO	38.6	77
Little Rock, AK	34.7	81
Bismarck, ND	46.8	69
Rapid City, SC	44.1	72
Des Moines, IA	41.6	73

Table 3.36 (Source: The World Almanac*)*

8. a) **The scatter plot has a linear form.**

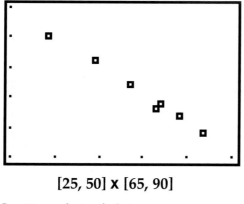

[25, 50] x [65, 90]

Scatter plot of data

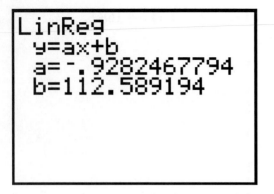

Least-squares equation: $y = -0.93x + 112.6$.

Residual plot

[25, 50] **x** [−1, 1]

b) **The equation of the least-squares line appears to adequately describe the data because the residuals seem to be relatively small and randomly scattered.**

9. Use **Table 3.37.**

Speed (mph)	Stopping Distance (ft)
20	42
30	73.5
40	116
50	173
60	248
70	343
80	464

Table 3.37 (Data based on tests conducted by the U.S. Bureau of Public Roads)

9. a) The scatter plot does not have linear form.

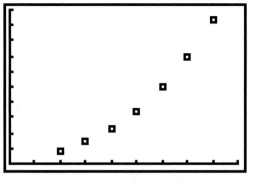

[0, 90] x [0, 500]

For 10–12, examine the residual plots and determine if the residuals are randomly distributed or show a pattern. If a pattern is observed, describe it.

10. See **Figure 3.45.**

Residuals

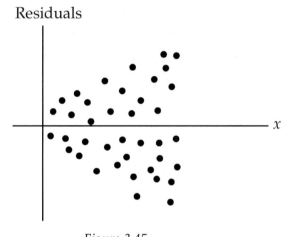

Figure 3.45

10. The residuals show a pattern. In this case, the pattern observed could be called a "fanning" pattern, with residuals close to the *x*-axis near the origin and then fanning out as *x* increases.

11. See **Figure 3.46.**

Residuals

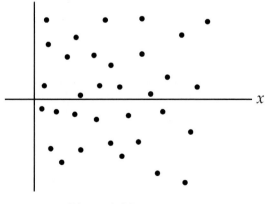

Figure 3.46

11. The residuals appear to be randomly scattered.

12. See **Figure 3.47.**

Residuals

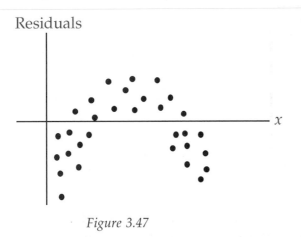

Figure 3.47

12. **The residuals show a pattern. The pattern appears to be curved, concave downward.**

13. A student fit a line with the equation $y = 0.5x + 2$ to the data in **Table 3.38.**

x	−4	−3	−2	−1	0	1	2
y	0	0	0.5	2	1.5	3	3

Table 3.38

a) Complete **Table 3.39** to find the residuals.

x	Actual y	Predicted y	Residual
−4	0		
−3	0		
−2	0.5		
−1	2		
0	1.5		
1	3		
2	3		

Table 3.39

13. a)

x	Actual y	Predicted y	Residual
–4	0	0	0
–3	0	0.5	–0.5
–2	0.5	1	–0.5
–1	2	1.5	0.5
0	1.5	2	–0.5
1	3	2.5	0.5
2	3	3	0

b) Make a residual plot (residuals versus the independent variable).

b) Residual plot

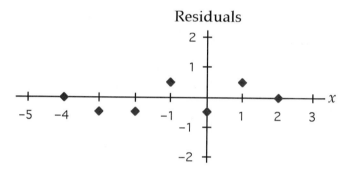

c) From examining the residual plot, do you think the equation $y = 0.5x + 2$ adequately describes the data? Why or why not?

c) Yes, the equation seems to adequately describe the data, as the residuals are randomly scattered.

14. A second student fit a line with the equation $y = 0.5x + 2$ to the data in **Table 3.40.**

x	–4	–3	–2	–1	0	1	2
y	0	0	0	0.5	1.5	2.5	4

Table 3.40

a) Complete **Table 3.41** to find the residuals.

x	Actual y	Predicted y	Residual
−4	0		
−3	0		
−2	0		
−1	0.5		
0	1.5		
1	2.5		
2	4		

Table 3.41

14. a)

x	Actual y	Predicted y	Residual
−4	0	**0**	**0**
−3	0	**0.5**	**−0.5**
−2	0	**1**	**−1**
−1	0.5	**1.5**	**−1**
0	1.5	**2**	**−0.5**
1	2.5	**2.5**	**0**
2	4	**3**	**1**

b) Make a residual plot (residuals versus the independent variable).

b) Residual plot

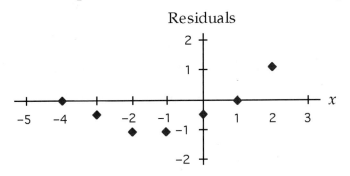

c) From examining the residual plot, do you think the equation $y = 0.5x + 2$ adequately describes the data? Why or why not?

c) No, the equation does not seem to adequately describe the data because the residuals are not randomly scattered. They exhibit a definite pattern that curves upward.

For 15–16, each data set has a point or points that could be considered an outlier(s).

a) Make a scatter plot of each data set. By sight, sketch a line that seems to fit the data well.

b) Enter the data without the outliers into the calculator. Find an equation for the least-squares line. Graph the least-squares line on your scatter plot.

c) Are the graphs of the lines from (a) and (b) the same line or different lines? If they are different, explain why.

15. Use **Table 3.42.**

x	2	3	4	5	6	7	8	9
y	3	4	6	7	9	4	11	13

Table 3.42

15. a)

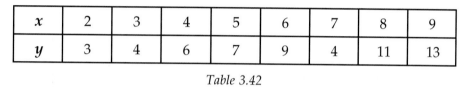

b) $y = 1.41x + 0.1$.

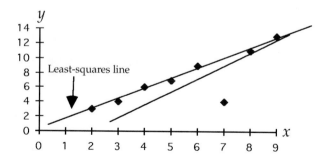

c) **Sample answer: The graphs of the lines are most likely different because the outlier "pulls" the first line down from the other data points. Removing the outlier from the data produces a line with a much better fit.**

16. Use **Table 3.43.**

x	−3	−1	0	1	2	4
y	9	5	3	5	−1	−5

Table 3.43

16. a)

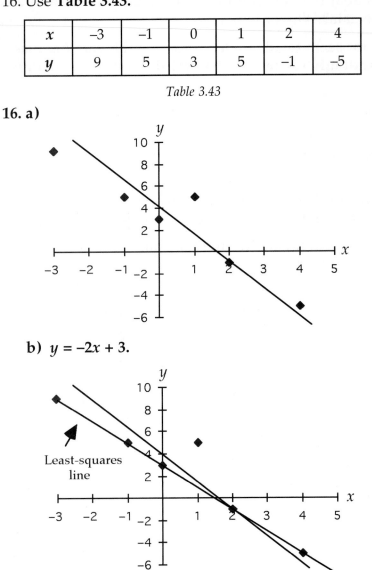

b) $y = -2x + 3.$

c) **Sample answer: The graphs of the lines are most likely different because the outlier "pulls" the first line up and away from the other data points. Removing the outlier from the data produces a line that fits the other data points perfectly.**

For 17–18,

a) Use a calculator or computer to make a scatter plot.

b) Use the calculator or computer to fit a line to the data.

17. Use **Table 3.44.**

x	10	20	30	40	50
y	60	52	45	35	29

Table 3.44

17. a) and b) $y = -0.79x + 67.9.$

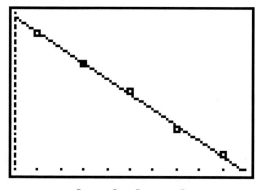

[5, 55] x [25, 65]

18. Use **Table 3.45.**

x	−30	−25	−22	−15	−10
y	47	60	70	85	96

Table 3.45

18. a) and b) $y = 2.44x + 121.4.$

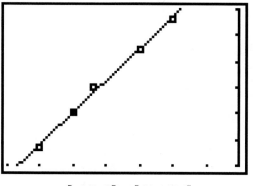

[−35, 0] x [40, 100]

19. a) The data in Table 3.37 in Exercise 9 showed the relationship between vehicular stopping distance and the speed of the vehicle. The scatter plot did not have a linear form. Describe the form of the scatter plot.

19. a) The scatter plot of the data appeared to curve upward rather than to form a straight line.

b) **Figure 3.48** shows the residual plot when a least-squares line is fit to the data. What does this plot tell us?

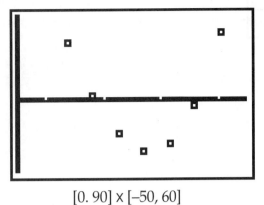

[0. 90] x [−50, 60]

Figure 3.48

b) **The residual plot shows a definite U-shaped pattern. This leads us to believe that there is no linear relationship between the two variables.**

c) Why would it not be a good idea to base predictions on a line or the equation of a line?

c) **It would not be a good idea to predict from a line because the data seem to be rising faster than a line would suggest.**

Chapter 3 Summary

Scatter plots

Data-driven linear models

Fitting a line to data

Making predictions

Residuals

Linear regression

Modeling process

Outliers

Chapter 3 Review *(SE pages 287–293)*

1. Write a summary of the important mathematical ideas found in Chapter 3.

1. **Answers will vary. Following are some of the important ideas that should be listed:**

   It is helpful to use a scatter plot to examine two-variable data.

   Some scatter plots exhibit a pattern that can be modeled with a linear equation.

   The model used to describe the pattern in data can be used to make predictions.

   Trial and error can be used to find a linear equation to fit data with a linear pattern.

   Residuals (errors) are found by calculating the difference between the actual values of the data and the predicted values ($y_{actual} - y_{predicted}$).

   Residuals can be used to help analyze the fit of a line to the data.

   The least-squares line is the line that gives the smallest sum of the squared errors (residuals).

   The modeling process is not complete until the model produces results that are accurate enough.

   If a line is a good fit for a data set, the residuals should be small and randomly scattered above and below the x-axis.

   Outliers can influence the least-squares line so that it does not describe the data as well as it could.

For 2–3,

    a) Sketch a line of best fit.

    b) Determine an equation for your line.

2. Use **Figure 3.49.**

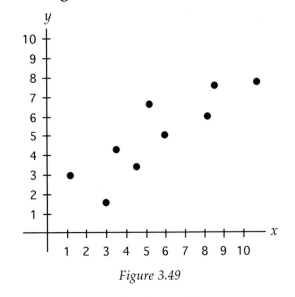

Figure 3.49

---

2. a) Sample answer:

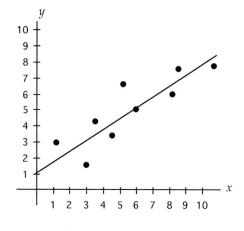

b) Equation: $y = \dfrac{5}{6}x + 1.$

3. Use **Figure 3.50.**

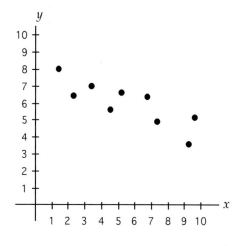

Figure 3.50

3. a) Sample answer:

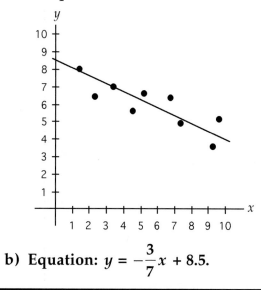

b) Equation: $y = -\dfrac{3}{7}x + 8.5.$

For 4–7, assess each scatter plot for form and strength. If the plot is linear in form, state whether the variables are positively or negatively related. (These plots do not show either the scales or the variables represented.)

4. Use **Figure 3.51.**

Figure 3.51

4. **The scatter plot shows a strong linear relationship. The variables are positively related.**

5. Use **Figure 3.52.**

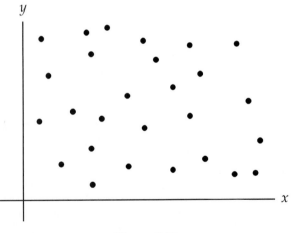

Figure 3.52

5. **This plot shows no relationship between the variables.**

6. Use **Figure 3.53.**

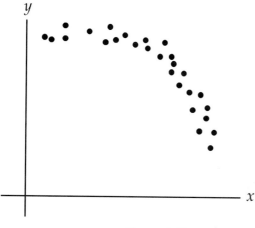

Figure 3.53

6. **The scatter plot has a strong nonlinear form.**

7. Use **Figure 3.54.**

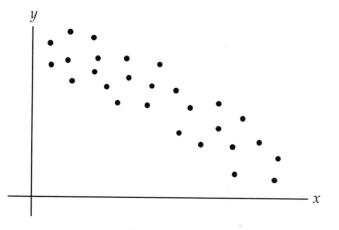

Figure 3.54

7. **The scatter plot shows a moderately strong linear relationship. The variables are negatively related.**

8. What if the pattern in a scatter plot moves from the lower right to the upper left? Are the variables positively or negatively related? Explain.

8. **They are negatively related. If the pattern starts in the lower right and moves to the upper left, the value of the dependent variable is increasing, whereas the value of the independent variable is decreasing.**

9. The data in **Table 3.46** represent two characteristics of the ponderosa pine: the diameter measured at chest height and the usable volume.

Diameter (in)	Usable Volume (thousands of cubic in)
36	276
28	163
28	127
41	423
19	40
32	177
22	73
38	363
25	81
17	23
31	203
20	46
25	124
19	30
39	333
33	269
17	32
37	295
23	83
39	382

Table 3.46
(Source: Data reported in Croxton, Cowden, and Klein,
Applied General Statistics, *p. 421)*

a) Use your calculator or computer to make a scatter plot of the data.

9. a) Scatter plot:

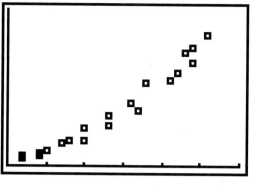

[15, 45] **x** [0, 500]

b) Use your calculator or computer to fit a line to the data. Write an equation for the least-squares line. Does the line appear to model the data well?

b) $y = 15.9x - 275.1$. **Sample answer: The least-squares line does not appear to be a good model, because many of the points lie below the line.**

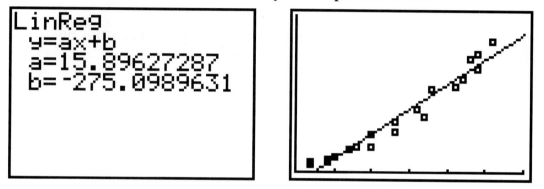

[15, 45] **x** [0, 500]

c) Use your calculator/computer to make a residual plot. Based on the residual plot, does this linear model appear to describe the data adequately?

c) It confirms that the least-squares line is not a good model for these data, because there is a definite U-shape to the pattern of the data points.

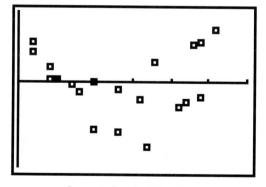

[15, 45] **x** [−75, 63]

For 10–12, decide whether the scatter plot suggests a linear relationship.

10. Use **Figure 3.55**.

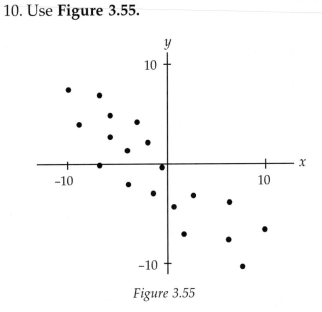

Figure 3.55

10. The scatter plot does suggest a linear relationship between the two variables.

11. Use **Figure 3.56**.

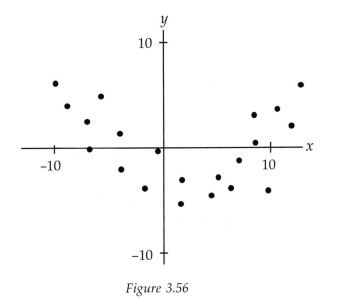

Figure 3.56

11. There appears to be a relationship between the two variables, but it is not linear.

12. Use **Figure 3.57.**

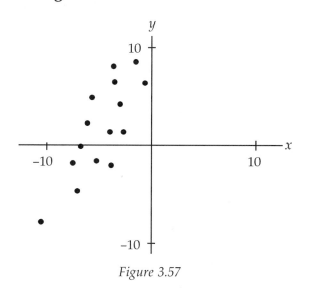

Figure 3.57

12. Yes, the scatter plot suggests a linear relationship.

For 13–14, use the data in **Tables 3.47** and **3.48,** which provide information on people's heights as children and again as adults.

Girls' Height at 1.5 Years (cm)	Girls' Adult Height (cm)
78.0	157.0
79.4	158.4
80.4	161.4
81.3	164.7
81.3	160.4
82.1	163.7
83.2	164.4
83.2	170.2
83.9	170.5
84.9	166.5
86.2	171.3
87.9	170.7
88.2	179.7
89.4	176.9
90.1	176.9

Table 3.47

Boys' Height at 2 Years (cm)	Boys' Adult Height (cm)
89.0	178.0
89.9	177.1
90.3	179.6
90.8	181.8
90.9	184.0
91.0	180.5
91.1	182.0
91.2	183.1
91.4	180.1
91.9	185.1
92.9	182.0
93.3	186.3
94.7	187.4
95.4	187.9
96.1	189.4

Table 3.48

13. Suppose you wanted to predict how tall a $1\frac{1}{2}$-year-old girl would be when she reached adulthood.

   a) Which is the independent variable, and which is the dependent variable?

13. a) The independent variable is girls' height at $1\frac{1}{2}$ years old; the dependent variable is girls' adult height.

   b) Make a scatter plot of the relationship between women's adult heights and their heights when they were $1\frac{1}{2}$ years old.

b) Answer:

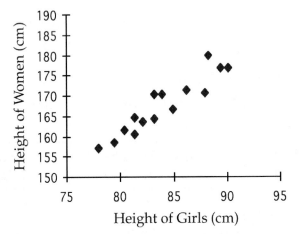

   c) Would you describe the relationship between women's heights and girls' heights as linear or nonlinear and as positive or negative? Explain.

c) The pattern in the scatter plot appears to have a linear form. The points appear scattered about a line. The relationship between women's heights and girls' heights is positive. Taller $1\frac{1}{2}$-year-old girls tend to become taller women.

d) Fit a least-squares line to the data in your scatter plot. Write its equation and sketch its graph on your scatter plot.

d) $y = 1.75x + 20.7$.

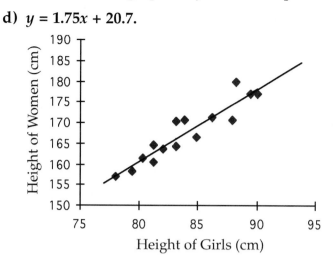

e) Make a residual plot. Based on your residual plot, does the least-squares line appear to describe adequately the relationship between women's adult height and childhood height? Explain.

e) Yes, the residuals appear randomly scattered.

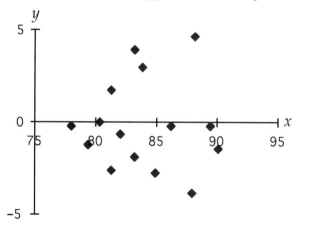

f) Use your equation to predict the adult height of a $1\frac{1}{2}$-year-old girl who is 82.5 cm tall.

f) $1.75(82.5) + 20.7 = 165.1$ cm.

14. a) Determine the least-squares line for predicting men's heights from their heights when they were 2 years old.

14. a) $y = 1.61x + 34.8$.

b) If two 2-year-old boys differ in height by 1 cm, predict how much their heights will differ when they are adults.

b) Their adult heights will differ by approximately 1.61 cm.

c) What if their heights as 2-year-olds differ by 2 cm?

c) Their adult heights will differ by approximately 3.22 cm.

d) Does the *y*-intercept of the least-squares line have any meaning in this context? Explain.

d) No. The *y*-intercept says that a 2-year-old who is 0 cm tall will grow up to be 34.8 cm tall.

e) Does the slope of the least-squares line have any meaning in this context? Explain.

e) Yes. The slope indicates that for every 1-cm change in height of a 2-year-old, there will be a corresponding change of 1.61 cm in height as an adult.

Chapter 4—Polynomials

Goals of the Chapter

- To recognize and use polynomials to model situations and solve problems

- To perform operations with polynomials

- To use properties of exponents to simplify expressions

Preparation Reading

Polynomials are used to model a variety of situations: the spread of diseases, planetary motion, resistance in electrical circuits, the design of suspension bridges, the way objects travel when they fall or are thrown, and the profitability of a company are just a few examples. The graphs of polynomial functions are smooth curves. This is the reason that they are used in engineering and in computer graphics to create curved parts of machines and figures.

Figure 4.1 shows the graph of a polynomial function. This graph models the average salary in thousands of dollars for professional baseball players in the United States in the years from 1976 to 1999.

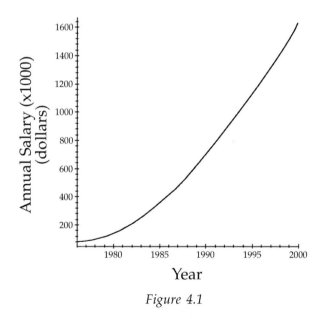

Figure 4.1

The expressions we have been using in the last two chapters are examples of polynomials. Polynomials are expressions that are made up of terms in which all variables have whole number exponents. The expression $1000 + 2000r + 1000r^2$ is an example of a polynomial expression that represents the amount of money available at the end of two years when $1000 is invested at an annual interest rate r.

Some polynomials are quite simple. For example, the polynomial e^3 can be used to represent the volume of a cube whose edge is e units long. On the other hand, other polynomials, such as the ones used in the codes that protect your compact disc player from errors, have hundreds of terms. Even our calculators use polynomials when performing some of their more complicated functions.

In this chapter we will develop the algebraic skills needed to work with polynomials. We will also examine polynomial functions and their graphs and use them to model real-world situations.

Reflect and Discuss

Earlier in this course, we encountered expressions whose terms had whole number exponents. For example, in Section 2.6 we used the first degree polynomial $5h - 200$ to express a person's ideal weight in terms of height. Identify several other examples.

Some examples are s^2 (an expression for finding the area of a square); $\frac{4}{3}\pi r^3$ (volume of a sphere); $3.7x + 2500$ (number of calories a person burns a day if they walk x minutes).

Section 4.1 Introduction to Polynomials

What You Need to Know

• How to use percents in calculations

What You Will Learn

• To model a real-world situation with a polynomial

Materials

• One-liter container (or larger)

• Food coloring

• Water

• Measuring container calibrated in metric units

The Environmental Protection Agency has designated numerous *Superfund sites* around the United States. Many of these involve large-scale contamination of groundwater by industrial and governmental activity. The water contained in the ground, called an *aquifer,* can enter public water supplies and private well water.

Environmental Science Services is one company that has been contracted to clean up a Superfund site in New England. The aquifer contains 1 billion pounds of water, and it is contaminated by about 100,000 pounds of hydrocarbons. They use more active methods to purify water than the one discussed in the activity. This is because the purified water must be returned to the aquifer after cleaning. Some removal processes are filtration, ultraviolet radiation, air stripping, and carbon absorption.

Small bodies of water often become contaminated by various kinds of pollutants. Industrial chemicals are a common cause of such pollution. There are several methods that can be used to clean up contaminated water. One fairly simple method that can be used in some cases is *dilution*. Polluted water can be removed a little at a time and replaced with clean water.

This process can be modeled with mathematical expressions called **polynomials** that contain whole number exponents. In the following activity, you will simulate the cleanup of a body of water through dilution and create a polynomial model to describe the cleanup.

Activity 4.1 A Model for Water Pollution Cleanup (SE pages 297–299)

1. Consider a small container full of a mixture of clean water and contaminant. Think about removing a portion of the mixture and replacing it with clean water. After repeating this process several times, what do you think happens to the amount of contaminant in the container?

1. **Sample answer: The amount of contaminant in the container will decrease after each removal/replacement procedure.**

We can create a physical model for using dilution to clean a body of polluted water. Carry out the following steps:

- Place 200 ml (milliliters) of dyed liquid and 800 ml of clear water in a container. The dyed liquid represents the contaminant, and the clear water represents the unpolluted water.
- Mark the 1-liter level on the container.
- To represent flushing contaminant from the water, remove 250 ml of liquid from the container.

2. How many milliliters of contaminant were in the original mixture?

2. **200 ml**

3. If 250 ml (25%) of the liquid in the container was removed, then we can assume that 25% of the contaminant was also removed. What percent of the original 200 ml of contaminant is still in the 1-liter container? How many milliliters of contaminant are left in the container?

3. **75%; 0.75(200) = 150 ml.**

- Refill your container to the 1-liter mark with clean water.
- For a second time, remove 250 ml of the water mixture from the container.

4. What percent of the remaining 150 ml of contaminant was removed this time? What percent of the 150 ml of contaminant is still in the 1-liter container? How many milliliters of contaminant are left in the container?

4. **25% of the 150 ml was removed; 75% of the 150 ml is still in the container; 0.75(150) = 112.5 ml remain.**

- Repeat refilling your container to the 1-liter mark with clean water. Then, for a third time, remove 250 ml of liquid from the container.

5. What percent of the amount of contaminant that was still in the container in item 4 was removed this time? What percent of the contaminant from item 4 is still in the one-liter container? How many milliliters of contaminant are left in the container?

5. **25% of the 112.5 ml was removed; 75% of the 112.5 ml is still in the container; 0.75(112.5) ≈ 84.4 ml remain.**

6. Complete **Table 4.1** to show the amount of contaminant remaining in the container after three, four, and five removal/replacement procedures. Note that the third column of the table contains an "expanded form" of the computation. The expanded form shows all the multiplications that are involved in computing each dilution. The fourth column shows the same computation written in the more compact exponent form.

Number of Flushing Procedures	Amount of Contaminant in Container (ml)	Amount of Contaminant, Expanded Form (ml)	Amount of Contaminant, Exponent Form (ml)
0	200	200	
1	200(0.75) = 150	200(0.75)	$200(0.75)^1$
2	150(0.75) = 112.5	200(0.75)(0.75)	$200(0.75)^2$
3			
4			
5			

Table 4.1

6.

Number of Flushing Procedures	Amount of Contaminant in Container (ml)	Amount of Contaminant, Expanded Form (ml)	Amount of Contaminant, Exponent Form (ml)
0	200	200	
1	200(0.75) = 150	200(0.75)	$200(0.75)^1$
2	150(0.75) = 112.5	200(0.75)(0.75)	$200(0.75)^2$
3	**112.5(0.75) ≈ 84.4**	**200(0.75)(0.75)(0.75)**	**$200(0.75)^3$**
4	**84.4(0.75) ≈ 63.3**	**200(0.75)(0.75)(0.75)(0.75)**	**$200(0.75)^4$**
5	63.3(0.75) ≈ 47.5	200(0.75)(0.75)(0.75)(0.75)(0.75)	$200(0.75)^5$

7. Look for a pattern in your completed Table 4.1, and use it to write an expression in exponent form for the amount of contaminant remaining in the container after eight flushings. Evaluate your expression to determine the amount of contaminant remaining.

7. **$200(0.75)^8$; approximately 20 ml.**

8. Did your physical modeling (removing and refilling the container) support your prediction in item 1 of this activity? Explain.

8. **Sample answer: Yes, the amount of contaminant decreased as predicted. Physically, the liquid got lighter. Algebraically, the number of milliliters of contaminant decreased.**

9. Complete **Table 4.2** for a mixture that contains 200 ml of contaminant. But now assume that 20% of the mixture is removed and replaced with clean water after each flushing. How much contaminant remains after five flushings? (Hint: 80% of the contaminant *remains* in the mixture after each flushing.)

Number of Flushing Procedures	Amount of Contaminant in Container (ml)	Amount of Contaminant, Expanded Form (ml)	Amount of Contaminant, Exponent Form (ml)
0	200	200	
1			
2			
3			
4			
5			

Table 4.2

9. **Approximately 164 liters of contaminant remains.**

Number of Flushing Procedures	Amount of Contaminant in Container (ml)	Amount of Contaminant, Expanded Form (ml)	Amount of Contaminant, Exponent Form (ml)
0	200	200	
1	200(0.80) = 160	200(0.80)	$200(0.80)^1$
2	160(0.80) = 128	200(0.80)(0.80)	$200(0.80)^2$
3	128(0.80) = 102.4	200(0.80)(0.80)(0.75)	$200(0.80)^3$
4	102.4(0.80) ≈ 81.9	200(0.80)(0.80)(0.80)(0.80)	$200(0.80)^4$
5	81.9(0.80) ≈ 65.5	200(0.80)(0.80)(0.80)(0.80)(0.80)	$200(0.80)^5$

10. Write an expression in exponent form for the amount of contaminant remaining in the container after eight flushings. Evaluate your expression to determine the amount of contaminant remaining.

10. $200(0.80)^8$; approximately 33.6 ml.

11. Your expression in item 7 represents the amount of contaminant left after eight flushings if the fraction of contaminant remaining after each flushing is 0.75. In item 10, your expression represented the amount remaining after eight flushings if the fraction remaining after each flushing is 0.80.

   Let r represent *any* value for the fraction remaining after each flushing. Write an expression in terms of r for the amount of contaminant left after eight flushings in this general case.

11. $200r^8$

The expression you have just written is an example of a polynomial.

A polynomial is an expression with any number of terms. Each term contains a product of a coefficient and one or more variables raised to whole number exponents. A polynomial in one variable x is an expression whose terms are of the form ax^k, where k is a whole number and a is any number.

Your polynomial from item 11 has only one term. But the polynomial $3x^2 + 4x + 7$ contains three terms, which are $3x^2$, $4x$, and 7.

Extend the Activity *(SE page 300)*

12. Consider a small pond that contains 150 gallons of contaminants. Assume that each time the owner attempts to dilute the amount of contaminants in the pond, he runs off 0.5% of the pond's water mixture and replaces it with clean water. Write an expression for the amount of contaminants remaining in the pond after six dilution procedures. Evaluate your expression to find the amount of contaminant remaining at that point.

12. The fraction of contaminants remaining after each dilution is 0.995. After six dilutions, $150(0.995)^6 \approx 146$ gallons of contaminant remain.

Section 4.2 Exponents

What You Need to Know

- How to evaluate an expression containing exponents

- How to express large numbers using scientific notation

What You Will Learn

- To use the properties of exponents to simplify expressions containing exponents

- To multiply and divide numbers expressed in scientific notation

Materials

- Graphing calculator, CBL and light probe

- LIGHTFIL program

- Flashlight

- Colored transparency film

- Tape

In the year 2001, the EPA placed on its priority list about 1500 Superfund sites. Cleanup of these sites will take many years. One estimate of the total cost of cleaning up the priority sites is approximately \$330 billion.

We can compute the average cost of cleaning up one of the Superfund priority sites by dividing the total cost for all sites by the number of sites:

$$\text{Average cost to clean one site} = \frac{330 \text{ billion dollars}}{1500 \text{ sites}}.$$

The numbers in this computation, especially the numerator, are large. As we saw in Section 1.6, scientific notation is a shorthand way of dealing with very large numbers by using exponents. Using scientific notation, we can write the average cost computation as:

$$\text{Average cost to clean one site} = \frac{3.3 \times 10^{11} \text{ dollars}}{1.5 \times 10^{3} \text{ sites}}.$$

Multiplying and dividing very large numbers in this form is often more efficient than working with numbers in standard numerical form. But to do so, we need to know how expressions containing exponents can be combined.

We used expressions involving exponents in Activity 4.1. Many of the geometry formulas from Chapter 1 also contain exponents. Recall that n^2 means n used as a factor 2 times or $(n)(n)$, and 3^5 means 3 used as a factor 5 times, or $(3)(3)(3)(3)(3)$. In the expression 3^5, 3 is called the **base** and 5 is the **exponent.** In this activity you will develop the basic properties of exponents.

1. For (a)–(d), use the definition of an exponent to rewrite each expression as a product.

   a) $2^2 = $ _____

   $2^3 = $ _____

   $(2)^2 (2)^3 = $ _____ $= 2^?$

1. a) $2 \cdot 2; 2 \cdot 2 \cdot 2; 2 \cdot 2 \cdot 2 \cdot 2 \cdot 2 = 2^5$.

   b) $3^2 = $ _____

   $3^2 = $ _____

   $(3)^2 (3)^2 = $ _____ $= 3^?$

b) $3 \cdot 3; 3 \cdot 3; 3 \cdot 3 \cdot 3 \cdot 3 = 3^4$.

   c) $(-2)^4 (-2)^3 = $ _____ $= (-2)^?$

c) $(-2)(-2)(-2)(-2)(-2)(-2)(-2) = (-2)^7$.

   d) $y^4 \cdot y^2 = $ _____ $= y^?$

d) $y \cdot y \cdot y \cdot y \cdot y \cdot y = y^6$.

2. In general, what did you notice when two expressions involving exponents of the same base were multiplied? Write a simpler form for $x^a \cdot x^b$. Explain.

2. When two powers of the same base are multiplied, the exponents are added.

$x^a \cdot x^b = x^{a+b}$ because $x^a = \underbrace{(x)(x)(x)...(x)}_{a \text{ factors}}$ and $x^b = \underbrace{(x)(x)(x)...(x)}_{b \text{ factors}}$. So,

$$x^a \cdot x^b = \left[\underbrace{(x)(x)(x)...(x)}_{a \text{ factors}} \right]\left[\underbrace{(x)(x)(x)...(x)}_{b \text{ factors}} \right] = \left[\underbrace{(x)(x)(x)(x)...(x)}_{a+b \text{ factors}} \right] = x^{a+b}.$$

3. Use the property you identified in item 2 to simplify each expression in (a)–(e).

   a) $2(x)^2 (x)^5$

3. a) $2x^7$

   b) $(3ab)(5a^3 b^2)$

b) $15a^4 b^3$

   c) $(2)^3 (3)^2 (2)^3 (x)^2$

c) $(2)^6 (3)^2 (x)^2 = 576x^2$.

d) $(10)^3(10)(10)^4$

d) 10^8

e) $(3.3 \times 10^2)(5.1 \times 10)$

e) 16.83×10^3

4. As in item 1, use the definition of an exponent to rewrite the expression as a base with one exponent.

a) $\dfrac{5^5}{5^3} = $ _____.

4. a) $\dfrac{5 \cdot 5 \cdot 5 \cdot 5 \cdot 5}{5 \cdot 5 \cdot 5} = 5^2$.

b) $\dfrac{(-3)^4}{(-3)^3} = $ _____.

b) $\dfrac{(-3) \cdot (-3) \cdot (-3) \cdot (-3)}{(-3) \cdot (-3) \cdot (-3)} = (-3)^1$.

c) $\dfrac{10^5}{10^2} = $ _____.

c) $\dfrac{10 \cdot 10 \cdot 10 \cdot 10 \cdot 10}{10 \cdot 10} = 10^3$.

d) $\dfrac{3^4}{3} = $ _____.

d) $\dfrac{3 \cdot 3 \cdot 3 \cdot 3}{3} = 3^3$:

5. In general, what did you notice when two expressions involving exponents of the same base are divided? Write a simpler form for $\dfrac{x^a}{x^b}$. Explain.

5. When two powers of the same base are divided, the exponent in the denominator is subtracted from the exponent in the numerator to find the exponent of the quotient.

$$\dfrac{x^a}{x^b} = x^{a-b}.$$

Explanations will vary but should be similar to the following.

$$\dfrac{x^a}{x^b} = \dfrac{\overbrace{(x)(x)(x)...(x)}^{a \text{ factors}}}{\underbrace{(x)(x)(x)...(x)}_{b \text{ factors}}}. \text{ Reduce to get } \underbrace{(x)(x)(x)...(x)}_{(a-b) \text{ factors}} \text{ or } x^{a-b}.$$

6. What happens when two expressions involving equal exponents of the same base are divided? For example, consider the expressions $\dfrac{5^3}{5^3}$, $\dfrac{3^4}{3^4}$, and $\dfrac{(-2)^5}{(-2)^5}$.

Notice that the result for each of these quotients is 1. Because the division of any number by itself equals 1, this seems perfectly reasonable.

Applying one of the properties of exponents to the first example, $\dfrac{5^3}{5^3} = 5^{3-3} = 5^0$. This reasoning holds for all bases except 0. (Recall that division by 0 is undefined.)

Summarize these findings by writing a statement about simplifying an expression involving any base x (except 0) raised to a power of 0.

6. **Any base (except 0) raised to the power 0 must equal 1, or $x^0 = 1$ for all $x \neq 0$.**

7. What could be the meaning of a negative exponent? To find out, look at the patterns in **Table 4.3** as you move from right to left. Notice that each number is divided by its base to produce the number to the left in the pattern. At the same time, the exponent in each column heading decreases by one.

x^{-3}	x^{-2}	x^{-1}	x^0	x^1	x^2	x^3	x^4
			1	6	36	216	1296
			1	5	25	125	625
			1	2	4	8	16
			1	1	1	1	1
			1	-2	4	-8	16

Table 4.3

What should be placed immediately to the left of the 1 in each row to continue the pattern? Complete the entire column. Continue the pattern you have discovered to complete the entire table.

7. **As you move from right to left in a row of the table, each number is equal to the number on the right divided by the value of the base for the row. If this pattern is to continue, the number to the left of the x^0 column should be $\dfrac{1}{x}$ for each base number x.**

x^{-3}	x^{-2}	x^{-1}
$\dfrac{1}{216}$	$\dfrac{1}{36}$	$\dfrac{1}{6}$
$\dfrac{1}{125}$	$\dfrac{1}{25}$	$\dfrac{1}{5}$
$\dfrac{1}{8}$	$\dfrac{1}{4}$	$\dfrac{1}{2}$
1	1	1
$-\dfrac{1}{8}$	$\dfrac{1}{4}$	$-\dfrac{1}{2}$

8. Examine your completed table from item 7. The first three columns can be rewritten in a different way using positive exponents; for example, $216 = 6^3$. Therefore, $\dfrac{1}{216} = \dfrac{1}{6^3}$. Hence, we can say that $6^{-3} = \dfrac{1}{6^3}$. How can 2^{-3} be rewritten using a positive exponent?

8. $\dfrac{1}{2^3}$

9. What is the meaning of x^{-1}? (Assume $x \neq 0$.)

9. $x^{-1} = \dfrac{1}{x}$.

10. Write each expression with only positive exponents. Assume all variables are nonzero.

   a) 16^{-1}

10. a) $\dfrac{1}{16}$

   b) 10^{-3}

   b) $\dfrac{1}{10^3}$

   c) n^{-3}

   c) $\dfrac{1}{n^3}$

   d) $5^{-1}x^{-2}$

   d) $\dfrac{1}{5x^2}$

e) $\left(\dfrac{1}{3}\right)^{-2}$

e) $\left(\dfrac{1}{3}\right)^{-2} = \dfrac{1}{\left(\dfrac{1}{3}\right)^{2}} = 1 \cdot \left(\dfrac{3}{1}\right)^{2} = \left(\dfrac{3}{1}\right)^{2}.$

f) $2x^{-3}$

f) $\dfrac{2}{x^3}$

g) $(3x)^{-2}$

g) $\dfrac{1}{(3x)^2}$ or $\dfrac{1}{9x^2}$

h) $5^{-1}x^4yz^{-1}$

h) $\dfrac{x^4 y}{5z}$

A cautionary note! Extra care must be taken when evaluating expressions that involve powers of negative numbers. Note especially that $-3^2 \neq (-3)^2$.

The placement of the parentheses changes the meaning of the second expression. The expression -3^2 is read as "the negative of the square of 3," so $-3^2 = -9$; whereas $(-3)^2$ is read as "the square of negative three," so $(-3)^2 = 9$. There is a subtle but important difference in the two notations.

11. To summarize your investigation of the properties of exponents, complete **Table 4.4.**

a)	$x^a \cdot x^b = ?$
b)	$\dfrac{x^a}{x^b} = ?$
c)	$x^0 = ?$
d)	$x^{-1} = ?$
e)	$x^{-n} = ?$

Table 4.4

11.

a)	$x^a \cdot x^b = x^{a+b}$
b)	$\dfrac{x^a}{x^b} = x^{a-b} \ (x \neq 0)$
c)	$x^0 = 1 \ (x \neq 0)$
d)	$x^{-1} = \dfrac{1}{x} \ (x \neq 0)$
e)	$x^{-n} = \dfrac{1}{x^n} \ (x \neq 0)$

Expressions Containing Exponents

In Discovery 4.1 you developed the basic properties of exponents and revealed the meaning of zero and negative exponents. However, there is often more than one way to correctly apply the properties to simplify an expression containing exponents.

Example 1

Find two different methods to evaluate $(3)^{-2}(3)^4$.

Solution:

Method 1 (using the property for multiplying):

$(3)^{-2}(3)^4 = (3)^2 = 9$.

Method 2 (using the definition of x^{-n}):

$(3)^{-2}(3)^4 = \left(\dfrac{1}{3^2}\right)(3)^4 = (3)^2 = 9$.

Example 2

Find two different methods to evaluate $\dfrac{6^2}{6^{-2}}$.

Solution:

Method 1 (using the property for dividing):

$\dfrac{6^2}{6^{-2}} = 6^{2-(-2)} = 6^4 = 2376$.

Method 2 (using the definition of x^{-n}):

$\dfrac{6^2}{6^{-2}} = \dfrac{6^2}{\dfrac{1}{6^2}} = 6^2 \cdot 6^2 = 6^4 = 2376$.

The exponent properties you developed apply in each of the following examples. (Assume all variables are nonzero.)

Example 3

Simplify $\dfrac{(2x^5y^3)(3x)}{x^3y^{-2}}$.

Solution:

Begin by simplifying the numerator and then divide.

$\dfrac{(2x^5y^3)(3x)}{x^3y^{-2}} = \dfrac{6x^6y^3}{x^3y^{-2}} = 6x^3y^5$.

Example 4

We can now return to the problem that began this section. Recall that the computation for the average cost of cleaning up one of the priority Superfund sites can be expressed using scientific notation:

$$\text{Average cost to clean one site} = \frac{3.3 \times 10^{11} \text{ dollars}}{1.5 \times 10^{3} \text{ sites}}.$$

Use the properties of exponents to simplify the computation and evaluate the average cost per gallon.

Solution:

$$\frac{3.3 \times 10^{11}}{1.5 \times 10^{3}} = \left(\frac{3.3}{1.5}\right) \times \left(\frac{10^{11}}{10^{3}}\right)$$

$$= 2.2 \times 10^{8}, \text{ or } 220,000,000 \text{ dollars per site.}$$

Negative Exponents and Scientific Notation

Recall from Chapter 1 that scientific notation involves using exponents to make very large numbers easier to write. A number written in scientific notation is expressed as a number between 1 and 10 multiplied by a power of 10. For example, 17,500 is written as 1.75×10^{4} from $17,500 = 1.75 \times 10,000$.

Similarly, we can use negative exponents to express very small numbers in scientific notation. For example, the time it takes for some personal computers to carry out a single instruction is 0.00000000250 seconds, which is difficult even to read when written this way. To write this number in scientific notation, begin by thinking of it as the product of a number between 1 and 10 and a unit decimal number.

$$0.00000000250 = 2.50 \times 0.000000001$$

$$= 2.50 \times \frac{1}{1,000,000,000}$$

$$= 2.50 \times \frac{1}{10^{9}}$$

$$= 2.50 \times 10^{-9}$$

A simple way of converting numbers to scientific notation is based on the following observation:

The value of the exponent equals the number of places the decimal point is moved to the left (exponent increases) or to the right (exponent decreases) to produce a leading number that is between 1 and 10. To express 0.0025 in scientific notation, move the decimal point three places to the right to produce 2.5, which is a number between 1 and 10. Then the exponent of 10 is –3.

Scientific notation makes clear how many significant figures are contained in the measurement. In this case, there are three significant figures. The inclusion of the final zero indicates that the precision of the measurement is one hundred-billionth (10^{-11}) of a second; the zeros before the 2 in the first version are merely placeholders.

Example 5

Write these numbers in scientific notation:

    a) 150

    b) 834,000

    c) 0.056

    d) 0.000370

Solution:

    a) $150 = 1.5 \times 100$

           $= 1.5 \times 10^2$

    b) $834{,}000 = 8.34 \times 100{,}000$

            $= 8.34 \times 10^5$

    c) $0.056 = 5.6 \times 0.01$

$$= 5.6 \times \frac{1}{100}$$

$$= 5.6 \times 10^{-2}$$

    d) $0.000370 = 3.70 \times 0.0001$

$$= 3.70 \times \frac{1}{10{,}000}$$

$$= 3.70 \times 10^{-4}$$

Example 6

Simplify $\left(\dfrac{1.8 \times 10^5}{9 \times 10^3}\right) \cdot (3.3 \times 10^{-4})$.

Solution:

By first dividing and then multiplying,

$$\left(\frac{1.8 \times 10^5}{9 \times 10^3}\right) \cdot (3.3 \times 10^{-4}) = (0.2 \times 10^2)(3.3 \times 10^{-4}) = 0.66 \times 10^{-2},$$

which is equal to 6.6×10^{-3}.

More Exponent Properties

Johannes Kepler (1571–1630) developed a mathematical formula, $T^2 = kD^3$, which gives the period of time T it takes a planet to make one revolution around the sun at an average distance D away from the sun. The constant is k, which is the same for every planet in the solar system.

This same formula relates the orbital period of an Earth satellite and its distance from Earth. If a satellite is D kilometers above Earth and the orbital period is measured in seconds, the constant k is $5.86 \times 10^{-2} \frac{s^2}{km^3}$.

If the orbital period of a NOAA (National Oceanographic and Atmospheric Administration) polar-orbiting satellite is 100 minutes (6000 s), then the satellite's altitude can be found by rewriting the equation $T^2 = kD^3$ in the form

$$D = 3\sqrt{\frac{T^2}{k}} = 3\sqrt{\frac{\left(6.00 \times 10^3 s\right)^2}{5.86 \times 10^{-2} \frac{s^2}{km^3}}}$$

This computation presents a situation in which a product, 6.00×10^3, must be raised to a power and in which the power expression 10^3 is itself raised to a power.

Power of a Product

$(a \cdot b)$ means $\underbrace{(ab)(ab)(ab)...(ab)}_{n \text{ factors}}$. Using the commutative and associative properties of multiplication,

$$(a \cdot b)^n = \underbrace{(ab)(ab)(ab)...(ab)}_{n \text{ factors}} = \left(\underbrace{a \cdot a \cdot a...a}_{n \text{ factors}}\right)\left(\underbrace{b \cdot b \cdot b...b}_{n \text{ factors}}\right) = a^n b^n.$$

The power of a product property, $(a \cdot b)^n = a^n b^n$, indicates that the value of $(2 \cdot 3)^4$ can be found by either of two sequences of steps:

1. Multiply the factors first and then raise the product to the power; or

2. Raise each factor to the power and then multiply.

Power of a Power

$(a^m)^n$ means $\underbrace{(a)^m (a)^m (a)^m ...(a)^m}_{n \text{ factors}}$. Using the multiplication property for exponents,

$$(a^m)^n = \underbrace{(a)^m (a)^m (a)^m ...(a)^m}_{n \text{ factors}} = a^{\overbrace{m+m+m+...+m}^{n \text{ terms}}} = a^{mn}.$$

In words, to raise a power expression to another power, multiply the exponents.

The power of a product property and power of a power property are shown in each of the following examples.

Example 7

Simplify $(2x^2y^3)^2$.

Solution:

$$(2x^2y^3)^2 = 2^2(x^2)^2(y^3)^2 = 4x^4y^6.$$

Example 8

Simplify $(-3a^{-2})^{-1}$.

Solution:

$$(-3a^{-2})^{-1} = (-3)^1(a^{-2})^{-1} = \frac{1}{-3}a^2 = -\frac{1}{3}a^2 \text{ or } -\frac{a^2}{3}.$$

Power of a Quotient

$\left(\dfrac{a}{b}\right)^n$ means $\underbrace{\left(\dfrac{a}{b}\right)\left(\dfrac{a}{b}\right)\left(\dfrac{a}{b}\right)\cdots\left(\dfrac{a}{b}\right)}_{n \text{ factors}}$, so we can write: $\left(\dfrac{a}{b}\right)^n = \dfrac{a^n}{b^n}$.

Example 9

Return to the problem on page 421 of determining the NOAA satellite's orbital altitude. To perform the necessary calculations, we can use the properties of exponents to simply the expression as follows:

$$\sqrt[3]{\frac{\left(6.00 \times 10^3\right)^2}{5.86 \times 10^{-2}}} = \sqrt[3]{\frac{(6.00)^2 \times \left(10^3\right)^2}{5.86 \times 10^{-2}}} = \sqrt[3]{\frac{36.0 \times 10^6}{5.86 \times 10^{-2}}} = \sqrt[3]{6.16 \times 10^8} \approx 850.$$

So the satellite's altitude is approximately 850 km.

The properties of exponents:

$$a^m \cdot a^n = a^{m+n}$$

$$\frac{a^m}{a^n} = a^{m-n}, \ a \neq 0 \qquad\qquad (a \cdot b)^n = a^n \cdot b^n$$

$$a^0 = 1, \ a \neq 0 \qquad\qquad\qquad \left(\frac{a}{b}\right)^n = \frac{a^n}{b^n}$$

$$a^{-1} = \frac{1}{a}, \ a \neq 0 \qquad\qquad\quad \left(a^m\right)^n = a^{mn}$$

$$a^{-n} = \frac{1}{a^n}, \ a \neq 0$$

These properties can be used to simplify expressions with variables. If you forget a property, remember that you can always return to the meaning of an exponent and redevelop the property.

Exercises 4.2

I. Investigations *(SE pages 310–313)*

1. On September 5, 1999, the *New York Times* news service reported that "the gap between rich and poor in this country has grown into an economic chasm so wide that this year, the richest 2.7 million Americans—the top 1 percent—will have as many after-tax dollars to spend as the bottom 100 million.... This ratio has more than doubled since 1977, when the top 1 percent had as much as the bottom 49 million...." The article went on to state, "In dollars, the richest 2.7 million people and the 100 million at the other end of the scale will each have about 620 billion to spend."

   a) The average amount of spending money that each person in the top 1% had in 1999 was $\dfrac{620,000,000,000 \text{ dollars}}{2,700,000 \text{ people}}$. Rewrite this ratio by expressing the numerator and denominator in scientific notation.

1. a) $\dfrac{6.2 \times 10^{11} \text{ dollars}}{2.7 \times 10^{6} \text{ people}}$

   b) Use the properties of exponents to evaluate the ratio in (a).

   b) $\left(\dfrac{6.2}{2.7}\right)\left(\dfrac{10^{11}}{10^{6}}\right)\left(\dfrac{\text{dollars}}{\text{people}}\right) = 2.3 \times 10^{5}$ or 230,000 dollars per person.

   c) The poorest 100 million Americans have a total after-tax spending capability of $\dfrac{620,000,000,000 \text{ dollars}}{100,000,000 \text{ people}}$. Rewrite this ratio by expressing the numerator and denominator in scientific notation.

   c) $\dfrac{6.2 \times 10^{11} \text{ dollars}}{1 \times 10^{8} \text{ people}}$

   d) Use the properties of exponents to evaluate the ratio in (c).

   d) $\left(\dfrac{6.2}{1}\right)\left(\dfrac{10^{11}}{10^{8}}\right)\left(\dfrac{\text{dollars}}{\text{people}}\right) = 6.2 \times 10^{3}$ or 6200 dollars per person.

2. a) In Exercise 21 of Section 1.2, the thickness of a wire in an integrated circuit was given as 0.00000025 m. If a typical copper wire has a diameter of about half a millimeter (0.0005 m), how many integrated circuit wires would fit across the diameter of a typical copper wire? Use scientific notation to perform the calculation.

2. a) $0.00000025 = 2.5 \times 10^{-7}$, and $0.0005 = 5 \times 10^{-4}$. **Divide the copper wire diameter by the integrated circuit wire diameter:**

   $\dfrac{5 \times 10^{-4} \text{ m}}{2.5 \times 10^{-7} \text{ m}} = \left(\dfrac{5}{2.5}\right)\left(\dfrac{10^{-4}}{10^{-7}}\right) = 2 \times 10^{-4-(-7)} = 2 \times 10^{3}$ or 2000 wires.

b) In Exercise 29 of Section 1.5, the volume of a buckyball was found to be 0.024 nm³. Expressing this volume in SI units of cubic meters would be quite awkward. Use scientific notation to write the volume of a buckyball in m³.

b) $(0.024 \text{ nm}^3)\left(\dfrac{1 \text{ m}}{10^9 \text{ nm}}\right)^3 = (0.024 \text{ nm}^3)\dfrac{(1 \text{ m})^3}{(10^9 \text{ nm})^3} =$

$(2.4 \times 10^{-2} \text{ nm}^3)\left(\dfrac{1 \text{ m}^3}{10^{27} \text{ nm}^3}\right) = 2.4 \times 10^{-2-27} \text{ m}^3 = 2.4 \times 10^{-29} \text{ m}^3.$

c) A basketball with a diameter of $9\dfrac{3}{8}$ in has a volume of 7.07×10^{-3} m³. How many times larger is the volume of a basketball than that of a buckyball?

c) $\dfrac{7.07 \times 10^{-3} \text{ m}^3}{2.4 \times 10^{-29} \text{ m}^3} = \left(\dfrac{7.07}{2.4}\right)\left(\dfrac{10^{-3}}{10^{-29}}\right) = 2.9 \times 10^{-3-(-29)} = 2.9 \times 10^{26}.$

3. Consider the list of time intervals measured in seconds in **Table 4.5**.

Description	Approximate Time in Seconds
One year	3.2×10^7 seconds
Age of Earth	1.3×10^{17} seconds
Time between normal human heartbeats	0.8 seconds
One day	8.6×10^4 seconds

Table 4.5

a) According to this table, how many times does a human heart beat in a year under normal circumstances?

3. a) $\dfrac{3.2 \times 10^7 \text{ s}}{0.8 \text{ s}} = 4 \times 10^7$ or **40 million heartbeats per year.**

b) According to this table, what is the age of Earth in years?

b) $(1.3 \times 10^{17} \text{ s})\left(\dfrac{1 \text{ yr}}{3.2 \times 10^7 \text{ s}}\right) = \left(\dfrac{1.3}{3.2}\right)\left(\dfrac{10^{17}}{10^7}\right) \text{ yr} = 0.41 \times 10^{10} \text{ yr} = 4.1 \times 10^9 \text{ yr}$

or **4.1 billion years.**

c) Calculate how many seconds are in 10 years.

c) $\left(\dfrac{8.6 \times 10^4 \text{ s}}{\text{day}}\right)\left(\dfrac{365 \text{ days}}{\text{yr}}\right)(10 \text{ yr}) = 31{,}390 \times 10^4 \text{ s} = 3.1 \times 10^8 \text{ s}.$

4. Personal computers often have storage devices measured in gigabytes. A recently purchased computer has a disk drive that is able to store 8.4 gigabytes (GB) of information. Things have changed considerably since IBM introduced the first personal computer with a hard disk drive in 1983. That computer had a 10 megabyte (MB) storage capacity.

 a) How many times larger is the new disk than a 10 MB disk drive? Use scientific notation.

4. a) 8.4 GB = 8.4 × 10⁹ bytes, and 10 MB = 10⁷ bytes. $\dfrac{8.4 \times 10^9 \text{ bytes}}{10^7 \text{ bytes}} = 8.4 \times 10^2$

or 840 times as large.

 b) A zip drive manufacturer advertises that its computer disk will store "as much data as 174 floppies." The zip disk stores 250 MB, and a floppy disk stores 1,440,000 bytes. Is the ad correct?

b) 250 MB is 2.50 × 10⁸ bytes and 1,440,000 is 1.44 × 10⁶.

$$\left(\frac{2.50 \times 10^8 \text{ bytes}}{1.44 \times 10^6 \text{ bytes}} \right) = 1.74 \times 10^2 = 174.$$

5. The Galileo spacecraft was launched in October 1989, and by 1995 it had arrived near enough to Jupiter to begin sending back information. Despite a malfunction of its high-gain antenna, which would have allowed it to send large amounts of information quickly, the spacecraft was able to send back about 1000 bits of information per second. These data have allowed scientists to learn more about the atmosphere on Jupiter and its moons.

According to an article in the September 1999 issue of *National Geographic* about this mission, Jupiter is about 470 million miles from Earth. How long did it take the information to travel between the spacecraft and Earth? Radio and television waves travel at the speed of light, which is 3.00×10^5 km/second. Also, because speed is defined as distance traveled per unit time, the time for the transmission equals distance divided by speed. (Remember: 1 mile = 1.609 km.)

5. $\left(\dfrac{(470 \times 10^6 \text{ mi})(1.609 \text{ km}/\text{mi})}{3.00 \times 10^5 \text{ km}/\text{s}} \right) = 2.52 \times 10^3$ **seconds, or about 42 minutes.**

6. We usually prefer that mathematical rules have no exceptions. To eliminate exceptions to the rules for multiplying and dividing expressions with exponents, we explored the meanings of both negative and zero exponents. However, one exception to the rule for dividing with exponents is unavoidable.

 a) Explain why the quotient $\dfrac{0^4}{0^2}$ requires an exception to the rule.

6. a) The answer would seem to be $0^{4-2} = 0^2 = 0$, but this cannot be correct because division by 0 has no meaning. So the rule that states $\dfrac{x^a}{x^b} = x^{a-b}$ has to include the disclaimer "$x \neq 0$."

b) Explain why 0^n is defined for any positive integer n but can have no meaning if n is a negative integer or zero.

b) If n is a positive integer, for example 3, then $0^3 = (0)(0)(0) = 0$. However, if n is –3, then $0^{-3} = 1/0^3 = 1/0$, which has no meaning, so we call the result "undefined." Recalling the origin of the meaning of an exponent of 0 (from Discovery 4.3, item 6), 0^0 would result from a quotient like $0^4/0^4 = 0^0$. Because this also involves division by 0, 0^0 it is also undefined.

7. In the United States today, 49% of the people drink coffee regularly. The average coffee drinker drinks 3–4 cups of coffee per day. According to many coffee drinkers, the caffeine in the coffee helps them wake up in the morning and provides mental alertness.

   Caffeine is eliminated from the body by the kidneys. The kidneys eliminate a constant fraction of the caffeine in the bloodstream each hour, similar to the way the dyed liquid was removed from the container in Activity 4.1.

   a) Suppose a coffee drinker has an 8-ounce cup of coffee with breakfast at 7:00 A.M. Complete **Table 4.6** to find how much caffeine is left in his bloodstream five hours later. Assume that there are 160 milligrams of caffeine in an average 8-ounce cup of brewed coffee. Also assume that in one hour this person's kidneys remove 15% of the caffeine that was present at the start of the hour. (Hint: This means that the fraction of caffeine remaining after an hour is 0.85.)

Time	Amount of Caffeine in Bloodstream (mg)	Amount of Caffeine in Expanded Form (mg)	Amount of Caffeine in Exponent Form (mg)
7:00 A.M.	160	160	$160(0.85)^0$
8:00 A.M.			
9:00 A.M.			
10:00 A.M.			
11:00 A.M.			
12:00 P.M.			

Table 4.6

7. **a)**

Time	Amount of Caffeine in Bloodstream (mg)	Amount of Caffeine in Expanded Form (mg)	Amount of Caffeine in Exponent Form (mg)
7:00 A.M.	160	160	$160(0.85)^0$
8:00 A.M.	$160(0.85) = 136$	$160(0.85)$	$160(0.85)^1$
9:00 A.M.	$136(0.85) = 115.6$	$160(0.85)(0.85)$	$160(0.85)^2$
10:00 A.M.	$115.6(0.85) \approx 98.3$	$160(0.85)(0.85)(0.85)$	$160(0.85)^3$
11:00 A.M.	$98.3(0.85) \approx 83.5$	$160(0.85)(0.85)(0.85)(0.85)$	$160(0.85)^4$
12:00 P.M.	$83.5(0.85) \approx 80.0$	$160(0.85)(0.85)(0.85)(0.85)(0.85)$	$160(0.85)^5$

b) The kidneys of different people may eliminate caffeine at slightly different rates. Repeat (a) for a person whose kidneys are more efficient so that 0.82 of the caffeine remains at the end of an hour.

b)

Time	Amount of Caffeine in Bloodstream (mg)	Amount of Caffeine in Expanded Form (mg)	Amount of Caffeine in Exponent Form (mg)
7:00 A.M.	160	160	$160(0.82)^0$
8:00 A.M.	$160(0.82) = 131.2$	$160(0.82)$	$160(0.82)^1$
9:00 A.M.	$131.2(0.82) \approx 107.6$	$160(0.82)(0.82)$	$160(0.82)^2$
10:00 A.M.	$107.6(0.82) \approx 88.2$	$160(0.82)(0.82)(0.82)$	$160(0.82)^3$
11:00 A.M.	$88.2(0.82) \approx 72.3$	$160(0.82)(0.82)(0.82)(0.82)$	$160(0.82)^4$
12:00 P.M.	$72.3(0.82) \approx 59.3$	$160(0.82)(0.82)(0.82)(0.82)(0.82)$	$160(0.82)^5$

c) Let the fraction of caffeine remaining after one hour for *any* person be represented by *r*. Write a one-term polynomial for the amount of caffeine remaining in the bloodstream after five hours for any person who drinks an 8-ounce cup of coffee at 7:00 A.M.

c) **$160r^5$**

d) If a person drinks *another* cup of coffee at 10:00 A.M., write a two-term polynomial for the amount of caffeine remaining in her bloodstream at 12:00 P.M.

d) **$160r^5 + 160r^2$**

II. Projects and Group Activities *(SE pages 313–314)*

8. Materials: graphing calculator, CBL and light probe, LIGHTFIL program, transparent plastic sheets (red, green, or other colors), flashlight, tape

Most automobile windshields contain clear glass to allow maximum light transmission, except for possibly a band of tinted glass at the top. This filters the sun's rays to help reduce their intensity.

In this activity you will investigate the transmission of light through a similar type of filter.

- Set up the equipment. Use tape to secure a flashlight and light probe approximately 80 cm apart on a flat surface as shown in **Figure 4.2.** Make sure the flashlight's beam is shining directly into the light probe. Once secured, do not move either the probe or the flashlight.

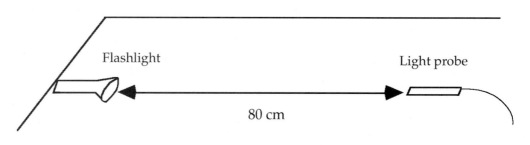

Flashlight

Light probe

80 cm

Figure 4.2

- Connect the light probe to the Channel 1 port (CH1) of the CBL unit, connect the CBL to your calculator, then turn on the CBL.

- Turn on the flashlight and start the LIGHTFIL program on the TI-83.

- When the program asks you to Enter Number of Samples, enter 5. (You may wish to collect more later.)

- The program then asks for the Number of Sheets. Begin with 0 sheets (no filters), turn the room lights off, and press Enter on the calculator to take the measurement. (It is essential to have the room as dark as possible with measuring the light intensity.)

- When collecting the next measurement, enter the number 1 when prompted by the calculator and hold 1 plastic sheet in front of the flashlight. Turn the room lights off and press ENTER to take the measurement. Continue collecting data using 2 plastic sheets, 3 sheets, and so forth, until you have taken as many measurements as you specified.

a) Your data (the number of plastic sheets) are found in L2. The corresponding light intensity measurements are found in L3. Record your data in a table similar to **Table 4.7**.

Number of Filters	Light Intensity
0	
1	
2	
3	
4	

Table 4.7

a) **Sample data (using sheets of red transparency film):**

0	0.880
1	0.631
2	0.476
3	0.351
4	0.268

b) Use your light intensity measurements from 0 filters and 1 filter to calculate the fraction of the light that passes through 1 filter.

b) $\dfrac{0.631}{0.880} = 0.72.$

In theory, if l is the fraction of the light that passes through 1 filter, then $(l)^n$ is the fraction of the light that passes through n filters.

c) Use the fraction of the light transmitted through 1 filter that you calculated in (b) to predict the fraction of the light that passes through 2 filters, 3 filters, and 4 filters.

c) **Using 0.72 from the sample answer in (b): 2 filters, 0.52; 3 filters, 0.37; 4 filters, 0.27.**

d) Compare the predictions from your theory-driven model in (c) with your data in Table 4.7. If your predictions do not exactly match the data, explain why. (If there is too much deviation, you may wish to repeat your data collection.)

d) Sample answers: There may have been outside light in the room when taking measurements, the filters may not have been exactly the same thickness, the light from the flashlight may not have been shining directly into the probe.

e) Suppose a glass filter 1 mm thick allows 80% of the light to pass through it. How much light will pass through a glass filter 2 mm thick? How much light will pass through a glass filter w mm thick?

e) $0.80)^2$, $(0.80)^w$

III. Additional Practice *(SE pages 314–316)*

9. Certain copying machines allow you to make an enlargement of the original document. Suppose that an enlargement is 1.15 times larger in linear dimensions. If you make copies of copies, and the original rectangular figure is 6 cm by 12 cm, what are the dimensions of the 2nd copy, the 4th copy, the 9th copy, and the nth copy?

9. 2nd copy: $(1.15)^2(6)$ cm x $(1.15)^2(12)$ cm or 7.9 cm x 15.9 cm

4th copy: $(1.15)^4(6)$ cm x $(1.15)^4(12)$ cm or 10.5 cm x 21.0 cm

9th copy: $(1.15)^9(6)$ cm x $(1.15)^9(12)$ cm or 21.1 cm x 42.2 cm

nth copy: $(1.15)^n(6)$ cm x $(1.15)^n(12)$ cm

10. When a rubber ball drops and bounces, it usually does not bounce up to its original height. The ratio of the rebound height to the original height is called the resiliency of the ball for whatever surface it is dropped on.

a) Suppose a ball is dropped onto a surface from 5.0 feet, and for that surface the ball's *resiliency* is 0.70. List the heights for the first three bounces.

10. a) 1st bounce: 0.70(5.0 ft) = 3.5 ft; 2nd bounce: $(0.70)^2(5.0$ ft) = 2.5 ft; 3rd bounce: $(0.70)^3(5.0$ ft) = 1.7 ft.

b) When the ball hits the ground the third time, what is the total vertical distance it has traveled?

b) 5.0 + 2(3.5) + 2(2.5) = 17 ft.

For 11–37, write each expression in a simpler form using the properties of exponents. Evaluate all numerical expressions, and simplify algebraic expressions containing variables. Write answers without negative exponents or parentheses. (Assume all variables are nonzero.)

11. $(5)^0(3)^2(3)^3$

11. $3^5 = 243$.

12. $(x^2)(x^4)(y^2)$

12. x^6y^2

13. $\dfrac{10^6}{10^2}$

13. 10,000

14. $(2x)^3$

14. $8x^3$

15. $\left(\dfrac{3x}{2}\right)^2$

15. $\dfrac{9x^2}{4}$ or $2.25x^2$

16. $(2x)^2(3x^2)$

16. $12x^4$

17. $(5)^{-2}(5x)^3$

17. $5x^3$

18. $6(x)^{-3}(x)^4(2x)^{-1}$

18. 3

19. $-7c^4(3c^2)$

19. $-21c^6$

20. $5(xy)^3$

20. $5x^3y^3$

21. 5^{-2}

21. $\dfrac{1}{25} = 0.04$.

22. $(2x)^3(3x)^2$

22. $72x^5$

23. $3^{-2} + 2^{-1}$

23. $\dfrac{1}{9} + \dfrac{1}{2} = \dfrac{11}{18}$.

24. $\dfrac{2}{y^{-2}}$

24. $2y^2$

25. $(2x^{-2}y^3)(3x^5y^{-3})$

25. $6x^3$

26. $\left(\dfrac{1}{5}\right)^0 + 6^0$

26. 2

27. $(-2)^{-3}(-2)^{-2}$

27. $-\dfrac{1}{32}$

28. $\left(\dfrac{1}{2}\right)^{-2}$

28. 4

29. $\left(\dfrac{2a}{b^2}\right)^3$

29. $\dfrac{8a^3}{b^6}$

30. $(-2x^2y)^3$

30. $-8x^6y^3$

31. $\left(\dfrac{2a^{-1}}{b}\right)^{-2}$

31. $\dfrac{a^2b^2}{4}$

32. $(2xy)(x^2y)^3$

32. $2x^7y^4$

33. $-3^2(2x)^{-1}$

33. $-\dfrac{9}{2x}$

34. $(3xy)(x^2y^3)(7x^3y)$

34. $21x^6y^5$

35. $(8n^3)(5nx^2)(n^2x)$

35. $40n^6x^3$

36. $\dfrac{\left(2a^3\right)\left(5a^5b^2\right)}{10a^4b^2}$

36. a^4

37. $\left(\dfrac{4x^3y}{x^2}\right) \cdot \left(\dfrac{x^5y^3}{2}\right)$

37. $2x^6y^4$

For 38–42, write each number in scientific notation.

38. 0.078

38. 7.8×10^{-2}

39. 0.00000054

39. 5.4×10^{-7}

40. 0.192

40. 1.92×10^{-1}

41. 0.0000000003

41. 3×10^{-10}

42. 0.0000160

42. 1.60×10^{-5}

For 43–47, write each number in standard numerical form.

43. 2.63×10^{-4}

43. 0.000263

44. 8×10^{-3}

44 0.008

45. 4.70×10^{-2}

45. 0.0470

46. 1.5×10^{-6}

46. 0.0000015

47. 7.1×10^{-9}

47. 0.0000000071

For 48–52, simplify and write each answer in scientific notation. Assume all given numbers result from measurement.

48. $\dfrac{4.5 \times 10^3}{2.5 \times 10^2}$

48. 1.8 x 10^1 = 18.

49. $(2.18 \times 10^5)(7.34 \times 10^3)$

49. 1.60 x 10^9

50. $(6.4 \times 10^5)(1.2 \times 10^{-9})$

50. 7.7 x 10^{-4}

51. $\left(\dfrac{6.7 \times 10^3}{1.9 \times 10^7}\right) \cdot (4.0 \times 10^9)$

51. 1.4 x 10^6

52. $\dfrac{9.26 \times 10^3}{3.25 \times 10^{-2}}$

52. 2.85 x 10^5

Section 4.3 Operations with Polynomials

What You Need to Know

- How to use the properties of exponents to simplify expressions containing exponents

- How to combine like terms

What You Will Learn

- To recognize a polynomial expression

- To add, subtract, and multiply polynomial expressions

- To divide a polynomial expression by a monomial

Materials Needed

- None

In Activity 4.1 we created a polynomial expression $200r^8$ that models the dilution of contaminated water. In that same section we described a polynomial expression as an algebraic expression in which each term has variables raised to whole number exponents. We now formalize this definition by using more precise mathematical symbols:

A **polynomial in** x is an expression of the form

$$A_n x^n + a_{n-1}x^{n-1} + a_{n-2}x^{n-2}\ldots + a_1 x + a_0.$$

If a_n is not zero, then the **degree of the polynomial** is n. The numbers $a_n, a_{n-1}, a_{n-2}, \ldots, a_1, a_0$ are called coefficients.

The exponents are all integers greater than or equal to zero.

For example, the expression $5p^4 - 6p^2 + 7$ is a polynomial of degree 4 and has three terms.

The expression e^3, which gives the volume of a cube with the length of an edge e, is a polynomial of degree 3. It has only one term.

The expression $2x^{-1} + 5x - 1$ is *not* a polynomial, because one of its terms contains a variable raised to a negative power.

Example 10

Indicate whether the expression is a polynomial. If it is a polynomial, give the number of terms and the degree of the polynomial. If it is not a polynomial, explain why not.

---

a) $2x^{-3} + 6x^2 - 5x$

b) $3z^5 + \dfrac{1}{2}z - \dfrac{3}{5}$

c) $3x - b$

d) $a^4 + 5a + \sqrt{a^3 - 7}$

Solutions:

a) No, this is not a polynomial because one of the terms has a negative exponent.

b) Yes, this is a polynomial of degree 5. It has three terms.

c) Yes, this is a polynomial of degree 1. It has two terms.

d) No, this is not a polynomial because the last term, $\sqrt{a^3 - 7}$, does not have the form of a variable raised to a whole number exponent multiplied by a nonzero coefficient.

Mathematicians have given specific names to certain polynomials. If a polynomial has only one term, such as $5y^2$, it is called a **monomial.** If it has two terms, such as $3r + 5$, it is called a **binomial.** And if it has three terms, such as $x^2 + 5x - 16$, it is called a **trinomial.**

Adding and Subtracting Polynomials

There are occasions when we need to add two or more polynomials. To add two polynomial expressions, we add like terms. In Discovery 4.2 we examine a visual model of like terms that can help us add polynomials.

Discovery 4.2 A Visual Model for Adding Polynomials *(SE pages 318–319)*

Consider the following expressions: x^2, $2x$, xy, x^2y, xy^2. Except for $2x$, each of these monomials has an understood numerical coefficient of 1. To determine whether any of these terms are like terms, it is sometimes helpful to represent them geometrically.

1. Fill in **Table 4.8** by drawing a representation of each term based on the given figures for x and y. Notice that x^2 can be represented by a square with sides of length x.

x	y	$2x$	x^2	y^2	xy	x^3	x^2y	xy^2

Table 4.8

1.

x	y	$2x$	x^2	y^2	xy	x^3	x^2y	xy^2
				☐	☐		▱	▱

In your table, notice that the only representations that look the same are x and $2x$. This indicates that these are the only two expressions in the table that are like terms. And because they are like terms, we can add them by adding their coefficients: $x + 2x = 3x$.

Figure 4.3 shows representations for $3xy$ and $2xy$. Notice that they are like terms. The figure also shows us why $3xy + 2xy$ can be simplified to $5xy$.

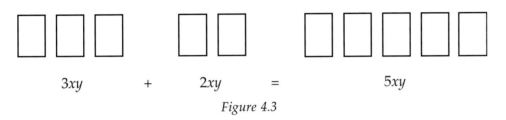

$$3xy \qquad + \qquad 2xy \qquad = \qquad 5xy$$

Figure 4.3

Suppose we want to add two monomials such as x^2y and xy^2. When we look at the representations of these two monomials in the table, we can see that they are not like terms. Hence, the best we can do is write the sum as $x^2y + xy^2$. The two terms cannot be combined into one monomial because they are not like terms. So we say that the expression $x^2y + xy^2$ is in **simplest terms.**

The representations in item 1 suggest that for terms to be like terms, not only do the variables have to be the same, but so do their corresponding exponents.

2. For (a)–(c), are the pairs of monomials like terms? If they are not like terms, explain why. If they are like terms, find their sum.

   a) x and x^2

2. a) Not like terms; the variables are the same, but the corresponding exponents are not.

   b) $3x^3$ and $2x^3$

   b) Like terms; $5x^3$

   c) $2x^6$ and $5y^6$

   c) Not like terms because the variables are not the same.

To add polynomials, we add the coefficients of the like terms. For example,

$(4x^2 + 3x + 6) + (3x^2 + 5x - 2) = 4x^2 + 3x + 6 + 3x^2 + 5x - 2 = 7x^2 + 8x + 4.$

3. For (a)–(c), add the polynomials. If you need to, draw a picture of the problem. State the number of terms in the resulting polynomial.

a) $(2x^2 + 5xy) + (3x + 2xy)$

3. **a) $2x^2 + 7xy + 3x$: The polynomial $2x^2 + 7xy + 3x$ has three terms.**

b) $(4x + 3y) + (x + 2y)$

b) $5x + 5y$: The polynomial $5x + 5y$ has 2 terms.

c) $(3x^2 + 2y^3) + (2x^3 + y^2)$

c) $2x^3 + 3x^2 + 2y^3 + y^2$: The polynomial $2x^3 + 3x^2 + 2y^3 + y^2$ has four terms. (There are no like terms to combine.)

We can subtract polynomial expressions as well as add them. Differences can also be simplified by combining like terms. Special care must be taken to avoid mistakes with the signs of the terms.

Example 11

Subtract: $(3x^2 - 2x + 7) - (x^2 - 4x + 8)$

Solution:

Use the distributive property to rewrite the example. Then combine the like terms.

$(3x^2 - 2x + 7) - (x^2 - 4x + 8) = 3x^2 - 2x + 7 - x^2 + 4x - 8 = 2x^2 + 2x - 1.$

Multiplying by a Monomial

The concept of multiplying polynomials is not new. In Section 4.2 we multiplied $(2x^2)(2x^3)$ and other similar expressions. These are examples of multiplying a monomial by a monomial.

In earlier chapters we used the distributive property of multiplication over addition to simplify expressions like $3(2t + 1)$. This is an example of polynomial multiplication where a binomial is multiplied by a monomial. To multiply $3t(2t + 1)$, we still use the distributive property but must then use the properties of exponents to simplify the results: $3t(2t + 1) = (3t)(2t) + (3t)(1) = 6t^2 + 3t$.

Example 12

Multiply (a)–(c), and give the degree of the resulting product.

a) $(3x^2)(2x^2 - x + 7)$ This is a multiplication of a second-degree trinomial by a second-degree monomial.

b) $5x(6x^2 + 3x - 2)$ This is a multiplication of a second-degree trinomial by a first-degree monomial.

c) $2x^3(5x - 1)$ This is a multiplication of a first-degree binomial by a third-degree monomial.

Solution:

a) $(3x^2)(2x^2 - x + 7) = 3x^2(2x^2) - 3x^2(x) + 3x^2(7) = 6x^4 - 3x^3 + 21x^2$; 4th degree

b) $5x(6x^2 + 3x - 2) = 5x(6x^2) + 5x(3x) - 5x(2) = 30x^3 + 15x^2 - 10x$; 3rd degree

c) $2x^3(5x - 1) = 2x^3(5x) - 2x^3(1) = 10x^4 - 2x^3$; 4th degree

---

Example 13

A community garden that is in the shape of a rectangle with dimensions of 50 feet by 60 feet has just been promised an extra strip of land along one of its sides. The strip is of uniform width, but the width in feet has not been specified. Draw two figures showing the two possible locations of the strip of land. Letting w represent the width of the extra strip of land, write an expression for the total area for the garden and the strip. (See **Figures 4.4a** and **4.4b**.)

Solution:

There are two ways the strip could be added to the garden—along the longer side or along the shorter side.

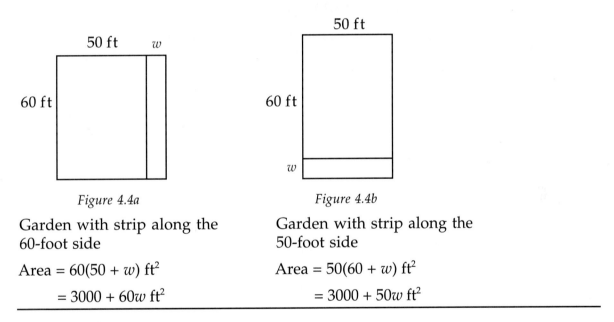

Figure 4.4a

Garden with strip along the 60-foot side

Area = 60(50 + w) ft²

   = 3000 + 60w ft²

Figure 4.4b

Garden with strip along the 50-foot side

Area = 50(60 + w) ft²

   = 3000 + 50w ft²

We can divide a polynomial by a monomial by dividing each term of the polynomial by the monomial.

Example 14

a) Divide $\dfrac{6x^2 + 8}{2}$.

b) Divide $5x^3 - 10x^2 + 25x$ by $5x$.

Solution:

a) $\dfrac{6x^2 + 8}{2} = \dfrac{6x^2}{2} + \dfrac{8}{2} = 3x^2 + 4$

b) $5x^3 - 10x^2 + 25x \div 5x = \dfrac{5x^3 - 10x^2 + 25x}{5x}$

$$= \dfrac{5x^3}{5x} - \dfrac{10x^2}{5x} + \dfrac{25x}{5x}$$

$$= x^2 - 2x + 5$$

Multiplying a Binomial by a Binomial

Consider the following problem: A builder has a lot that measures 100 feet by 120 feet. The builder plans to build a warehouse on this lot. The architect has suggested that the width of the open area on the sides of the lot be three times the width of the open area in the front and the back of the warehouse. (See **Figure 4.5.**) Write an expression for the amount of area available for the warehouse.

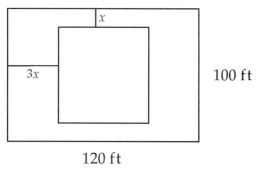

120 ft

Figure 4.5

Using Figure 4.5, we can express the area of the warehouse as $(120 - 6x)(100 - 2x)$ ft^2.

This expression is an example of the multiplication of a binomial by a binomial, but how do we do this multiplication? There are several ways to think about this process, all of which involve applying the properties we have been using. Two methods are shown as follows:

Method 1

Use the distributive property twice:

$$(120 - 6x)(100 - 2x) = (120)(100 - 2x) - (6x)(100 - 2x) \qquad \text{Distributive property}$$
$$= (120)(100) - (120)(2x) - (6x)(100) + (6x)(2x) \qquad \text{Distributive property}$$
$$= 12{,}000 - 240x - 600x + 12x^2 \qquad \text{Multiply.}$$
$$= 12{,}000 - 840x + 12x^2 \qquad \text{Add like terms.}$$

Method 2

Polynomials can also be multiplied by placing one polynomial under the other and multiplying each term of one polynomial by every term of the other.

To multiply $(120 - 6x)(100 - 2x)$ $\qquad 100 - 2x$

$\qquad \qquad \qquad \qquad \qquad \qquad \qquad \underline{120 - 6x}$

Multiply $100 - 2x$ by 120. $\qquad \qquad 12{,}000 - 240x$

Multiply $100 - 2x$ by $-6x$. $\qquad \underline{\qquad -600x + 12x^2}$

Add like terms. $\qquad \qquad \qquad 12{,}000 - 840x + 12x^2$

Each step of the distributive process can be seen in this method. Some people find that writing the two factors vertically helps them keep track of the terms.

Example 15

a) Multiply $(3x - y)(x + 2y)$

b) Multiply $(2x^2 + 5)(x - 3)$

Solutions:

a) Use the distributive property twice:

$$(3x - y)(x + 2y) = (3x)(x + 2y) - (y)(x + 2y)$$
$$= 3x^2 + 6xy - xy - 2y^2$$
$$= 3x^2 + 5xy - 2y^2$$

b) Use the distributive property twice:

$$(2x^2 + 5)(x - 3) = (2x^2)(x - 3) + (5)(x - 3)$$
$$= 2x^3 - 6x^2 + 5x - 15$$

In this example, there are no like terms to add. It is customary, but not necessary, to write the terms of the polynomial in descending order of the powers of the variable.

Exercises 4.3

I. Investigations *(SE pages 324–329)*

1. The shape in **Figure 4.6** is a cube with each edge measuring n centimeters.

   a) Write an expression for the volume of the cube. Write an expression for the surface area (the sum of the areas of each of the faces of the cube). Indicate the degree and the number of terms in your polynomial expressions.

   Figure 4.6

   a) **Volume: n^3; Surface area: $6n^2$**

   In this form, the volume is a third-degree monomial, and the surface area is a second-degree monomial. If the surface area were expressed as the sum of 6 terms, it would be a second-degree polynomial with 6 terms.

   b) **Figure 4.7** shows a rectangular solid made up of two cubes. Let the length of one edge of each cube measure x feet. Write an expression for the volume of the shape and for the surface area (the sum of the areas of the faces of the rectangular solid).

   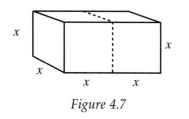

   Figure 4.7

   b) **Volume: $x(x)(2x) = 2x^3$; Surface area: $2(x)(x) + 4(x)(2x) = 2x^2 + 8x^2$ or $10x^2$.**

   c) Write expressions for the volume and the surface area of the solid in **Figure 4.8.**

   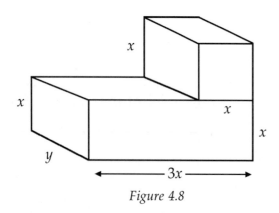

   Figure 4.8

c) **Volume:** $3x^2y + x^2y$ or $4x^2y$;
   Surface area $= 5xy + 2x^2 + 2(3x)(x) + (3x)(y) + y(3x - x)$,
   which simplifies to $8x^2 + 10xy$.

2. Suppose you are asked to design a new drink can that is twice as tall as it is wide.

   a) Write a polynomial expression to represent the volume of a cylinder with diameter n and height $2n$. Write an expression to represent the surface area of the cylinder. (See **Figure 4.9.**)

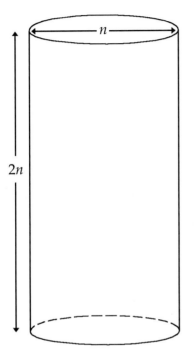

Figure 4.9

2. a) **Volume:** $\pi\left(\dfrac{n}{2}\right)^2(2n) = \dfrac{\pi n^3}{2}$; **Area:** $2\pi\left(\dfrac{n}{2}\right)^2 + \pi n(2n) = \dfrac{\pi n^2}{2} + 2\pi n^2$ or $\dfrac{5\pi n^2}{2}$.

b) Use your polynomial expressions to complete **Table 4.9.** Round your answers to the nearest tenth. (Hint: To make your job easier, try using your calculator table features or a computer spreadsheet.)

Diameter	Volume (cm³)	Surface Area (cm²)
3 cm		
3.5 cm		
4 cm		
4.5 cm		
5 cm		
5.5 cm		

Table 4.9

b)

Diameter	Volume (cm³)	Surface Area (cm²)
3 cm	42.4	70.7
3.5 cm	67.3	96.2
4 cm	100.5	125.7
4.5 cm	143.1	159.0
5 cm	196.4	196.4
5.5 cm	261.3	237.6

c) Expand the table to find a measurement that makes the volume approximately 250 cubic cm. What is the surface area for this measurement?

c) Using guess and check, a diameter of 5.42 cm gives a value close to 250 cubic cm for the volume. The surface area when the diameter is 5.42 cm is 230.7 square cm.

3. The owner of a lot 50 feet wide and 100 feet long has been notified that new street repairs will take a strip of land from one of the shorter sides of her lot. The removed strip will be of uniform width, but it is not yet known how wide it will be. She will be paid $20 per square foot for the land.

a) Draw a picture of this situation. Label the width of the strip w.

3. **a)** **Sample drawing:**

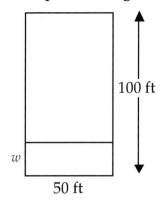

w

50 ft

100 ft

b) Write an expression for the land area to be taken by the street repairs.

b) **0w square feet**

c) Write an expression for the amount of money the owner will be paid.

c) **\$20(50w) = \$1000w.**

d) Write an expression for the land area she will have left.

d) **50(100 − w) = 5000 − 50w square feet.**

e) Use your expression from (d) to find the land area remaining if a 12.5-foot strip is removed.

e) **5000 − 50w; 5000 − 50(12.5) = 4375 square feet.**

4. An area model can be used to show a pictorial representation of a product. For example, the product of 15 and 13 can be shown with the model in **Figure 4.10.**

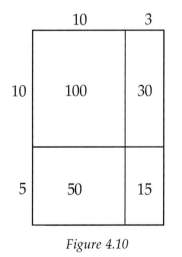

Figure 4.10

From the drawing, we can see by finding the sum of the individual areas that 15 x 13 = 100 + 30 + 50 + 15 = 195.

a) Use an area model to multiply 12 x 18.

4. a) Answer:

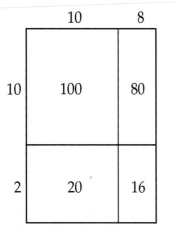

12 x 18 = 100 + 80 + 20 +16 = 216.

b) In a similar manner, we can use an area model to multiply binomials. The area model in **Figure 4.11** can be used to show the product of $(x + 5)$ and $(x + 2)$. Complete the area model by replacing each question mark with the area for the indicated rectangle.

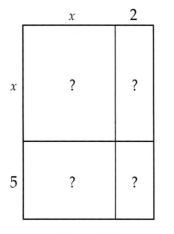

Figure 4.11

b) Answer:

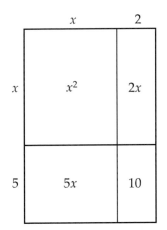

c) Use the area model in (b) to find a polynomial expression for $(x + 5)(x + 2)$.

c) $x^2 + 2x + 5x + 10 = x^2 + 7x + 10.$

d) Verify your result in (c) algebraically.

d) $(x + 5)(x + 2) = x(x + 2) + 5(x + 2) = x^2 + 2x + 5x + 10 = x^2 + 7x + 10.$

e) Use an area model to find $(2t + 1)(t + 3)$.

e) $2t^2 + t + 6t + 3 = 2t^2 + 7t + 3.$

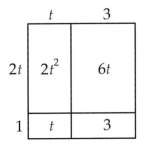

5. The Hardy-Weinberg equation, $(p + q)^2 = 1$, is based on the distributions of alleles in the gene pool of a population. Alleles are forms of a gene, and different alleles produce different traits. For example, the gene for eye color may have two alleles: blue eyes and not blue eyes.

This model represents a situation where there are only two alleles: p represents the fraction of all the alleles with one trait, and q represents the fraction of all the alleles with the other trait. Because there are no other possibilities, $p + q = 1$. Squaring $(p + q)$ allows us to represent algebraically all the combinations of alleles. Hence, $(p + q)^2 = 1^2$ or $p^2 + 2pq + q^2 = 1$.

We can also visualize this by making an area model that shows the various allele combinations in offspring of the population. (See **Figure 4.12.**)

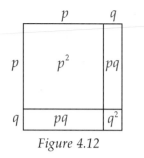

Figure 4.12

Because genes are inherited from two parents, we all have two alleles for each gene. Some people have two different alleles, say Aa. Others have two of the same alleles, either AA or aa. In both the equation and the area model, the expression q^2 represents the fractional part of the population that has two identical alleles for a trait, for example, blue eyes. p^2 is the fractional part of the population that has two copies of the other allele (which would be for the opposite trait, *not* having blue eyes). The $2pq$ term is the fractional part of the population that has two different alleles. (This group may not display the trait if the trait is recessive. An example is the hereditary disease *cystic fibrosis.*)

Public health scientists use the Hardy-Weinberg equation to estimate the percentages of people carrying the alleles for some inherited diseases. The metabolic disorder *phenylketonuria* (PKU) is an inherited inability to break down a certain amino acid. It occurs in about 1 out of 10,000 babies born in the United States. If left untreated, it results in severe mental retardation. If you have the disease, it means you have two copies of the allele that causes the disease. If you have the allele for this along with another different allele, you do not have the disease but are said to *carry* the disease. In this case, you may pass it on to your children.

We know that $\dfrac{1}{10,000}$ of the babies born have PKU, so the term q^2 in the Hardy-Weinberg equation equals $\dfrac{1}{10,000}$ or 0.0001.

a) What is the value of q? Keep in mind that q is the fraction of all the alleles in the gene pool that carry the disease. Here we are counting genes, not people.

5. **a) Because $q^2 = 0.0001$, $q = \sqrt{0.0001} = 0.01$.**

b) Because we know that $p + q = 1$, we can write $p = 1 - q$. So p is the fraction of the alleles in the gene pool that do not carry the disease. What is the value of p?

b) $p = 1 - 0.01 = 0.99$; p is the fraction of the non-PKU alleles in the gene pool.

c) Because we know p and q, we can compute $2pq$, the fractional part of the population that has two different alleles. People in this group do not have the disease but can pass it on to their offspring. What fractional part of the population is in this category?

c) 2(0.99)(0.01) = 0.0198.

Being able to estimate the fractional part of a population that carries a harmful allele is important in making public health decisions.

d) Again, this can be represented with an area model in which p and q are assigned values. Complete the model in **Figure 4.13** using the indicated values of p and q. Then compare the areas with the values of p^2 and q^2 in (a) and (c).

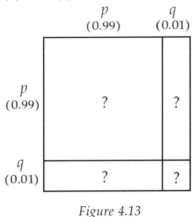

Figure 4.13

d) **p^2 = 0.9801; pq = 0.0099; and q^2 = 0.0001. These areas are identical to the values in (a) and (c).**

e) People with albinism lack pigment in their skin, hair, and eyes. The trait for albinism follows the same pattern as that of PKU. There are two alleles. The one that does not cause the disease is dominant. If 1 out of 22,000 people exhibit this trait, what fractional part of the population carries an allele for albinism even though it does not have the trait?

e) **$q^2 = \dfrac{1}{22,000} = 0.000045$, so $q = \sqrt{0.000045} = 0.0067$. This means $p = 1 - 0.0067$ and $2pq$ = 0.0134, or 1.34% of people carry the allele for albinism but do not have the trait.**

II. Projects and Group Activities *(SE page 329)*

6. The pattern of numbers shown in **Figure 4.14** is known as Pascal's triangle. This triangular table appeared as early at 1303 in China. It was used in the 17th century by Blaise Pascal to investigate probabilities. Within the triangle itself, there are many different patterns. In this problem we will use one such pattern to help us raise a binomial to positive integer powers.

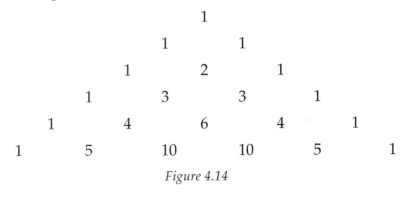

Figure 4.14

a) Raise the binomial $(a + b)$ to the 0 power. Then raise $(a + b)$ to the powers of 1, 2, 3, and 4. Examine the coefficients of the expanded binomials and Pascal's triangle. What do you notice?

6. **a)** $(a + b)^0 = 1$, $(a + b)^1 = a + b$, $(a + b)^2 = a^2 + 2ab + b^2$, $(a + b)^3 = a^3 + 3a^2b + 3ab^2 + b^3$, $(a + b)^4 = a^4 + 4a^3b + 6a^2b^2 + 4ab^3 + b^4$. **The coefficients of the product correspond to the numbers of a row of Pascal's triangle.**

b) Use Pascal's triangle to write the expansion of $(a + b)^5$.

b) $(a + b)^5 = a^5 + 5a^4b + 10a^3b^2 + 10a^2b^3 + 5ab^4 + b^5$.

c) Write the next row in the triangle by continuing the pattern. This row gives the coefficients of $(a + b)$ to what power?

c) **The next row is 1, 6, 15, 20, 15, 6, 1. This would correspond to $(a + b)^6$.**

III. Additional Practice *(SE pages 330–332)*

7. In **Figure 4.15,** represent the area of the shaded region between the two rectangles in terms of x and y.

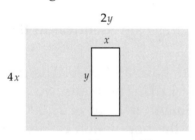

Figure 4.15

7. $(4x)(2y) - xy = 7xy$.

8. In **Figure 4.16,** represent the area of the shaded region between the two rectangles in terms of p.

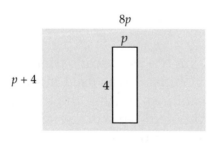

Figure 4.16

8. $8p(p + 4) - 4p = 8p^2 + 32p - 4p = 8p^2 + 28p$.

9. In **Figure 4.17,** represent the area of the shaded region between the square and the triangle in terms of x.

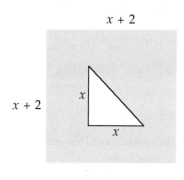

Figure 4.17

9. $(x + 2)^2 - \dfrac{1}{2}x^2 = x^2 + 4x + 4 - \dfrac{1}{2}x^2 = \dfrac{1}{2}x^2 + 4x + 4.$

10. In **Figure 4.18,** represent the area of the shaded region between the square and the trapezoid in terms of t.

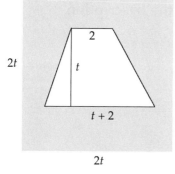

Figure 4.18

10. $(2t)^2 - \left(\dfrac{1}{2}(t + 2 + 2)(t) \right) = 4t^2 - \dfrac{1}{2}(t^2 + 4t) = 4t^2 - \dfrac{1}{2}t^2 - \dfrac{1}{2}(4t) = \dfrac{7}{2}t^2 - 2t.$

For 11–13, indicate whether the expression is a polynomial. If it is not a polynomial, tell why. If it is a polynomial, state the number of terms and the degree of the polynomial.

11. $-3p^{-3} - \dfrac{3}{5}p + \sqrt{2}$

11. **No, this is not a polynomial because one of the exponents is negative.**

12. $3.6721x + 70.124x^5 - 6.092$

12. **Yes, this is a polynomial of degree five with three terms.**

13. $4t - (2t)^{\frac{1}{2}} + 7t^2$

13. No, because one of the variables has a fractional exponent.

14. The expression $\dfrac{4}{3}\pi r^3$ is used to find the volume of a sphere with radius r. Is this expression a polynomial? If it is not a polynomial, tell why. If it is, state how many terms it has and its degree.

14. Yes, this is a polynomial of degree three with one term.

15. The expression $12 + 300t - 16t^2$ might be used to determine the height of a model rocket t seconds after it is launched. Is this expression a polynomial? If it is, state how many terms it has and its degree.

15. Yes this is a polynomial of degree two with three terms.

16. The expression $1.225w^{\frac{1}{2}}$ can be used to determine the diameter of a fiber line needed to lift a load weighing w tons. Is this expression a polynomial? If it is not a polynomial, tell why. If it is, state how many terms it has and its degree.

16. No, this is not a polynomial because the variable has a fractional exponent.

For 17–21, write an example of a polynomial that fits the description.

17. A third-degree polynomial with two terms

17. Sample answer: $2n^3 + 5$

18. A polynomial of degree one with one term

18. Sample answer: $10y$

19. A fifth-degree polynomial with fractional coefficients

19. Sample answer: $\dfrac{2}{3}x^5 - \dfrac{1}{5}x^4 + \dfrac{5}{6}x^2 - 0.8$

20. A third-degree polynomial with all negative coefficients

20. Sample answer: $-5y^3 - 1.5y^2 - 21y - 8$

21. A third-degree polynomial that has two terms

21. Sample answer: $7x^3 + 5x^2$

For 22–27, add or subtract as indicated.

22. $(3m^3 - 5m^2 + 7) + (m^2 - 4m + 8)$

22. $3m^3 - 4m^2 - 4m + 15$

23. $(5x^2 - x + 3) - (x^2 - 8x + 6)$

23. $4x^2 + 7x - 3$

24. $(6y^2 - 3y + 7) - (11 - 5y + 6y^2)$

24. $2y - 4$

25. $(2x + 3) - (x^2 - 1) + (2x^2 - 3x + 5)$

25. $x^2 - x + 9$

26. $(4t^2 + 6s^2) + (3t^2 + 2s)$

26. $7t^2 + 6s^2 + 2s$

27. $-3n^2 + (5n - 4) - (n^2 - 3n)$

27. $-4n^2 + 8n - 4$

For 28–51, perform the indicated operation and combine like terms when possible.

28. $x(10x^3 - 6x)$

28. $10x^4 - 6x^2$

29. $-5(b^5 + b^3 - b + 20)$

29. $-5b^5 - 5b^3 + 5b - 100$

30. $(6y^2 - 3y + 1)(7y^2)$

30. $42y^4 - 21y^3 + 7y^2$

31. $\dfrac{10x^2 + 4x - 16}{4}$

31. $2.5x^2 + x - 4$

32. $\dfrac{10.2a^3 - 2.2a^2 - 5.5a}{2a}$

32. $5.1a^2 - 1.1a - 2.75$

33. Divide $21y^6 - 12y^4 + 8y$ by $3y$.

33. $7y^5 - 4y^3 + \dfrac{8}{3}$

34. Divide $z^3 - 8z^2$ by $(-z)$.

34. $-z^2 + 8z$

35. $(x + 3)(2x - 3)$

35. $2x^2 + 3x - 9$

36. $(2t - 3)(2t - 3)$

36. $4t^2 - 12t + 9$

37. $(2x - 5)(x^2 - 1)$

37. $2x^3 - 5x^2 - 2x + 5$

38. $(a - 2)(a + 2)$

38. $a^2 - 4$

39. $(2x - 3)(y + 4)$

39. $2xy - 3y + 8x - 12$

40. $(2r^2 - 1)(r + 3)4$

40. $8r^3 + 24r^2 - 4r - 12$

41. $(2x^2 - 4)(3x + 2)$

41. $6x^3 + 4x^2 - 12x - 8$

42. $(3m - 1)^2$

42. $9m^2 - 6m + 1$

43. $(x^3 - 2x + 5)(5x - 1)$

43. $5x^4 - x^3 - 10x^2 + 27x - 5$

44. $(c - 1)(c + 1)$

44. $c^2 - 1$

45. $(3p - 2)(3p + 2)$

45. $9p^2 - 4$

46. $(7y^2 + 3y - 2)(y^2 + 1)$

46. $7y^4 + 3y^3 + 5y^2 + 3y - 2$

47. $(3x + 2)(3x + 2)$

47. $9x^2 + 12x + 4$

48. $(3t - 7)(3t + 7)$

48. $9t^2 - 49$

49. $(5g + 3)(5g - 3)$

49. $25g^2 - 9$

50. $(x + 3)^3$

50. $x^3 + 9x^2 + 27x + 27$

51. $(t - 2)^3$

51. $t^3 - 6t^2 + 12t - 8$

Section 4.4 Factoring Polynomials

What You Need to Know

- How to add, subtract, and multiply polynomials

- How to apply the properties of exponents

What You Will Learn

- To factor polynomial expressions

- To recognize prime numbers and prime polynomial expressions

Materials

- None

Students involved in the Watermelon Toss at a local university developed this theory-driven model for the height of a watermelon tossed into the air from a height of 48 feet: $h = -16t^2 + 32t + 48$. In this model the height h is in feet and time t is in seconds. To determine the time at which the melon hits the ground, we would need to solve this polynomial function for t when $h = 0$. One way to solve the resulting equation is to factor it. In this section we will examine what it means to factor a number or expression. In Section 4.5 we will solve polynomial equations.

To **factor** a number means to write it as a product of two or more numbers. Each of these numbers is called a factor of the original number. For example, the number 30 is equal to $6 \cdot 5$, so 6 and 5 are both factors of 30. In fact, all of the numbers 1, 2, 3, 5, 6, 10, and 15 are factors of 30. However, some of these numbers can themselves be written as products.

The numbers 2, 3, and 5 are called **prime numbers** (or simply **primes**) because their only factors are themselves and 1. All numbers greater than 1 and that are not prime are called **composite numbers.**

A number, N, is considered to be **factored completely** when it is written as a product of its prime factors. The product of prime factors is sometimes referred to as the **prime factorization** of N.

Throughout this section, we will seek only factors containing integers when we factor numbers or algebraic expressions. The number 30 could be factored into $\frac{1}{2} \cdot 60$, but this type of factoring will not be considered here. There are also advanced engineering applications that require factors that include a type of number called a complex number, but we will restrict ourselves to using only real numbers. For our purposes, a number will be considered prime if it has no *integer* factors other than itself and 1.

Example 16

Factor 45 completely.

Solution:

We know that 45 is equal to $5 \cdot 9$ or $3 \cdot 15$, but both 9 and 15 can be factored further. So a prime factorization is $1 \cdot 3 \cdot 3 \cdot 5$. The 1 in the prime factorization is often omitted because every integer has 1 as a factor. Also, because 3 appears as a factor twice, exponent notation can be used to write $45 = 3^2 \cdot 5$.

When we factor a polynomial, we write it as a product of prime factors. Factored polynomials can be of help in simplifying algebraic expressions and in solving equations. An algebraic expression may contain variables as well as numbers. For example, the expression $3x^2$ contains a factor of 3 and two factors of the variable x.

The purpose of this section is to examine some methods for factoring polynomials and to find ways to recognize polynomials that cannot be factored.

Factoring large numbers can be involved and time-consuming (see Exercise 5). Computer security systems rely on this difficulty to prevent unauthorized use of information. So-called *encryption keys* are based on numbers with 100 or more digits that take hours or years of time to factor. These large numbers used in building encryption codes are obtained by multiplying two large prime numbers. Mathematicians working in a branch of mathematics known as number theory continue to look for better methods of factoring. Companies marketing security systems run contests offering prizes to people who can factor large numbers.

Common Monomial Factoring

The first step in factoring a polynomial is to identify the terms in the polynomial. Every term must be examined for factors that the terms have in common. For instance, $12x^3 - 2x^2 + 4x$ is a trinomial, and each of the three terms has a common factor of 2 as well as a common factor of x.

The distributive property can be thought of in two ways. It can be used to multiply, as in $a(b + c) = ab + ac$, and it can be used to factor, as in $ab + ac = a(b + c)$.

So each term can be factored into $2x$ multiplied by something: $2x(6x^2) - 2x(x) + 2x(2)$. Applying the distributive property, the polynomial can be expressed as a product, $(2x)(6x^2 - x + 2)$.

Thus, we have written the polynomial $12x^3 - 2x^2 + 4x$, which has three terms, in an equivalent form, $2x(6x^2 - x + 2)$, which is made up of three prime factors: 2, x, and $(6x^2 - x + 2)$.

Example 17

Factor $3x(x - 1) + 2(x - 1)^2$

Solution:

To factor $3x(x - 1) + 2(x - 1)^2$, first identify the terms. This polynomial has two terms: $3x(x - 1)$ and $2(x - 1)^2$.

Notice that each term has a factor of $(x - 1)$, so this expression can be factored.

$$3x(x - 1) + 2(x - 1)^2 = (x - 1)[3x + 2(x - 1)]$$
$$= (x - 1)(3x + 2x - 2)$$
$$= (x - 1)(5x - 2)$$

Factoring Quadratic Trinomials

Multiplying the two binomials $(x + a)$ and $(x + b)$ reveals a useful pattern: $(x + a)(x + b) = x^2 + ax + bx + ab$, which can be written $x^2 + (a + b)x + ab$. For any two nonzero numbers, a and b, this last type of expression is called a **quadratic trinomial.** Provided that the coefficient of the x^2 term is 1, we can see two important properties: (1) the coefficient of the x term is made up of the sum of the two numbers a and b, (2) the constant term is the product of the same two numbers.

For example, $(x + 3)(x + 7) = x^2 + 10x + 21$, which is $x^2 + (3 + 7)x + 3 \cdot 7$. In this case, a and b are the numbers 3 and 7.

Keeping this in mind can help us factor trinomials.

Discovery 4.3 Factoring Trinomials *(SE pages 335–336)*

When the leading coefficient of a trinomial is not equal to 1, the method discussed here will not work. In such cases, factoring the trinomial may be somewhat more challenging. Often, some kind of trial-and-error method is necessary (see Exercise 1).

Factoring trinomials depends on recognizing some number patterns and solving a puzzle. When factoring a trinomial with a leading coefficient of 1, think of two numbers whose product is the constant term and whose sum is the coefficient of the first-degree term. For example, in the quadratic trinomial $x^2 - 15x - 250$, the constant term is –250 and the coefficient of the first-degree term is –15. So what two numbers have a product of –250 and a sum of –15? The *only* possibilities are 10 and –25.

1. Complete **Table 4.10** by first finding the numbers a and b. Write the factors of each trinomial and check by multiplication.

Factor the Trinomial	Product of Two Numbers	Sum of Two Numbers	Two Numbers	The Factors of the Trinomial	Check
$n^2 + 9n + 20$	20	9	4 and 5	$(n+4)(n+5)$	$(n+4)(n+5) = n^2 + 9n + 20$
$a^2 + 12a + 35$	35	12			
$x^2 - 2x - 15$	−15	−2			
$b^2 + 18b - 40$	−40	18			
$n^2 + 22n + 21$	21	22			
$t^2 + 4t - 5$	−5	4			
$x^2 + 20x + 19$	19	20			
$t^2 + 25t + 100$	100	25			

Table 4.10

1.

$n^2 + 9n + 20$	20	9	4 and 5	$(n+4)(n+5)$	$(n+4)(n+5) = n^2 + 9n + 20$
$a^2 + 12a + 35$	35	12	**7 and 5**	$(a+7)(a+5)$	$(a+7)(a+5) = a^2 + 12a + 35$
$x^2 - 2x - 15$	−15	−2	**3 and −5**	$(x+3)(x-5)$	$(x+3)(x-5) = x^2 - 2x - 15$
$b^2 + 18b - 40$	−40	18	**20 and −2**	$(b+20)(b-2)$	$(b+20)(b-2) = b^2 + 18b - 40$
$n^2 + 22n + 21$	21	22	**21 and 1**	$(n+21)(n+1)$	$(n+21)(n+1) = n^2 + 22n + 21$
$t^2 + 4t - 5$	−5	4	**5 and −1**	$(t+5)(t-1)$	$(t+5)(t-1) = t^2 + 4t - 5$
$x^2 + 20x + 19$	19	20	**19 and 1**	$(x+19)(x+1)$	$(x+19)(x+1) = x^2 + 20x + 19$
$t^2 + 25t + 100$	100	25	**20 and 5**	$(t+20)(t+5)$	$(t+20)(t+5) = t^2 + 25t + 100$

2. Create a list of several factorable quadratic trinomials in a table similar to the one in item 1. To create the trinomials, choose two binomials and multiply them together. Exchange lists with another student, and complete each other's tables for practice.

2. Answers will depend on the problems written by each student.

3. Now try factoring some trinomials directly, without the help of a table:

$x^2 - 7x + 6$ Think: What two numbers multiply to 6 and add to −7?

Sum   Product   Only −1 and −6 will work. So $x^2 - 7x + 6 = (x-1)(x-6)$.

Factor:

a) $x^2 - 5x - 14 = (x \quad)(x \quad)$.

3. **a)** $(x - 7)(x + 2)$

   b) $n^2 + 17n + 70 = (n\ \ \ \ )(n\ \ \ \ ).$

   b) $(n + 10)(n + 7)$

   c) $y^2 + 16y - 17 = (y\ \ \ \ )(y\ \ \ \ ).$

   c) $(y + 17)(y - 1)$

4. Factor: (Hint: Look for a common factor first. If there is one, rewrite the expression as a product of the common factor and a polynomial. Then factor the polynomial.)

   a) $2t^2 + 12t + 16$

4. **a) $2(t + 4)(t + 2)$**

   b) $5x^2 - 20x + 15$

   b) $5(x - 3)(x - 1)$

Not all trinomials can be factored. Some are prime. The trinomial $a^2 + 3a + 4$ cannot be factored because there is no pair of integers with a product of 4 and a sum of 3.

Factoring Special Forms

When trying to factor a polynomial, look for these forms:

- **Perfect square trinomials.** When a binomial is squared, the resulting trinomial takes the form of $(ax + b)^2 = (ax)^2 + 2abx + b^2$ or $a^2x^2 + 2abx + b^2$.

  To look for this form in a trinomial, notice if the first coefficient and the last coefficient are perfect squares a^2 and b^2. If they are, then look to see that the middle term is twice the product of a and b.

Example 18

Factor $25x^2 + 20x + 4$.

Solution:

$25x^2$ is $(5x)^2$ and 4 is 2^2. Twenty is twice the product of 5 and 2. Therefore, we can write $25x^2 + 20x + 4 = (5x + 2)^2$.

- **The difference of two squares.** When two binomials that are the sum and difference of the same terms are multiplied, the result is a binomial that is the difference of two squares.

  $(ax - b)(ax + b) = (ax)(ax) + (ax)(b) - (b)(ax) - b^2 = a^2x^2 - b^2$.

  Notice that there is no middle term.

  To recognize this form, look for polynomials with only two terms, where one is being subtracted from the other. Both terms must be perfect squares.

Example 19

Factor the following expressions:

a) $121n^2 - 144$

b) $2y^2 - 32$

Solution:

a) $121n^2 = (11n)^2$ and $144 = 12^2$. There are only two terms, and they are being subtracted.

$$121n^2 - 144 = (11n)^2 - (12)^2 = (11n - 12)(11n + 12)$$

b) Because there is a factor common to each term, rewrite $2y^2 - 32$ as $2(y^2 - 16)$. Then notice that the factor $y^2 - 16$ is the difference of two squares and can be factored as $(y - 4)(y + 4)$. So $2y^2 - 32 = 2(y - 4)(y + 4)$.

Note: The sum of two squares cannot be factored.

The ability to factor a polynomial is an important aid in solving equations, as we will see in Section 4.5. Factoring can also be helpful for writing algebraic expressions in simpler forms and for understanding the graphs of many types of functions.

Steps in Factoring a Polynomial

1. Look for common factors. If there is a factor common to all of the terms, rewrite the polynomial as a product of two factors, one of which is the common factor.

2. Organize the polynomial in descending degrees of the terms.

3. Look for a special form. Recognizing a perfect square trinomial or the difference of two squares makes a complicated problem easier.

4. If the polynomial is not a special form but a trinomial with a leading coefficient of 1, find two numbers that have a product equal to the constant term and a sum equal to the coefficient of the middle term. If two such numbers cannot be found, you are safe in declaring the polynomial "prime."

5. If the polynomial has a leading coefficient not equal to 1, several different methods may be used to factor the polynomial. (See Exercise 1 for one such method.)

6. After you have factored a polynomial, *always* check your answer by multiplying the factors to see if you get the original polynomial.

Exercises 4.4

I. Investigations *(SE pages 339–342)*

1. When the leading coefficient of a trinomial is not equal to 1, the factoring method discussed in Discovery 4.3 does not work and a more involved process is required.

   Consider the more general trinomial $ax^2 + bx + c$, where a is an integer not equal to 1. Many trinomials of this type can be generated by multiplying two binomials; for example, $(x + 3)(5x - 1) = 5x^2 + 14x - 3$. Notice that the coefficients of x in the binomials are factors of the coefficient of the x^2 term in the trinomial, and the constant terms in the binomials are factors of the constant term in the trinomial. We could factor the trinomial by first factoring the coefficient of x^2 and the constant term, then using those numbers to generate the binomial factors.

   For example, if our task were to factor $5x^2 + 14x - 3$, we would need to consider all the pairs of binomial factors that produce the correct x^2 and constant terms. Examine the following pairs:

   $(5x + 3)(x - 1)$

   $(5x - 3)(x + 1)$

   $(5x + 1)(x - 3)$

   $(5x - 1)(x + 3)$

   Only the last of these pairs produces the correct middle term of $14x$ when multiplied.

   Care must be exercised in writing the signs of the constant terms in the binomials so that the correct linear term (the "x" term) results when the binomials are multiplied. Several possibilities may have to be tested to find the factors.

   a) Factor the following trinomials using this method:
      $7x^2 + 4x - 3$; $5x^2 + 9x - 2$; $2x^2 - 13x + 11$

1. **a)** $7x^2 + 4x - 3 = (7x - 3)(x + 1)$; $5x^2 + 9x - 2 = (5x - 1)(x + 2)$; $2x^2 - 13x + 11 = (2x - 11)(x - 1)$

Not all trinomials factor. For example, the trinomial $3x^2 - 6x - 2$ cannot be factored. The only linear factors of $3x^2$ are $3x$ and x, while the only factors of 2 are 2 and 1, although one of the binomials would have to contain a negative constant term in order to produce the -2 in the trinomial. Therefore, the only possible binomial factors of $3x^2 - 6x - 2$ are:

$(3x + 2)(x - 1)$

$(3x - 2)(x + 1)$

$(3x + 1)(x - 2)$

$(3x - 1)(x + 2)$

Because none of these pairs will produce a middle term of $-6x$ when multiplied, the trinomial $3x^2 - 6x - 2$ is prime.

Because the coefficients of x^2 and the constant terms were prime numbers, the factored forms of the polynomials have so far been relatively easy to determine. However, if the coefficient of the x^2 term and the constant term are not prime numbers, there may be many possible binomial factors that must be tested until the factors are found.

Consider the trinomial $15x^2 - 14x - 8$. Factors of 15 include the pairs (15)(1) and (5)(3), while those of 8 include (8)(1) and (4)(2). All of the following 16 binomial pairs might have to be tested as possible factors:

$(15x + 8)(x - 1)$	$(15x - 8)(x + 1)$	$(15x + 1)(x - 8)$	$(15x - 1)(x + 8)$
$(15x + 4)(x - 2)$	$(15x - 4)(x + 2)$	$(15x + 2)(x - 4)$	$(15x - 2)(x + 4)$
$(5x + 8)(3x - 1)$	$(5x - 8)(3x + 1)$	$(5x + 1)(3x - 8)$	$(5x - 1)(3x + 8)$
$(5x + 4)(3x - 2)$	$(5x - 4)(3x + 2)$	$(5x + 2)(3x - 4)$	$(5x - 2)(3x + 4)$

b) Factor the following quadratic trinomials. If the expression is not factorable, write prime.

$6x^2 + 11x + 3$

$14x^2 + 13x + 3$

$5x^2 - x - 4$

$5x^2 + 9x + 4$

$8x^2 + 15x - 12$

$6x^2 + 41x - 56$

b) $(3x + 1)(2x + 3)$; $(7x + 3)(2x + 1)$; $(5x + 4)(x - 1)$; $(5x + 4)(x + 1)$; prime; $(6x - 7)(x + 8)$

2. A rectangular room is 5 feet longer than it is wide. (See **Figure 4.19.**)

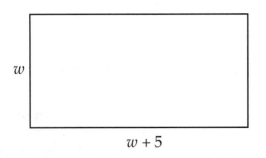

w

$w + 5$

Figure 4.19

a) Write an expression for the floor area of the room.

2. a) $w(w + 5)$

b) If the floor space of this room is an area of 300 square feet, what are the dimensions of the room? Answer this question by thinking of two numbers that have a product of 300 and a difference of 5.

b) The numbers are 15 and 20.

c) Now write an equation that sets the expression from (a) equal to the given area.

c) $w(w + 5) = 300$.

d) Expand the left-hand side of the equation from (c), and then collect all the terms on the left-hand side. How is this equation related to factoring polynomials? (Hint: Consider the answer to (b).)

d) The equation becomes $w^2 + 5w - 300 = 0$. The factors of the left-hand side are $(w - 15)(w + 20)$, which contain the numbers that solve the area question. The thinking involved in factoring the trinomial is similar to the thinking needed to find the dimensions in the area problem.

3. A farm with a large square field that measures x meters on each side (see **Figure 4.20**) is to be watered with a central pivot system, a watering system consisting of a well located in the center of a circle.

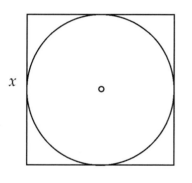

Figure 4.20

Water is pumped through a single pipe with a radius equal to one-half the length of the field and that rotates (pivots) about the center. When flying over western and midwestern America, it is not uncommon to see circles formed by this type of irrigation.

a) In Figure 4.20, assume the well and one end of the pivot are located in the middle of the square field. Write an expression in terms of x for the area of the field that is watered. Write an expression for the area of the field that is *not* watered.

3. a) The radius of the circle is $\dfrac{x}{2}$, so the area being watered is $\pi\left(\dfrac{x}{2}\right)^2$. The expression for the part of the field not being watered is $x^2 - \pi\left(\dfrac{x}{2}\right)^2$.

b) Factor the expression for the area not watered in (a). Rewrite the factored form as a monomial with a decimal coefficient.

b) $x^2 - \pi\left(\dfrac{x}{2}\right)^2 = x^2 - \dfrac{\pi x^2}{4} = x^2\left(1 - \dfrac{\pi}{4}\right) \approx 0.215x^2.$

What if the field were watered by a system of several smaller central pivot systems? Would more or less of the field be watered? How much more or less?

In (c)–(f) we will examine this situation and answer these questions.

c) **Figure 4.21** shows the same square field, x meters on a side but with four central pivot systems in place. What is the radius of each circle?

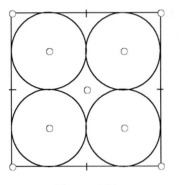

Figure 4.21

c) The radius of each small circle is $\dfrac{x}{4}$.

d) Write an expression in terms of x for the part of the field that is watered.

d) The part of field being watered is $4\pi\left(\dfrac{x}{4}\right)^2.$

e) Write an expression in terms of x for the amount of area of the field that is *not* watered using this system. Then factor it and rewrite the factored form as a monomial with a decimal coefficient.

e) $x^2 - 4\pi\left(\dfrac{x}{4}\right)^2 = x^2 - \dfrac{4\pi x^2}{16} = x^2\left(1 - \dfrac{\pi}{4}\right) \approx 0.215x^2.$

f) Compare the fraction of the field watered by one pivot and the fraction of the field watered by four pivots.

f) Both arrangements water the same fraction of the field.

4. Here are a few divisibility rules that can be helpful when factoring large numbers.

- Any even number is divisible by 2.

- If the sum of a number's digits is divisible by 3, the number itself is divisible by 3.

- If the sum of a number's digits is divisible by 9, the number itself is divisible by 9.

- If the last two digits of a number form a number divisible by 4, the entire number is divisible by 4.

- If the last digit of a number is a 5 or a 0, the number itself is divisible by 5.

- If the last digit of a number is 0, the number is divisible by 10 (and similarly for 100, 1000, etc.).

Consider the following numbers: 1394, 7443, 852, 6620, 189, 9048, 1365.

a) Which of these numbers have 2 for a factor? Explain.

4. a) 1394, 852, 6620, 9048. Any even number is divisible by 2.

b) Which have 3 for a factor?

b) 7443, 852, 189, 9048, 1365. If the sum of a number's digits is divisible by 3, the number itself is divisible by 3.

c) Which have 4 for a factor?

c) 852, 6620, 9048. If the last two digits of a number form a number divisible by 4, the entire number is divisible by 4.

d) Which have 5 for a factor?

d) 6620, 1365. If the last digit of a number is a 5 or a 0, the number itself is divisible by 5.

e) Which have 9 for a factor?

e) 7443, 189. If the sum of a number's digits is divisible by 9, the number itself is divisible by 9.

f) Which have 10 for a factor?

f) 6620. If the last digit of a number is 0, the number is divisible by 10.

5. Recall that a prime number is a number (2, 3, 5, 7, etc.) that has no factors other than itself and 1.

a) Why is 2 the only even prime number?

5. a) All larger even numbers have 2 as a factor.

b) Write the next 10 primes after 11.

b) 13, 17, 19, 23, 29, 31, 37, 41, 43, 47

c) Find the prime factorization of 345.

c) Because the sum of the digits is 12, 345 is divisible by 3, and because it ends in 5, it is also divisible by 5. 345 = (3)(5)(23). Because 23 is prime, this is a prime factorization of 345.

d) Find the prime factorization of 1457.

d) Using the divisibility rules from Exercise 4, we can see that 1457 has no factors of 2, 3, 4, or 5 (and consequently of 6, 8, 9, and 10). A trial of successively larger primes may then reveal possible factors. It turns out that 31 will work, and 1457 = (31)(47).

This last example suggests why factoring has become important in encryption for computer security purposes. If an extremely large composite number has only two large prime factors, it can be almost impossible to factor by normal methods (even computer-generated searches). But knowledge of one of the factors (the "key") makes it possible to find the other one and to factor the composite number.

II. Projects and Group Activities *(SE page 343)*

6. Write 10 quadratic trinomials for another student to factor. (Make sure that most of them will indeed factor, by multiplying two binomials.) Trade with another person and factor the polynomials.

6. Answers will depend on the problems written by each student.

7. In the 15th century, it was thought that $2^n - 1$ was a prime number if n was a prime number. As people began to study these numbers, many of them were shown to be composite. With the exception of the first three or four, all of these numbers have put into the history books the people who have shown that the number was prime or composite.

In 1644, a French monk, Marin Mersenne, claimed that $2^n - 1$ was prime when $n = 2, 3, 5, 7, 13, 17, 19, 31, 67, 127,$ and 257, and they were composite for all other positive integers n less than 257. He was incorrect but still got his name attached to these numbers, and today prime numbers in the form $2^n - 1$ are called Mersenne primes.

Mathematicians, both professional and amateur, are taking part in a competition to find new Mersenne primes. At stake are prize money and a chance of making history through a mathematical discovery. Find out more about the search for Mersenne primes by researching the topic on the Internet and writing a short report on your findings.

7. Answers will vary but should reflect adequate research of the topic.

III. Additional Practice *(SE pages 343–345)*

For 8–14, complete each factorization.

8. $x^2 + 10x + 21 = (x + 3)(x \quad)$

8. $(x + 7)$

9. $n^2 - n - 20 = (n + 4)(n \quad)$

9. $(n - 5)$

10. $x^2 - 3x + 2 = (x - 1)(x \quad)$

10. $(x - 2)$

11. $y^2 - 10y + 16 = (y \quad)(y \quad)$

11. $(y - 8)(y - 2)$

12. $x^2 + 4x - 21 = (x \quad)(x \quad)$

12. $(x + 7)(x - 3)$

13. $55 + 16n + n^2 = (n \quad)(\quad n)$

13. $(5 + n)(11 + n)$

14. $16 - 8x + x^2 = (\quad x)(\quad x)$

14. $(4 - x)(4 - x)$

For 15–45, factor the given expression completely. If the expression is not factorable, write "Prime." (Hint: Don't forget to look for common factors and special forms.)

15. $6xy + 2y + 4y^2$

15. $2y(3x + 1 + 2y)$

16. $5x^3 - 10x$

16. $5x(x^2 - 2)$

17. **Figure 4.22** shows a structural beam of length L, anchored in a wall at one end and supported on a post at the other. The vertical deflection of the beam at any horizontal distance from the left end is given by the polynomial

$$\frac{wx^4}{24EI} - \frac{wLx^3}{16EI} + \frac{wL^3x}{48EI}.$$

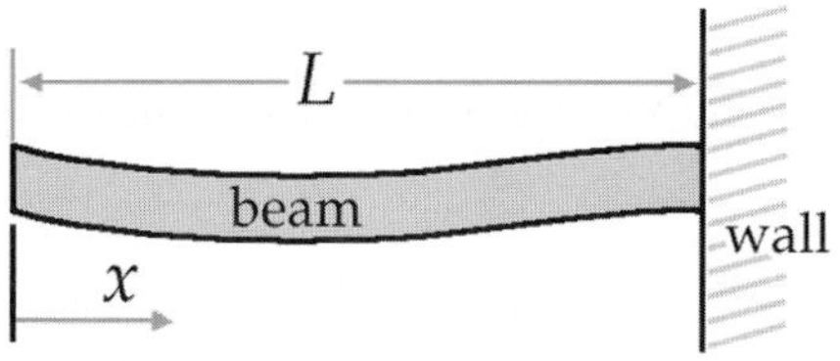

Figure 4.22

17. $\dfrac{wx}{8EI}\left(\dfrac{x^3}{3} - \dfrac{Lx^2}{2} + \dfrac{L^3}{6}\right)$

18. $3a^2b - 12ab + 18ab^3$

18. $3ab(a - 4 + 6b^2)$

19. $14x^5 - 21x^4 + 28x^2$

19. $7x^2(2x^3 - 3x^2 + 4)$

20. $3(a + b) - 4(a + b)^2$

20. $(a + b)[3 - 4(a + b)] = (a + b)(3 - 4a - 4b)$.

21. $77x^3y + 22xy^3 - 55x^2y^2 + 121xy$

21. $11xy(7x^2 + 2y^2 - 5xy + 11)$

22. $32n^3 - 48n^2 + 80n$

22. $16n(2n^2 - 3n + 5)$

23. $3x(y - 1)^2 + 6x(y - 1)$

23. $3x(y - 1)[(y - 1) + 2] = 3x(y - 1)(y + 1)$.

24. $16abc - a^2b + 3ac^3$

24. $a(16bc - ab + 3c^3)$

25. $15xy - 5x + 3y^2$

25. Prime

26. $a^2 - 9$

26. $(a + 3)(a - 3)$

27. $80 - 125x^2$

27. $5(16 - 25x^2) = 5(4 + 5x)(4 - 5x)$.

28. $2x^2 - 44x + 242$

28. $2(x^2 - 22x + 121) = 2(x - 11)^2$.

29. $2n^2 - 4n + 2$

29. $2(n^2 - 2n + 1) = 2(n - 1)^2$.

30. **Figure 4.23** is a diagram of an electrical circuit. To predict the current in the circuit, an electronic engineer would examine a mathematical expression called a *Laplace transform*. The Laplace transform for this circuit is $s^2 + 270s + 5000$.

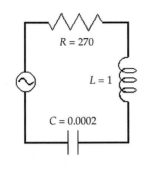

Figure 4.23

30. $(x + 20)(x + 250)$

31. $x^2 - 5x - 6$

31. $(x + 1)(x - 6)$

32. $y^2 - y - 12$

32. $(y - 4)(y + 3)$

33. $d^2 - 13d + 42$

33. $(d - 7)(d - 6)$

34. $s^2 + 17s + 60$

34. $(s + 12)(s + 5)$

35. $t^2 - 4t - 5$

35. $(t - 5)(t + 1)$

36. $b^2 + 11b + 30$

36. $(b + 5)(b + 6)$

37. $x^2 - 15x + 56$

37. $(x - 7)(x - 8)$

38. $2a^2 + 2a - 84$

38. $2(a^2 + a - 42) = 2(a + 7)(a - 6)$.

39. $3v^2 - 63v + 330$

39. $3(v^2 - 21v + 110) = 3(v - 10)(v - 11)$.

40. The volume of an open-top box that could be constructed from a 12-in x 10-in piece of sheet metal (see **Figure 4.24**) is given by the expression $4x^3 - 44x^2 + 120x$.

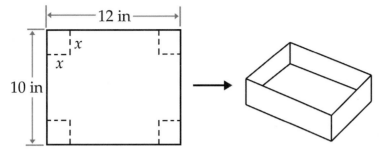

Figure 4.24

40. $(4x)(x - 5)(x - 6)$

41. $81x^2 - 18x + 1$

41. $(9x - 1)^2$

42. $4a^2 - 28a + 49$

42. $(2a - 7)^2$

43. $9x^2 + 48x + 64$

43. $(3x + 8)^2$

44. The moment of inertia of a flywheel like the one in **Figure 4.25** is given by the expression $\dfrac{\pi r b}{2g}(r_o^{\;4} - r_i^{\;4})$.

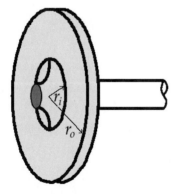

Figure 4.25

44. $\dfrac{\pi r b}{2g}\left(r_o^{\;2} + r_i^{\;2}\right)\left(r_o^{\;2} - r_i^{\;2}\right) = \dfrac{\pi r b}{2g}\left(r_o^2 + r_i^2\right)\left(r_o + r_i\right)\left(r_o - r_i\right)$.

45. $x^4 - 16$

45. $(x^2 + 4)(x^2 - 4) = (x^2 + 4)(x + 2)(x - 2)$.

Section 4.5 Modeling with Polynomial Functions

What You Need to Know

- How to graph a linear function

- How to evaluate polynomial expressions

What You Will Learn

- To model some situations with polynomial functions

- To graph polynomial functions

- To solve equations containing factorable polynomials

Materials

- None

In Chapter 1 we investigated possible designs for boxes made from rectangular cardboard. In Discovery 4.4 we will investigate how the volumes of these boxes can be modeled using **polynomial functions.**

Discovery 4.4 Container Design (Revisited) *(SE pages 346–347)*

Consider the problem of making a covered box out of one sheet of cardboard that measures 24 inches by 50 inches. One possible design is illustrated in **Figure 4.26.** A strip of uniform width x would be folded up on all sides as well as in the middle of the sheet. With appropriate short cuts, the resulting box might be appropriate for holding something like a pizza.

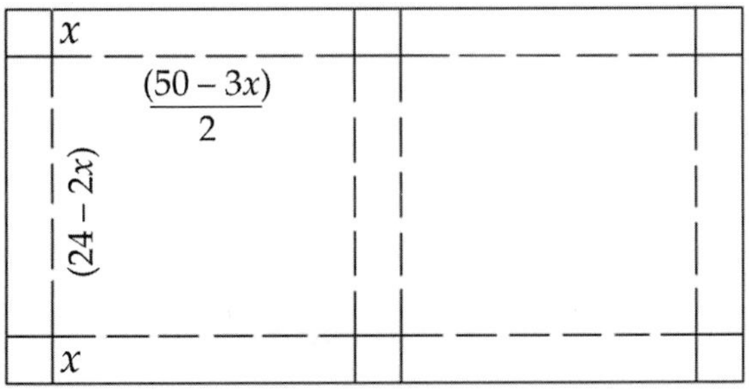

Figure 4.26

The expressions written on the figure represent the dimensions of the box that would result, all of which depend on the value of x.

1. Write an expression for the volume of the box by using these variable dimensions. (Note that the length can also be written as 25 − 1.5x.)

1. **Volume = (length)(width)(depth) = $\left(\dfrac{50 - 3x}{2}\right)$(24 − 2x)(x).**

2. By expanding this expression for volume, write the volume in the form of a polynomial function, with V as the dependent variable and x as the independent variable.

2. **$V = 600x − 86x^2 + 3x^3$ or $V = 3x^3 − 86x^2 + 600x$.**

3. As you recall from earlier chapters, a function can be represented by an equation, a table, or a graph, or it can sometimes be described in words. Create a table of values for your function by using as large a range of x values as possible that could actually result in a real box.

3.

x = Depth (in)	V = Volume (in³)
1	517 in³
2	880 in³
3	1107 in³
4	1216
4.5	1231.9
5	1225
6	1152
7	1015
8	832
9	621
10	400
11	187
12	0

The table feature of a calculator could be used here to investigate the possibilities more thoroughly.

4. Explain why there are limits on the set of feasible values for x.

4. **It is impossible to have a dimension less than 0, so $x > 0$. If the depth were 12 inches, after folding the cardboard there would be no material left for the bottom and top of the box, so $x < 12$.**

5. In item 4 you identified a problem domain for your volume function, which is the set of *x* values that can produce a real box. (See Exercise 4 of Section 1.5.) How does this compare with the domain of the function from item 2?

5. **The domain of $V = 3x^3 - 86x^2 + 600x$ is all real numbers. The problem domain is a subset of the complete domain.**

6. Construct a graph of the volume function that goes beyond the feasible values of *x* for the box. A good interval for *x* might be $-3 \leq x \leq 20$. If you use a graphing calculator, think carefully about an appropriate window for the graph. The table feature can be used to explore some possibilities.

6. **Sample graph:**

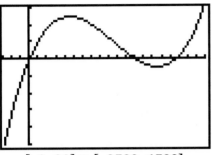

[−3, 20] x [−2500, 1500]

7. Using your graph and/or table, determine the value of *x* that would result in the largest possible volume for the box. Would this be a good design for a pizza box?

7. **Maximum volume occurs when the depth $x = 4.5914881 \approx 4.6$ inches, which results in a length of approximately 18.1 inches, a width of approximately 14.8 inches, and a volume of about 1232 inches^3. It would be appropriate only for a *very* deep-dish pizza; otherwise, there would be much wasted space (and material). It would be more cost effective to use a shallower box.**

8. Notice that in addition to the relative maximum point that represents the box with the largest possible volume, your graph shows a relative minimum point at a larger value of *x*. Find the coordinates of this point. Is there any physical meaning to this minimum point?

8. **The relative minimum has approximate coordinates of $x = 14.5$, $V = -235.6$. No, this point has no physical significance. It would require dividing the cardboard's 24-inch dimension into two parts, each 14.5 inches long, which is impossible.**

Properties of Polynomials

The following two important and general properties of polynomial functions were revealed in Discovery 4.4:

- The domain of a polynomial function includes all real numbers.
- The graph of a polynomial function is a smooth curve.

Example 20

The polynomial function $C = 0.002t^3 - 0.14t^2 + 2.2t + 3.0$ can be used to model the concentration of a drug in the bloodstream in parts per million as a function of time t in hours after the drug is administered.

a) Find the size of the initial dose and the concentration of the drug in the bloodstream 5 hours after it is administered.

b) Use a table and/or a graph of the function to determine the problem domain for this situation.

c) Determine the maximum bloodstream concentration of the drug and the time that concentration is reached.

Solution:

a) The initial dose is the value of C when $t = 0$, which is $0.002(0)^3 - 0.14(0)^2 + 2.2(0) + 3.0 = 3.0$ parts per million. After 5 hours, the concentration equals the value of the function when $t = 5$, or $0.002(5)^3 - 0.14(5)^2 + 2.2(5) + 3.0 = 10.75$ parts per million.

b) Both the graph of the function (**Figure 4.27**) and **Table 4.11** show that shortly after 26 hours, the value of C becomes negative, which makes no sense physically, as a negative concentration for a drug is impossible. Negative values for time also make no sense in this context. So the problem domain is approximately $0 \le t < 26$.

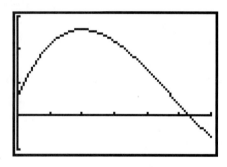

[0, 30] x [−5, 15]

Figure 4.27

c) Examination of the graph or table shows that the maximum concentration of 13.0 parts per million occurs 10 hours after taking the medication.

t (hr)	C (ppm)	t (hr)	C (ppm)
0	3.0	15	11.25
1	5.062	16	10.552
2	6.856	17	9.766
3	8.394	18	8.904
4	9.688	19	7.978
5	10.75	20	7.0
6	11.592	21	5.982
7	12.226	22	4.936
8	12.664	23	3.874
9	12.918	24	2.808
10	13	25	1.75
11	12.922	26	0.712
12	12.696	27	−0.294
13	12.344	28	−1.256
14	11.848	29	−2.162

Table 4.11

Solving Polynomial Equations: The Zero Product Property

The volume function in Discovery 4.4 can be expressed as $V = 3x^3 - 86x^2 + 600x$, which is a useful form for graphing and is also simple to write. However, one way of expressing the original factored form of the function is:

$$V = \left(\frac{1}{2}\right)(50 - 3x)(24 - 2x)(x).$$

This form has advantages also. One is that it shows where the function originates, because all of the numbers can be directly related to the original design problem. It also makes a direct determination of the problem domain possible and provides more information about the function's graph. To see how, consider the following question: For what values of x is the volume of the box 0?

If V is set equal to zero, the following equation results:

$$\left(\frac{1}{2}\right)(50 - 3x)(24 - 2x)(x) = 0.$$

To solve this equation, we can use the fact that if the product of two or more numbers is zero, then at least one of the factors is zero. Although a fairly simple concept, this is such an important fact that it is worth special emphasis.

Zero Product Property
If a and b are numbers and $a \cdot b = 0$, then either a or b (or both) must be equal to 0.

Also, if *any* product of numbers is equal to zero, then at least one of the factors must be equal to 0.

Return to our volume problem. Because each of the expressions $(50 - 3x)$, $(24 - 2x)$, and (x) stands for some number, the equation $\left(\frac{1}{2}\right)(50 - 3x)(24 - 2x)(x) = 0$ can only be true if at least one of the four factors on the left-hand side of the equation is equal to zero.

Clearly, the factor $\left(\frac{1}{2}\right)$ is not zero. So the only way the equation can represent a true statement is if either $(50 - 3x) = 0$ or $(24 - 2x) = 0$ or $x = 0$. To solve the original equation, we only have to solve three linear equations:

$50 - 3x = 0$ is true only if $x = \dfrac{50}{3}$.

$24 - 2x = 0$ is true only if $x = 12$.

$x = 0$.

Therefore, there are three possible solutions to the equation $\left(\frac{1}{2}\right)(50 - 3x)(24 - 2x)(x) = 0$. They are 0, 12, and $\dfrac{50}{3}$ (or $16\frac{2}{3}$). These numbers are also called the **zeros**, or roots, of the polynomial function $V = 3x^3 - 86x^2 + 600x$.

All three zeros are also the x-coordinates of the x–intercepts on the graph of the function $V = 3x^3 - 86x^2 + 600x$. Note that $\dfrac{50}{3}$ is not in the problem domain for the volume of the box; therefore, we disregard this possible solution. So for this situation, the volume of the box is 0 when $x = 0$ inches and when $x = 12$ inches.

The zero product property can be applied in a similar manner to solve any polynomial equation that can be factored.

Example 21

Find all solutions of the equation $(x + 4)(3x - 7)(6x + 3) = 0$.

Solution:

The product of three factors is zero, and the zero product property requires that at least one of the factors be zero.

Either $x + 4 = 0$, which implies $x = -4$, or

$3x - 7 = 0$, which implies $x = \dfrac{7}{3}$, or

$6x + 3 = 0$, which implies $x = -\dfrac{1}{2}$.

The solutions are -4, $-\dfrac{1}{2}$, and $\dfrac{7}{3}$.

Example 22

At the beginning of Section 4.4, we posed a problem asking when a watermelon would hit the ground if it were tossed into the air from a height of 48 feet. The model given was $h = -16t^2 + 32t + 48$, where h is in feet and time t is in seconds. We are now able to solve that problem.

Solution:

Because we are interested in when the melon hits the ground ($h = 0$), we set h equal to 0 in the equation and solve for t.

$-16t^2 + 32t + 48 = 0$

$-16(t^2 - 2t - 3) = 0$

$-16(t - 3)(t + 1) = 0$

Either $t - 3 = 0$, which implies $t = 3$ seconds, or
$t + 1 = 0$, which implies $t = -1$ seconds.

Because -1 second has no meaning in this problem, the watermelon hits the ground 3 seconds after being thrown into the air.

Example 23

Find all solutions of the equation $x^3 + 60x = 17x^2$.

Although the left-hand side of the equation can be factored, the right-hand side does not equal zero, so the zero product property cannot be used to solve the equation in its given form. However, if the $17x^2$ term is subtracted from both sides of the equation, the zero product property can be applied to the new equation:

$x^3 - 17x^2 + 60x = 0$

$x(x - 12)(x - 5) = 0$

Either $x = 0$ or $x - 12 = 0$ or $x - 5 = 0$.

The solutions are 0, 5, and 12.

To summarize the relationships among the solutions to a polynomial equation, the factors of the polynomial, and the zeros or roots of the polynomial function, let's examine the polynomial function $y = x^2 + 5x - 14$. If we set the polynomial equal to zero and solve for x, we get

$0 = x^2 + 5x - 14,$

$0 = (x + 7)(x - 2),$ and

$x = 2$ or $x = -7.$

We now know that the solutions to the polynomial equation are 2 and –7. We can also say that the zeros of the polynomial function are 2 and –7. We also know that the factors of the polynomial are $(x + 7)$ and $(x - 2)$.

We can generalize this by saying that if k is a zero of a polynomial function, then $(x - k)$ is a factor of the polynomial. This statement suggests that finding zeros of polynomial functions graphically can help us factor polynomials. (See Exercise 4.)

Exercises 4.5

I. Investigations *(SE pages 352–357)*

1. A small pond contains 5 pounds of a hydrocarbon contaminant. The pond is to be cleaned in a manner similar to the dilution method that was introduced in Section 4.1. A portion of the contaminated pond water will be removed each day, completely cleaned, and then returned to the pond.

   a) Let r represent the fraction of the hydrocarbons that is *not* removed each day by the cleaning process. Write a one-term polynomial function for the amount H (in pounds) of hydrocarbons in the pond after 30 days in terms of r.

1. a) $H = 5r^{30}$.

   b) Use a graphing calculator or computer to create a graph of your function for values of r between 0 and 1.

b)

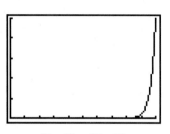

[0, 1] x [0, 5]

   c) Use your graph to find a value for r that will reduce the amount of hydrocarbons in the pond to approximately 0.5 pounds in 30 days.

c)

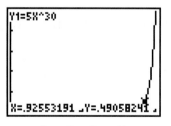

[0, 1] x [0, 5]

The amount of hydrocarbons remaining after 30 days is about 0.49 pounds if $r \approx 0.9255$.

   d) What percent of the pond's water must to be removed and cleaned each day to accomplish this task?

d) $1 - 0.9255 = 0.0745$, **or about 7.5%.**

   e) Suppose that during the cleanup, additional hydrocarbon contaminant enters the pond. One pound of hydrocarbons enters on the second day, and another pound enters on the fifth day. Write a new polynomial function for the total amount of hydrocarbons in the pond in terms of r.

e) $H = 5r^{30} + 1r^{28} + 1r^{25}$.

f) Repeat (b)–(d) to determine the percent of the pond's water that must be removed and cleaned each day in this case.

f)

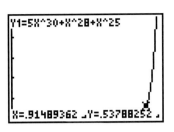

[0, 1] x [0, 5]

H **will be about 0.54 pounds if** *r* **is 0.914..., so** *r* **must be about 0.91 to achieve the desired level. The fraction removed each day is then 1 – 0.91 = 0.09, so 9% of the pond's water must be removed and cleaned each day.**

2. Suppose you have been hired to plan the layout for a summer music concert in a large city park. (See **Figure 4.28.**) The concert will be on the banks of a lake and surrounded by a fence. There will be an entrance fee. The city police have given a permit and will patrol the fence, but they say you can have only 1200 feet of fence because of the personnel needed for the patrol. You have been asked to decide how to use this 1200 feet of fencing to produce the largest area for the concert crowd. The concert organizer wants the space to be rectangular. (One side of the rectangle borders the lake and does not need to be fenced off.) A drawing of the site is provided. Decide what dimensions will give maximum area.

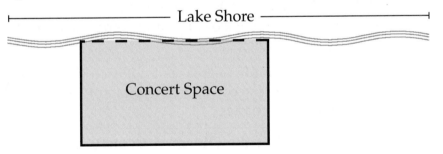

Figure 4.28

a) Write a function giving area as a function of one of the dimensions. Use a table and a graph to help decide the maximum area. What dimensions result in this area?

2. **a)** $A = x(1200 – 2x)$ **or** $A = -2x^2 + 1200x$, **where** *A* **is the area in square feet and** *x* **is the width in feet. The maximum area is 180,000 square feet using a width of 300 feet.**

b) Write a letter to the concert organizer telling her what the dimensions should be and explaining how you decided.

b) Answers will vary but should reflect an explanation of the mathematics from (a).

3. The polynomial expression $220 - 49t - 16t^2$ gives the height in feet of an object t seconds after it is thrown downward from a height of 220 feet above ground.

a) Use this expression to complete **Table 4.12**.

Time after Object Is Released (s)	Height of the Object (ft)
0	
0.5	
1	
1.5	
2	
2.5	
3	

Table 4.12

3. a) See the completed table in (c).

b) At 3 seconds, the polynomial has a negative value. What happened between 2.5 s and 3 s?

b) The object hit the ground.

c) Add another column to your table and label it "Change in Height per Unit Time (0.5 s)." Subtract the entries in the distance column to obtain the change in the height of the object in the previous half second. What do you notice? By looking at your table, could you have predicted that the relationship was not linear? Explain.

c) The number of feet per 0.5 seconds decreases by 8 each time interval. Yes, the distance fallen per half second is not constant. In other words, there is not a constant rate of change.

Time after Object Is Released (s)	Height of the Object (ft)	Change in Height per Unit Time (0.5 s)
0	220	---
0.5	196	196 – 220 = –24
1	164	–32
1.5	124	–40
2	76	–48
2.5	20	–56
3	–44	–64

4. To use a graphing calculator to aid in factoring, consider the polynomial expression $x^2 - 3x - 4$. We know this expression factors into $(x - 4)(x + 1)$.

   a) To see how the calculator can help identify the factors of this expression, graph the function $y = x^2 - 3x - 4$. What are the zeros of the function?

4. a) 4 and –1

   b) Factor the polynomial $x^2 - 8x - 9$, and graph the polynomial function $y = x^2 - 8x - 9$ on your calculator. What do you notice about the zeros of the function and the factors of the polynomial?

b) $(x - 9)(x + 1)$ are the factors; the zeros are 9 and –1.

   c) If k is one of the zeros of a function, what is one of the factors?

c) $(x - k)$

   d) Graphing $y = 2x^2 - x - 10$ shows zeros of –2 and 2.5. (See **Figures 4.29** and **4.30**.) The –2 suggests a factor of $(x + 2)$. The other zero of 2.5 is equivalent to $\frac{5}{2}$. This suggests that the second factor could be $(2x - 5)$. Show that this is true by multiplying the two factors $(x + 2)$ and $(2x - 5)$.

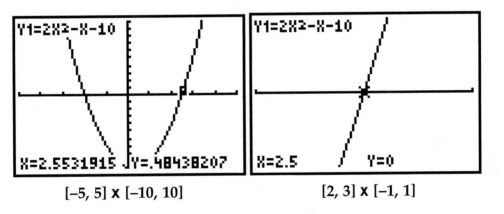

[–5, 5] x [–10, 10]   [2, 3] x [–1, 1]

Figure 4.29 Original graph   *Figure 4.30 Zooming in*

d) The product $(x + 2)(2x - 5)$ does equal $2x^2 - x - 10$.

   e) We can generalize by saying that for any two integers A and B, if $\frac{B}{A}$ is a zero of the polynomial function, then $(Ax - B)$ is a factor of the expression. Use the calculator to factor $3x^2 + x - 4$. Use multiplication to check your factors.

e) The zeros are –1.33 and 1. The decimal –1.33 suggests the fraction $-\frac{4}{3}$. So the factors are $(x - 1)$ and $(3x + 4)$.

   f) Use the calculator to factor $20x^2 - 13x - 15$. Use multiplication to check your factors.

f) The zeros are 1.25 or $\frac{5}{4}$ and –0.6 or $\frac{-3}{5}$. The factors are $(4x - 5)$ and $(5x + 3)$.

5. The function $D = -0.000014x^4 + 0.00034x^3 - 0.0244x$ gives the *deflection curve* that describes the shape of a 12-foot-long, 2" x 10" beam (a *joist*) that helps support the floor of a house. (See **Figure 4.31**.) The beam is being supported by posts on each end and carries a uniformly distributed load of 400 pounds per foot. The distance x from the left end of the beam and the deflection D are both measured in feet.

Figure 4.31

a) Make a table similar to **Table 4.13** to show the value of the function over the length of the beam. (Round off your deflection values to three decimal places.)

x (feet)	D (feet)
0	
1	
2	
3	
⋮	
12	

Table 4.13

5. a)

x (feet)	D (feet)
0	0
1	−0.024
2	−0.046
3	−0.065
4	−0.079
5	−0.088
6	−0.091
7	−0.088
8	−0.078
9	−0.064
10	−0.044
11	−0.021
12	0.004

b) Decide what the maximum deflection is for this beam. Where along the beam does this occur? What is the amount of deflection measured in *inches*? (Note: The deflection is negative because the deflection is *downward*.)

b) **Maximum deflection occurs in the center of the beam (at $x = 6$ feet) and is equal to 0.091 feet (downward), or about 1.1 inches.**

c) To see the broader behavior of the polynomial function given here, create a graph of the deflection curve that extends 10 feet past each end of the beam. (Give careful thought to choosing an appropriate window if you use a graphing calculator or computer.) Notice that the beam shape is only one part of the entire graph.

c) **Sample graph:**

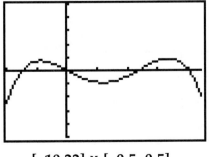

[−10,22] **x** [−0.5, 0.5]

6. Icebergs are tracked by satellite when they break off from the Antarctic ice sheets. Since January 1992, The National Ice Center has been tracking a very large iceberg that broke off from the Thwaites Ice Tongue. In the summer of 1995, the iceberg broke into two pieces. The larger piece is referred to as B10A. (See Exercise 27 of Section 1.5.) In the fall of 1999, this iceberg entered shipping lanes between the Antarctic Peninsula and South America and posed a threat. Since then, its location and size have been closely watched.

Icebergs are monitored until they break up into smaller icebergs that are too small to threaten ships. Even small icebergs 1 kilometer square pose a threat to shipping. Contributing to the danger is the fact that only about $\frac{1}{7}$ or $\frac{1}{8}$ of an iceberg is visible above water, and each iceberg has a different shape underwater.

On 26 August 1999, Iceberg B10A was roughly rectangular and measured 24 miles wide by 48 miles long. As it moved into warmer water, the ice slowly melted. By January 2000, the iceberg had shrunk to roughly 14 miles wide by 38 miles long. Both the length and width of the iceberg were decreasing at an average rate of about $\frac{1}{13}$ mile per day during this time.

a) Write an algebraic function for the area of the iceberg A after d days past 26 August. Multiply to get a polynomial expression for the area.

6. a) If the dimensions were 24 miles by 48 miles on 26 August and the length and width are both decreasing by $\frac{1}{13}$ miles per day, the length x days after 26 August can be written as $(48 - \left(\frac{1}{13}\right)x)$ and the width as $(24 - \left(\frac{1}{13}\right)x)$. The area function is $A(x) = \left(48 - \frac{1}{13}x\right)\left(24 - \frac{1}{13}x\right) = 1152 - \left(\frac{72}{13}\right)x + \left(\frac{1}{169}\right)x^2$.

b) Create a graph of the area of the iceberg versus the number of days since 26 August.

b) Sample graph:

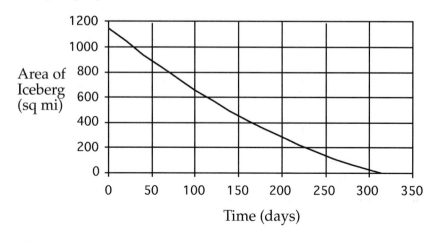

c) Use your graph from (b) to predict when the iceberg will be completely broken up.

c) According to this model, it will take approximately 310 days until the iceberg is broken up.

7. **Figure 4.32** shows a scatter plot of the amount of ozone near the Antarctic measured in Dobson Units (DU). The dots represent the monthly averages for the month of October for each year shown.

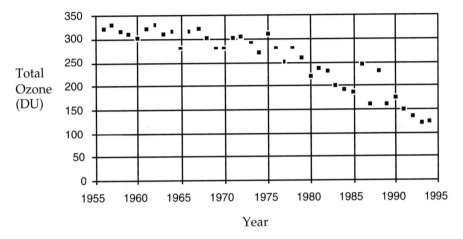

Figure 4.32

a) From the scatter plot, make a table showing all of the years that are divisible by 5 and the ozone levels in those years.

7. **a) Sample table:**

Year	Ozone Level (DU)
1960	300
1965	280
1970	280
1975	310
1980	220
1985	185
1990	175

b) Use your calculator's statistical calculation feature to explore nonlinear regression and find a polynomial function that models the data in your table from (a). Typical options are for second-degree (quadratic), third-degree (cubic), and fourth-degree (quartic) regression. Some calculators will perform more sophisticated polynomial regressions.

b) If calculator regression options are explored, the rather high value for 1975 makes a fourth-degree polynomial appear visually to be a better fit than either a third-degree or second-degree polynomial. The function is approximately $y = 0.0032x^4 - 25.37x^3 + 75135x^2 - 98,899,585x + 48,817,001,118$.

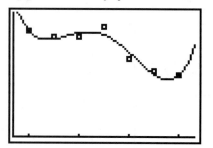

c) What does your best model from (b) predict for the year 2000?

c) Sample answer: For quartic regression, the model predicts an ozone level of 917 DU. This is not a very reasonable prediction, as it is almost three times as much as any level during the past four decades.

d) How does your polynomial function compare with the data for the years 1960, 1975, and 1985?

d) For the quartic model: The model gives an ozone level of 300 DU for 1960, a level of 288 DU for 1975, and a level of 176 DU for 1985. It is exactly correct for 1960, within 22 DU for 1975, and within 9 DU for 1985.

e) If you add more data points to your table, does the shape of the graph change? Is it more accurate?

e) Additional data:

Year	Ozone Level (DU)	Year	Ozone Level (DU)	Year	Ozone Level (DU)	Year	Ozone Level (DU)
1956	320	1966	315	1976	280	1986	245
1957	330	1967	320	1977	250	1987	160
1958	315	1968	300	1978	280	1988	230
1959	310	1969	280	1979	260	1989	160
1960	300	1970	280	1980	220	1990	175
1961	320	1971	300	1981	235	1991	150
1962	330	1972	305	1982	230	1992	135
1963	310	1973	290	1983	200	1993	120
1964	315	1974	270	1984	190	1994	125
1965	280	1975	310	1985	185		

When all the data are used, a second-degree model seems (again visually) to model the data as well as the third-degree or fourth-degree models. Because it is a simpler model, it is probably a better choice. The function is approximately $y = -0.1559x^2 + 610.6x - 597{,}584$.

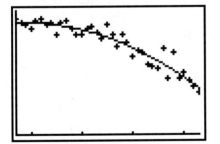

The model is less accurate for the dates examined in (d), giving ozone levels of 316 DU, 274 DU, and 207 DU. But its prediction of 48 DU for year 2000 is probably more reasonable than the prediction of 917 DU from the previous quartic model.

8. a) Graph the two functions $Y_1 = 0.7x^3 - 6.3x^2 + 12.6x$ and $Y_2 = -0.25x^2 + 1.75x$.

8. a)

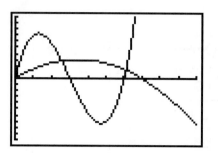

b) Over the interval $0 \le x \le 10$, for what values of x are these two functions equal? Estimate the answer to the nearest tenth in a manner similar to that used in Exercise 8 of Section 2.5.

b) The intersections can be estimated (using the TRACE feature or more powerful calculation features) as being located at $x = 0.0, 2.5,$ and 6.1.

c) For what values of x is Y_1 greater than Y_2?

c) $Y_1 > Y_2$ on the approximate intervals $0 < x < 2.5$ and $x > 6.1$.

9. The National Oceanic and Atmospheric Administration (NOAA) has satellites that orbit Earth at an altitude of a little over 500 miles. They scan a portion of Earth taking photographs 6 times per second. Data are sent to NOAA and can be analyzed to detect forest fires and fires in grasslands and prairies.

In 1996, one such fire was detected in Wyoming shortly after it was started by a lightning storm. When it was first detected, it was 2 km across and roughly in the shape of a circle. On the next satellite image eight hours later, it was 4 km across. Twenty-four hours after the second picture, another satellite image showed that the fire was still raging and was now 10 km across.

a) Write a linear equation that expresses the radius r of the fire as a function of time t. Assume the fire had a diameter of 2 km at time 0.

9. a) From the given information, it can be determined that the points $(0, 1)$, $(8, 2)$, and $(32, 5)$ are points on the graph of the equation. Using any two of the points, an equation can be found that expresses the radius as a function of time. One possible equation is $r = \dfrac{1}{8}t + 1$.

b) Use the equation from (a) to complete **Table 4.14.**

Time (hr)	Radius (km)	Area (sq km)
0		
8		
24		
32		
40		
48		

Table 4.14

b)

Time (hr)	Radius (km)	Area (sq km)
0	1	$\pi \approx 3.1$
8	2	$4\pi \approx 12.6$
24	4	$16\pi \approx 50.3$
32	5	$25\pi \approx 78.5$
40	6	$36\pi \approx 113$
48	7	$49\pi \approx 154$

c) Make a scatter plot of the data in Table 4.14. Use time as the independent variable and radius as the dependent variable. Describe the form of the scatter plot.

c) The scatter plot has linear form.

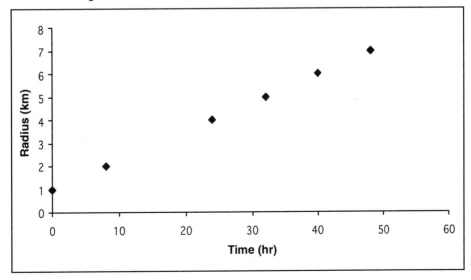

d) Use Table 4.14, your graph from (c), or your function from (a) to predict how long it will take the fire to reach a town that is 18 km away from the center of the fire.

d) When $r = 18$ km, $18 = \dfrac{1}{8}t + 1$. $t = 136$ hrs.

e) Create a second scatter plot using time as the independent variable and area as the dependent variable. Describe the form of the scatter plot. If the form of the data is different from the form in (c), explain why.

f) The scatter plot has a nonlinear form because it shows a relationship between time and the square of the radius. The rate of change is not constant.

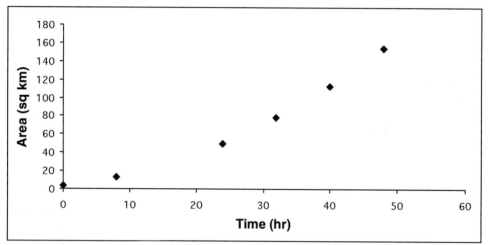

f) Use your equation from (a) to find an equation expressing the area as a function of time. Multiply and combine like terms.

f) If $r = \dfrac{1}{8}t + 1$, then $A = \pi r^2$. So $A = \pi\left(\dfrac{1}{8}t + 1\right)^2$; $A = \dfrac{\pi}{64}t^2 + \dfrac{\pi}{4}t + \pi$.

II. Projects and Group Activities (SE page 358)

10. After experimenting with price changes, an espresso stand owner knows that when she charges $1.35 cents per cup of coffee, she can sell 500 cups of coffee per week. However, if she raises the price to $1.50 per cup, she sells only 350 cups per week. Her overhead costs are $120 per week, and each cup of coffee costs her $0.32.

   a) Assume that the number of cups sold per week is a linear function of the price charged per cup. Write an equation that gives the number of cups sold N as a function of the price per cup p (in dollars). Graph the function for prices from $0 to $2.00.

10. a) Using the two points (1.50, 350) and (1.35, 500), N = –1000p + 1850.

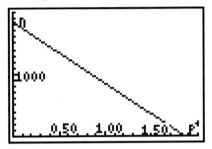

   b) What is the slope of the graph of this linear function (including units)?

b) –1000 cups per dollar change in price

   c) According to this function, how many cups could be sold if $1.40 per cup were charged?

c) (–1000)(1.40) + 1850 = 450 cups.

   d) What price should be charged to sell 750 cups? (Caution: Because this part requires extrapolating beyond the data, it may be an unreliable projection.)

d) To sell 750 cups, she should charge $1.10.

   e) Write a polynomial function that gives revenue (income) R as a function of the price per cup. Revenue is computed as (price per cup)(number of cups sold).

e) $R = p(-1000p + 1850) = -1000p^2 + 1850p$.

   f) Graph the revenue function from (e).

g) Sample graph:

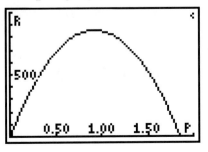

g) Notice that both of the graphs you have drawn have a *p*-intercept in common. Explain why.

g) For a price of $1.85 per cup, there would (theoretically, at least) be no sales and therefore no revenue.

h) Use your revenue graph and/or table to estimate the price that should be charged to maximize revenue.

h) She should charge $0.925, or 93 cents.

i) Write an equation expressing total cost *C* as a function of the price per cup. (Remember that there are overhead costs as well as unit costs per cup.) Graph this function on the same graph as the revenue function.

i) $C = 120 + 0.32(-1000p + 1850) = -32p + 712$.

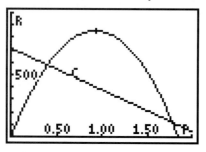

j) What are the approximate coordinates of the intersection points? What is the significance of these points?

j) The two graphs intersect in two places. They occur at about $0.40 per cup when costs and revenue are both about $582 and at $1.76 per cup when costs and revenue are both about $147. Because these are the points where cost and revenue are equal, they represent prices for which profit will be zero.

k) Write an equation expressing total profit *P* as a function of the price per cup (profit = revenue – cost). Graph this function. Then determine the maximum profit that can be made in a week and what should be charged per cup to make this profit.

k) $P = x(-1000x + 1850) - [120 + 0.32(-1000x + 1850)] = -1000x^2 + 2170x - 712$.

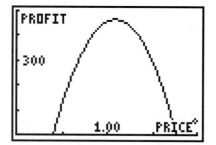

The maximum profit is about $465, at a price of $1.09 per cup.

III. Additional Practice *(SE pages 359–360)*

11. The population of a town is given by the function $P = -8t^2 + 250t + 1500$, where P is population and t is time in years beginning in 1950 (that is, a value of $t = 0$ corresponds to the year 1950).

   a) What was the population in 1960?

11. a) $-8(10^2) + 250(10) + 1500 = 3200$.

   b) Use your graphing calculator to estimate the year that the population was the largest.

b) Population is 3453 when $t \approx 15.6$, which corresponds to about midway through 1965.

   c) This town, a small farming community, fell upon hard times and became a ghost town. In what year did the town cease to exist?

c) Population is 0 for $t \approx 36.4$, during the year 1986.

For 12–37, find all solutions of each equation.

12. $(x - 7)(x + 8) = 0$.

12. $x = -8$ or 7.

13. $(3t + 1)(t + 12) = 0$.

13. $t = -12$ or $-\dfrac{1}{3}$.

14. $D(7D - 2)(2D - 5) = 0$.

14. $D = 0$, $\dfrac{2}{7}$, or $\dfrac{5}{2}$.

15. $(r - 1)(4r - 9)(12r - 5) = 0$.

15. $r = \dfrac{5}{12}$, 1, or $\dfrac{9}{4}$.

16. $t^2 - 5t - 24 = 0$.

16. $(t + 3)(t - 8) = 0$; $t = -3$ or 8.

17. $y^2 - 5y - 6 = 0$.

17. $(y + 1)(y - 6) = 0$; $y = -1$ or 6.

18. $x^3 - 5x^2 - 14x = 0$.

18. $x(x - 7)(x + 2) = 0$; $x = -2$, 0, or 7.

19. $a^4 - 9a^3 + 20a^2 = 0$.

19. $a^2(a - 5)(a - 4) = 0$; $a = 0$, 4, or 5.

20. $x^2 + 12x = -36$.

20. $(x + 6)(x + 6) = 0$; $x = -6$.

21. $s^2 = 6s + 27$.

21. $(s + 3)(s - 9) = 0$; $s = -3$ or 9.

22. $w^3 + w = 2w^2$.

22. $w(w - 1)(w - 1) = 0$; $w = 0$ or 1.

23. $b^3 + 2b^2 = 35b$.

23. $b(b + 7)(b - 5) = 0$; $b = -7$, 0, or 5.

24. $x(3x + 2)(x - 12)(2x - 7) = 0$.

24. $x = -\dfrac{2}{3}, 0, \dfrac{7}{2},$ or 12.

25. $v^2 + 16v + 64 = 0$.

25. $(v + 8)(v + 8) = 0$; $v = -8$.

26. $y^2 = y + 72$.

26. $(y + 8)(y - 9) = 0$; $y = -8$ or 9.

27. $(6h - 7)(2h + 9)(h - 3)(4h + 11) = 0$.

27. $h = -\dfrac{9}{2}, -\dfrac{11}{4}, \dfrac{7}{6},$ or 3.

28. $x^3 - 11x^2 + 18x = 0$.

28. $x(x - 9)(x - 2) = 0$; $x = 0$, 2, or 9.

29. $m^2 + 3m = 4$.

29. $(m + 4)(m - 1) = 0$; $m = -4$ or 1.

30. $2a^2 + 16a + 14 = 0$.

30. $2(a + 7)(a + 1) = 0$; $a = -7$ or -1.

31. $3x^2 - 12x - 15$

31. $3(x - 5)(x + 1)$; $x = -1$ or 5.

32. $5C^2 - 30C - 80 = 0$.

32. $5(C + 2)(C - 8) = 0$; $C = -2$ or 8.

33. $7n^2 - 56n + 105 = 0$.

33. $7(n - 3)(n - 5) = 0$; $n = 3$ or 5.

34. $F^3 + 12F^2 - 13F = 0$.

34. $F(F - 1)(F + 13) = 0$; $F = -13$, 0, or 1.

35. $p^2(5p + 6)(5p + 6) = 0$.

35. $p = -\dfrac{6}{5}$ or 0.

36. $q^3 + 16q = 8q^2$.

36. $q(q - 4)(q - 4) = 0$; $q = 0$ or 4.

37. $x^4 = 9x^2$.

37. $x^2(x + 3)(x - 3) = 0$; $x = -3, 0,$ or 3.

Chapter 4 Summary

Recognition of polynomial expressions

Modeling with polynomials

Properties of exponents

Operations with scientific notation

Operations with polynomials

Factoring polynomial expressions

Prime numbers and prime polynomial expressions

Graphs of polynomial functions

Solving equations containing factorable polynomials

Chapter 4 Review

1. Write a summary of the important mathematical ideas found in Chapter 4.

1. Answers will vary. Following are some of the important ideas that should be listed:

Polynomials and polynomial functions can be used to model real-world situations.

The properties of exponents can be used to simplify expressions that contain exponents.

Negative exponents can be used to write very small numbers in scientific notation.

A polynomial expression is an algebraic expression in which each term has variables raised to whole number powers.

Polynomials can be added and subtracted by adding and subtracting like terms.

The distributive property can be used to multiply polynomials.

We divide a polynomial by a monomial by dividing each term of the polynomial by the monomial.

The properties of exponents help us multiply and divide polynomials.

A prime number is a number whose only factors are 1 and the number. Numbers that are not prime are called composite numbers.

When we factor a polynomial, we write it as a product of prime factors.

When we factor a polynomial, we first look for a common monomial.

When factoring a polynomial, we also look for special forms such as the difference of two squares and perfect square trinomials.

If a trinomial written in descending order has a leading coefficient of 1, we can try to factor it by finding two numbers that have a product equal to the constant term and a sum equal to the coefficient of the middle term.

Some polynomial equations can be solved by factoring and then using the zero product property.

The zero product property says that if the product of two numbers is zero, then one or both of the numbers equals zero.

Graphs of polynomial functions are smooth curves.

For 2–5, write each expression in a simpler form using the properties of exponents. Evaluate all numerical expressions. Simplify algebraic expressions containing variables. Write answers without negative exponents or parentheses. (Assume all variables are nonzero.)

2. $(3x^2)(5x^{-3})(x^2 y)^3$

2. $15x^5 y^3$

3. $\dfrac{12a^5b}{\left(2a^4b^{-3}\right)^2}$

3. $\dfrac{3b^7}{a^3}$

4. $\left(\dfrac{30x}{5x^{-2}}\right)^{-3}$

4. $\dfrac{1}{216x^9}$

5. $(2.5 \times 10^{-5})(3.0 \times 10^4)^2$

5. **2.25×10^4**

6. In 1975, about 18 billion aluminum cans were manufactured. Every 22 cans produced used 1 pound of aluminum.

   a) How many tons of aluminum were processed to make the 18 billion cans? (Use scientific notation.)

6. a) **$(1.8 \times 10^{10}\text{ cans})\left(\dfrac{1\text{ lb}}{22\text{ cans}}\right)\left(\dfrac{1\text{ ton}}{2 \times 10^3\text{ lb}}\right) \approx 4.1 \times 10^5\text{ tons.}$**

   b) In 1997, there were 99 billion aluminum cans manufactured. Every 32 cans used up 1 pound of aluminum, and the average can contained about 51% recycled aluminum. How much aluminum ore was processed to make the 99 billion cans in 1997?

   b) **If the average can contained 51% recycled aluminum, it used 49% new aluminum.**

   $\left(9.9 \times 10^{10}\text{ cans}\right)\left(\dfrac{1\text{ lb aluminum}}{32\text{ cans}}\right)\left(\dfrac{0.49\text{ lb virgin aluminum}}{1\text{ lb aluminum}}\right)\left(\dfrac{1\text{ ton}}{2 \times 10^3\text{ lb}}\right) \approx$

   7.6×10^5 tons.

7. Write 0.00036 in scientific notation.

7. **3.6×10^{-4}**

8. Write 5.92×10^{-6} in standard notation.

8. **0.00000592**

9. Consider the expression $3p^4 - \dfrac{2}{3}p^2 + p + \sqrt{7}$. Is this expression a polynomial? If it is not a polynomial, indicate why. If it is a polynomial, state the number of terms and degree.

9. **Yes, it is a polynomial of degree four with four terms.**

10. The expression $x^3 - 4x^2 + \dfrac{2}{x}$ is used to find the *reactance* of a particular electrical circuit. Is this expression a polynomial? If it is not a polynomial, indicate why. If it is a polynomial, state the number of terms and degree.

10. No, it is not a polynomial because the third term is not of the form ax^k, where k is a whole number.

11. Write an example of a two-term polynomial of degree five.

11. One possibility is $2x^5 - 8x^2$.

12. In **Figure 4.33,** represent the area of the shaded region between the rectangle and the square in terms of y.

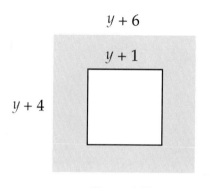

Figure 4.33

12. $(y + 6)(y + 4) - (y + 1)^2 = y^2 + 10y + 24 - (y^2 + 2y + 1) =$
$y^2 + 10y + 24 - y^2 - 2y - 1 = 8y + 23.$

13. A tank is to be designed as a cylinder 2.04 m in length with a half-sphere on each end. (See **Figure 4.34.**)

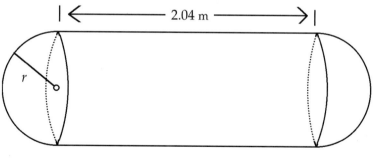

Figure 4.34

a) Write a polynomial expression in terms of the radius r that gives the volume of the tank.

13. a) Total volume = volume of sphere with radius r + volume of cylinder with length 2.04 m and radius r $= \dfrac{4}{3}\pi r^3 + \pi r^2(2.04) = \dfrac{4}{3}\pi r^3 + 2.04\pi r^2.$

b) Find the volume of the cylinder for $r = 0.62$ meters.

b) $\dfrac{4}{3}\pi(0.62)^3 + 2.04\pi(0.62)^2 = 3.4618... \approx 3.5 \text{ m}^3.$

For 14–19, perform the indicated operations and combine like terms.

14. $(12x^3 - 18x + 6) + (3x^2 + 4x - 6)$

14. $12x^3 + 3x^2 - 14x$

15. $(7b^2t + 5bt^2 - 2t^3) - (6b^2t - 5t^3)$

15. $b^2t + 5bt^2 + 3t^3$

16. $(-3x)(4x^3 - 0.4x)$

16. $-12x^4 + 1.2x^2$

17. $\dfrac{7t^6 + 56t^3 - 14t^2}{7t^2} \quad (t \neq 0)$

17. $t^4 + 8t - 2$

18. $(4a + 3)(8a - 7)$

18. $32a^2 - 4a - 21$

19. $(H^2 - 3H)(5H + 2)$

19. $5H^3 - 13H^2 - 6H$

For 20–25, factor each expression completely. If it is not factorable, write "Prime."

20. $x^3 + 6x$

20. $x(x^2 + 6)$

21. $9a^2 + 12a + 4$

21. $(3a + 2)^2$

22. $B^2 - 2B - 48$

22. $(B + 6)(B - 8)$

23. $25n^2 - 16$

23. $(5n + 4)(5n - 4)$

24. $D^2 + 3D - 1$

24. Prime

25. $2x^2y - 28xy + 90y$

25. $2y(x - 5)(x - 9)$

26. Consider the function $y = x^3 - 4x$.

a) Complete **Table 4.15**, and then graph the function.

x	y
–3	
–3	
–1	
0	
1	
2	
3	

Table 4.15

26. a)

x	y
–3	**–15**
–3	**0**
–1	**3**
0	**0**
1	**–3**
2	**0**
3	**15**

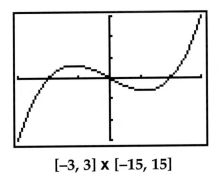

[–3, 3] x [–15, 15]

b) Find the x-intercepts of the graph by solving the equation $x^3 - 4x = 0$.

b) $x^3 - 4x = x(x + 2)(x - 2) = 0$, **with solutions** $x = -2$, 0, **or** 2, **which are the** x**–coordinates of the intercepts.**

27. A kennel owner wants to build three adjoining pens for animals. She has 120 feet of fencing available and plans an arrangement like the one in **Figure 4.35.**

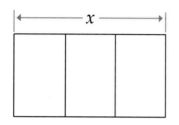

Figure 4.35

a) Write an equation that gives the total area A in terms of the length x. Assume that all three pens are the same size.

27. a) Each of the shorter sides has length $\dfrac{(120-2x)}{4}$**. Total area is then**

$$A = \text{(total length)(total width)} = x\left[\frac{(120-2x)}{4}\right] = 30x - \frac{x^2}{2}.$$

b) Graph your equation from (a). Determine the dimensions that will result in maximum total area.

b)

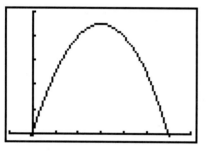

$[-10, 70]$ **x** $[0, 500]$

Maximum area of 450 feet^2 occurs for $x = 30$ feet. Overall dimensions are 30 feet x 20 feet.

For 28–34, find all solutions of each equation.

28. $(3x - 7)(5x + 8) = 0.$

28. $x = -\dfrac{8}{5}$ or $\dfrac{7}{3}$.

29. $(k + 4)(10k + 3)(2k - 9) = 0.$

29. $k = -4, -\dfrac{3}{10},$ or $\dfrac{9}{2}$.

30. $y^2 - 8y - 33 = 0.$

30. $(y + 3)(y - 11) = 0$; $y = -3$ or 11.

31. $x^3 + x^2 - 12x = 0.$

31. $x(x + 4)(x - 3) = 0$; $x = -4, 0,$ or 3.

32. $A^3 - A = 0.$

32. $A(A - 1)(A + 1) = 0$; $A = -1, 0,$ or 1.

33. $t^2 + 9 = 6t.$

33. $(t - 3)^2 = 0$; $t = 3$.

34. $s^3 = 7s^2 + 8s.$

34. $s(s - 8)(s + 1) = 0$; $s = -1, 0,$ or 8.

Appendix

Units and Conversions

Quantity	SI	U.S. Customary	Conversions
Length	meter (m)	foot (ft)	1 m = 3.281 ft = 39.37 in
		1 ft = 12 inches (in)	1 in = 2.54 cm
		1 yard (yd) = 3 ft	1 mi = 1.609 km
		1 mile (mi) = 5280 ft	1 km = 0.6214 mi
		1 in = 1000 mils	
Area	square meter (m^2)	square foot (ft^2)	1 hectare = 2.471 acres
	1 hectare = 10,000 m^2	1 acre = 43,560 ft^2	
Volume	cubic meter (m^3)	cubic foot (ft^3)	1 l = 0.03531 ft^3
	1 liter (l) = 1000 cm^3	1 ft^3 = 7.48 US gallons (gal)	
		1 gal = 231 in^3	
Weight	newton (N)	pound (lb)	1 lb = 4.448 N
		1 lb = 16 ounces (oz)	
		1 ton = 2000 lb	
Mass	kilogram (kg)	slug	1 kg = 2.205 lb*
	1 metric ton (tonne) = 1000 kg		1 oz = 454 g*
Time	second (s)	second (s)	

* Note: These are convenience conversions between mass units and weight units that are strictly valid only at sea level on the Earth.

Geometry Formulas

Two-Dimensional Figures

Figure	Area	Perimeter
Circle radius r, diameter d	$A = \pi r^2 = \pi d^2 / 4$	Circumference $C = 2\pi r = \pi d$
Rectangle length l, width w	$A = lw$	$P = 2l + 2w$
Square side s	$A = s^2$	$P = 4s$
Triangle base b, height h	$A = \dfrac{1}{2} bh$	
Parallelogram base b, height h	$A = bh$	
Trapezoid bases b_1, b_2, height h	$A = \dfrac{1}{2}(b_1 + b_2)h$	

Three-Dimensional Figures

Figure	Volume	Surface Area
Rectangular box length l, width w, height h	$V = lwh$	$SA = 2lw + 2lh + 2wh$
Cube side s	$V = s^3$	$SA = 6s^2$
Sphere radius r	$V = \dfrac{4}{3}\pi r^3$	$SA = 4\pi r^2$
Circular Cylinder radius r, diameter d, height h	$V = \pi r^2 h$	$SA = 2\pi rh = \pi dh$
Cone or Pyramid base area B, height h	$V = \dfrac{1}{3}Bh$	

Metric Prefixes

Prefix	Meaning
tera-	trillions
giga-	billions
mega-	millions
kilo-	thousands
hecto-	hundreds
deca-	tens
deci-	tenths
centi-	hundredths
milli-	thousandths
micro-	millionths
nano-	billionths
pico-	trillionths
femto-	quadrillionths

Index

A

Abbott, Edwin, 55
accuracy. *See* precision of measurement
addition
adding measurements, 18
distributive property, 122–123
order of operations, 8–10
polynomials, 318–320
solving equations, 137
algebraic expressions, 118, 120–125
combining like terms, 139–143
distributive property, 122–123
evaluating using technology, 124–125
order of operations, 123
solving equations, 136–143
solving inequalities, 152–153
algebraic logic, 129
angle measurement, 95
approximate numbers, 99–100
area, 55–63. *See also* surface area
converting units of, 56
formulas for, 58–63
uncertainty of measurement, 66–67
area models, 123
arrow diagrams, 8–10
for inverse operations, 136
representing functions, 161
assessing quality of fit, 271–274
assumptions to build models, 270
average rates of change, 177–179
axis, 175

B

bar graphs, 41
Pareto diagrams, 42
base (in exponential notation), 302
base of three-dimensional objects, 77–79
bimodal data, 30
binomials, 318
difference of two squares, 337–338
multiplying binomials together, 322–323

C

calculator
evaluating algebraic expressions, 124–125, 129
making geometric observations from, 215
calculus, 95
capacity, understanding, 80, 85
categorical data, 41
circles, 11, 60
circumference, 11

classes of data, 37
coding, 147–148
encryption keys, 334
keyword matrix, 155
coefficients in algebraic expressions, 140
combining like terms, 139–143
common monomial factoring, 334
comparing models, 274–275
compass rose, 101
composite numbers, 333
container design, 82, 346–347
continuous data, 31
control chart, 47
converting measurement units, 15, 56
coordinate plane, 175
correlation coefficient, 275
cubes, 79, 83
cubic units, 77
cylinders, 79, 83

D

data-driven models, 228
finding the prediction equation, 261–262
linear models, 233–237
lines of best fit, 252–254
making predictions from, 270–274
residuals, 256–259
degree of a polynomial, 317
Deming, W. Edwards, 47
dependent variables, 59
direct variation function, 190
descriptive statistics, 28
diagonals of rectangles, 12–14
difference of two squares, 337–338
dimensions, 103
direct variation function, 190
direction of a vector, 98
direction of variable relationship, 252–254
directly proportional variables, 190
discrete data, 31
discrete variables, 189
displacement vectors, 102
distributive property, 122–123
common monomial factoring, 334
division
measured numbers, 66–67
order of operations, 8–10
solving equations, 137
domain of a function, 160
polynomial functions, 347–348
dot plots, 36

E

edges of objects, 77
encryption, 147–148
keys for, 334
keyword matrix, 155

engineering notation, 98
equality properties, 137
equations. *See also* formulas
finding equations for lines, 186–187
how to write, **133**–134
least-squares prediction equation, 261–262
literal equations (formulas), 144–145
point-slope equation of a line, 206–207
slope-intercept form, 185–186
solving algebraically, 136–143
system of linear equations, 195
zero product property, 349–351
equivalent equations, 136
error. *See* precision of measurement
Escher, M. C., 56
estimating. *See also* precision of measurement
order of magnitude, 104
Pearson's correlation coefficient, 275
evaluating algebraic expressions. *See* algebraic
  expressions
exact numbers, 99–100
exponents, 302–309
properties of, 309
extrapolation, 237

F

faces of objects, 77
factoring polynomials, 333–338
common monomial factoring, 334
difference of two squares, 337–338
perfect square trinomials, 335–336
prime factorization, 333
quadratic trinomials, 335–336
factors in algebraic expressions, 140
50th percentile, 29
Flatland, 55
flop (computational operation), 107
Ford, Henry, 190
formulas, 7–8, 144–145. *See also* equations
area, 58–63
order of operations, 8–10
volume, 79
frequency histograms, 36–38
frequency table, 31
Fuller, Buckminster, 75, 90
Functions, 59
direct variation function, 190
domains and ranges, 160
input/output tables, 159–160
linear functions, 174–187
piecewise linear functions, 214
polynomials. *See* polynomials
representations of, 161–164
    vertical line test, 168

G

geometric models, 7

geometry formulas, 7–8
graphs
interpreting, 209–211
linear functions, 179–180
Pareto diagrams, 42
polynomial functions, 347–348
representing functions, **162**
residual plots, 272
scatter plots, 231, 233–234, 238–239, 253
slope-intercept form, 185–186
vertical line test, 168
visual models, 35–38
greater than (inequality), 32–34
greater than or equal to (inequality), 32–34
grouped frequency, 37

H

Hardy-Weinberg equation, 327–328
histograms, 36–38, 45
horizontal axis, 175
horizontal coordinate of ordered pairs, **164**
horizontal lines, equation for, 193
hypotenuse of right triangle, 13–14

I

implied multiplication, 8
independent variables, 59
indirect measurement, 116
inequalities, 32–34, 152–153
input/output tables, 159–160
intercept, 176, 192
slope-intercept form, 185–186
International System (SI), 95
inverse operations, 135, 136
irrational numbers, 99
isosceles triangles, 10, 65

J

Joule, James, 96
Juran, Joseph, 42

K

Kepler, Johannes, 307
keyword matrix, 155

L

Laplace transform, 344
least-squares criterion, 259
least-squares line, 259
leg of right triangles, finding, 14–15
length, definition of, 4
length measurements, 2–4
algebraic expressions for, 120–122
less than (inequality), 32–34

less than or equal to (inequality), 32–34
like terms, 139–143
linear equations. *See also* formulas
finding equations for lines, 186–187
graphing with slope-intercept form, 185–186
how to write, 133–134
least-squares prediction equation, 261–262
literal equations (formulas), 144–145
point-slope equation of a line, 206–207
slope-intercept form, 185–186
solving algebraically, 136–143
system of linear equations, 195
zero product property, 349–351
linear form of scatter plots, 253
linear functions, 174–187
graphing, 179–180
modeling, 204–211
piecewise linear functions, 214
linear least squares, 259–262
finding the prediction equation, 261–262
linear models, 114, 205–211
assessing quality of fit, 271–274
building from data, 233–237
point-slope form, 206
regression, 262
linear regression, 262
lines
finding equations for, 186–187
horizontal and vertical, equations for, 193
intercept, 176, 192
parallel and perpendicular, 208–209
point-slope equation of a line, 206–207
slope, 180–185
slope-intercept form, 185–186
lines of best fit, 252–254
finding the prediction equation, 261–262
least-squares line, 259–262
residuals, 256–259
literal equations, 144–145

M

magnitude of a vector, 98
making assumptions to build models, 270
mass and weight, 117
mathematical models. *See* models
matrices, 155
maximum likely error, 3, 58
mean, 4, 28, 30–31
comparing means, 32–34
decisions based on, 35
trimmed mean, 39
weighted mean, 40
measurement, 2–4
adding and subtracting, 18
angle measurement, 95
area, 55–63, 66–67
indirect measurement, 116
measuring from a calculator screen, 215

precision. *See* precision of measurement
rates, 95
significant figures, 18
statistics, 28
surface area, 65
time measurement, 94
uncertainty. *See* precision of measurement
volume, 77–81, 174–176
weights and masses, 117
median, 29, 30–31
Mersenne, Marin, 343
metric system, 94
modal time, 40
mode, 30
models, 1, 30–31
algebraic models, 8
comparing, 274–275
data-driven, 228, 233–237, 252–262, 270–274
geometric, 7
linear, 114, 204–211, 233–237, 262, 271–274
making predictions from, 270–274
with polynomial functions, 318–320, 346–351
theory-driven, 228
verbal, 7
visual, 35–38
monomials
common monomial factoring, 334
multiplying polynomials by, 320–322
multimodal data, 30
multiplication
binomials and binomials, 322–323
distributive property, 122–123
factors of, 140
implied multiplication, 8
measured numbers, 66–67
order of operations, 8–10
polynomials and monomials, 320–322
solving equations, 137

N

negative exponents, 303, 306
negative reciprocals, 209
negatively related variables, 252–254
Newton, Isaac, 99
nonlinear form of scatter plots, 253
notation
engineering notation, 98
exponential notation, 302, 304
scientific notation, 97–98, 306
number line, 33
numbers
exact and approximate, 99–100
precision. *See* precision of measurement
prime and composite numbers, 333
rational and irrational, 99
scientific notation, 97–98

O

one-dimensional axis, **33**
order of magnitude, 104
order of operations, 8–10
  evaluating algebraic expressions, 123
  solving equations, 137
ordered pairs, 164
origin of a coordinate graph, **164**
outliers, 278
output, understanding, 85

P

parallel lines, 208–209
Pareto diagrams, 42
Pareto, Vilfredo, 42
Pascal, Blaise, 329
Pascal's triangle, 329
Pearson's correlation coefficient, 275
percent error, 5
perfect square trinomials, 337
perimeters, 4, 11–12, 55
  form for, 7
  rectangle, 10
  triangles, 10
perpendicular lines, 208–209
piecewise linear functions, 214
planes, 55–56
plotting residuals, 272
point-slope form, 206
polygons, area of, 64
polynomials, 294–**296,** 299, 317–323
  adding and subtracting, 318–320
  degrees of, 317
  exponent properties, 309
  factoring, 333–338
  models with polynomial functions, 346–351
  multiplying binomials together, 322–323
  multiplying by monomials, 320–322
  properties of polynomials, 347–348
  quadratic trinomials, factoring, 335–336
  zero product property, 349–351
positively related variables, 252–254
power of a power, 308
power of a product, 308
power of a quotient, 309
powers, rounding, 67
precision of measurement, 3, 17
  assessing quality of fit, 271–274
  exact and approximate numbers, 99–100
  making predictions from models, 270–274
  order of magnitude, 104
  Pearson's correlation coefficient, 275
  percent error, 5
  residuals, 256–259
  significant figures, 18
  uncertainty of measurement, 58, 66–67
predictions from data, 235–237

  assessing quality of fit, 271–274
  making from models, 270–274
  Pearson's correlation coefficient, 275
  residuals, 256–259
prefixes, 3
prime factorization, 333
prime numbers, 333
problem domain, 160
problem identification, 270
properties of equality, 137
proportion, 5
Pythagoras, 14
Pythagorean Theorem, 13–14

Q

quadrants of a graph, 175
quadratic trinomials, factoring, 335–336
qualitative graphs, 168
quality of statistics, 47

R

range of a function, 160
range of data, 30
rates, 95
  of change, 95, 177–179
rational numbers, 99
rectangles
  area of, 58–59
  diagonals, 12–14
  perimeter, 10
rectangular solids, 79, 83
regression, 262
relative frequency histogram, 44
representing functions, 161–164
residual plots, 272
residuals, 256
right solids, 77–79
right triangles, 13–15
roots, rounding, 67
rounding, 67
rule of thumb, 131

S

sample data set, 4
sample mean, 4, 28, 30–31
  comparing means, 32–34
  decisions based on, 35
  trimmed mean, 39
  weighted mean, 40
scatter plots, 231, 233–234
  linear and nonlinear forms, 253
  residuals, 256–259
  shape of, 238–239
  strong and weak relationships, 253
schematics, 19
scientific notation, 97–98, 306

secret codes, 147–148
encryption keys, 334
keyword matrix, 155
Shewhart, Walter, 47
SI units, 95
sigma (_), 28
significant figures, 18
simplest terms of polynomials, 319
simplifying to build models, 270
size, understanding, 85
slope of a line, 180–185
slope-intercept form, 185–186
solution, 136
solving equations. *See* equations
spheres, 79, 83
spreadsheets, 125
evaluating algebraic expressions, 125
representing functions, 162
square units, 56
squares, area of, 59
statistics, 28
statistical quality, 47
strong relationships in scatter plots, 253
subscripts, 19
subtraction
binomials, 337–338
measurement subtraction, 18
order of operations, 8–10
polynomials, 318
solving equations, 137
surface area, 65. *See also* area
system of linear equations, 195

T

tables
evaluating algebraic expressions, 124–125
graphs of linear functions, 179–180
representing functions, 162
temperature gradient, 102
terms of algebraic expressions, **139**
theory-driven models, 228
tiling the plane, 56
time measurement, 94
trapezoids, area of, 60
triangles
area of, 60
hypotenuse of right triangles, 13–14
isosceles triangles, 10, 65
legs of right triangles, 14–15
    perimeter, 10
trimmed mean, 39
trinomials, 318, 335–336
Trotter, Mildred, 230
two-dimensional figures, perimeters of, 11–12

U

uncertainty of measurement, 58, 66–67
units of measurement
area, 55–57
converting between, 15, 56
difference between unit and dimension, 103
International System (SI), 95
metric system, 94
paying attention to, 96
prefixes for, 3
volume, 77
weights and masses, 117
U.S. Customary units, 95

V

Variables, 8
dependent and independent, 59
directly proportional, 190
discrete, 189
positively and negatively related, 252–254
vectors, 98–99, 101
displacement vectors, 102
verbal descriptions of functions, 161
verbal models, 7
versus, defined, 233
vertical axis, 175
vertical coordinate of ordered pairs, 164
vertical line test, 168
vertical lines, equation for, 193
vertices of objects, 77
visual models, 35–38
polynomial addition, 318–320
volume, 77–81
formulas, 79
relationship with weight, 174–176

W

weak relationships in scatter plots, 253
weight
difference between weight and mass, 117
relationship with height, 205
relationship with volume, 174–176
weighted mean, 40
width, definition of, 4

X

x-axis, *x*-coordinates, and *xy*-plane, 175

Y

y-axis and *y*-coordinates, 175

Z

zero product property, 349–351